Russian Tanks, 1900-1970

Galahad Books

RUSSIAN TANKS
1900-1970

The complete illustrated history of Soviet armoured theory and design

by John Milsom

Published by Galahad Books, a division of A & W
Promotional Book Corporation, 95 Madison Ave-
nue, New York, N.Y. 10016, by arrangement with
Stackpole Books, Cameron and Kelker Streets,
Harrisburg, Pa. 17105
Library of Congress Catalog Card No.: 73–81665
ISBN: 0–88365–052–5

To my wife, Vicky

Contents

PART I: MECHANIZATION OF THE RUSSIAN ARMY

Introduction

Russian Tanks, 1900–1970 is the product of study of the subject over a period of several years. Part I describes the gradual development of armoured vehicles in the Soviet Union from both technical and tactical viewpoints, the expansion of the munitions and automotive industries, and the effects of politics and wars on the growth of the Soviet armoured forces. Part II describes in great detail the technical evolution of individual vehicle types—light, medium and heavy tanks, self-propelled weapons and finally armoured cars and miscellaneous tracked vehicles.

I have refrained from making direct comparison between either Soviet tactical doctrines or technical evolution and those of its adversaries, since I do not believe this may be achieved adequately without relating parallel developments taking place within those national spheres to be compared. In this respect, I have felt it sufficient to quote eminent personalities on both sides of the fence and then leave the reader to draw his own conclusions as to the validity or significance of their statements and opinions. I must emphasize strongly that not a little bias on each side may be encountered owing to political or propaganda requirements; but since this is often the only material which has been made available it must be included.

Regarding the smaller members of the Warsaw Pact forces, or indeed, other countries employing Soviet equipment, I have deliberately kept to a minimum any associated discussion. Apart from the fact that each member country has a history of its own armoured forces going back way beyond its absorption into the Soviet sphere of influence, it would be dangerous to draw any conclusions regarding the performance capabilities of Soviet forces from studies of the application of their equipment by others. Thus, no mention has been made, for example, of Suez or the Israeli-Arab Wars, and only to a very limited degree of Korea; for in these actions Soviet equipment showed no advances not already known from their Soviet usage. Nor can the Soviet occupation of Czechoslovakia provide any special indication of the Soviet application of mechanized forces apart from their associated logistic capability in moving large forces of armoured equipment in such a short period of time.

It will no doubt be appreciated that there are many difficulties involved in collecting photographs of Russian vehicles. The illustrations in this book have been gathered from many sources, but, because many are old or were taken under poor conditions with inferior photographic equipment, the reproduction of some may well leave something to be desired. Where poorer quality photographs have been used it should be understood that these are rare pictures of material which otherwise has not been photographed for use in the West.

I would like to thank the many people and establishments who have assisted me in compiling the information for this book, many of whom are listed in the bibliography and quotes. I would especially like to mention, however, the following: Peter Chamberlain, Colonel R. J. Icks and Christopher Foss for their help in obtaining some of the rarer photographs; the Imperial War Museum; the Museum of the Armoured Corps of the USSR; the Centralna Biblioteka Wojskowa, Warsaw; Colonel Offerd for permission to reproduce material on Russian Tanks authored by the Armour School (formerly STT) Bovington; and Colonel A. ('Busty') Cooper RAC (Retd) for his professional opinions and criticism of the work at various stages of its production.

Locations of strategic and industrial significance to Russian Armour Development

This map shows the principal areas in the USSR associated with the historical, technological, industrial and military aspects of armour. In addition to the Soviet tendency to rename various places from time to time and to deliberately distort the geographical representations of the USSR, a certain amount of inaccuracy may have resulted during the preparation of this map. Many of the locations shown therein have been extracted from not altogether reliable sources and one must be heedful of their dubious validity. It should also be noted that the omission or inclusion of a particular place, as well as the emphasis on that place, is proportional to its relationship within the sphere of armour.

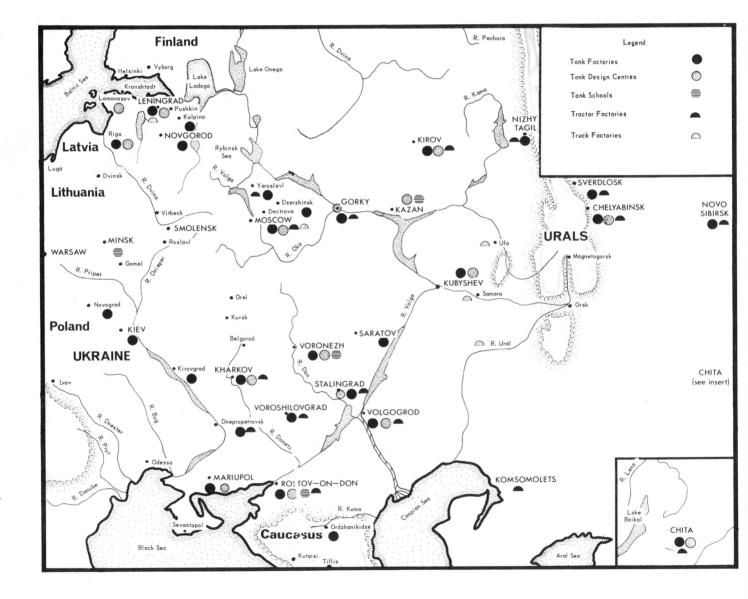

PART I
Mechanization of the Russian Army

1 Pre-Revolutionary Concepts

It will, no doubt, be appreciated that the production of modern armaments—particularly tanks and other military fighting vehicles, is only possible in a society possessing a highly-developed technological and industrial basis. In addition, that society must have an open mind regarding new concepts of warfare from both a scientific and tactical viewpoint. Whereas during the first quarter of the twentieth century, most of the European countries and the USA possessed such a basis—established gradually over the preceding century—Russia was virtually void of any organized or advanced industrial basis whatsoever, and prior to the Revolution little effort was made to establish one. Furthermore, any ingenuity or innovating zeal shown by scientists or tacticians was, more often than not, suppressed or waved aside.

In spite of this difficult situation, pre-Revolutionary Russia made several contributions to the development of the armoured fighting vehicle—in fact, the first completely assembled prototype armoured track-laying fighting vehicle was actually built in Russia. Russian military theory of the nineteenth and early twentieth centuries was no less developed than that of other countries for this time; by developing independently it was unrestricted and skilfully adapted the best military theories of other armies. Several early attempts made in Russia to produce experimental armoured fighting vehicles demonstrated that the Russians were not retarded in their conceptions of future warfare, and that they appreciated the value of an armoured mobile arm. The Russians' claim that they were working on tank projects concurrently with, and independent of, the British and French has since been substantiated.

Pre-twentieth century development. Pre-twentieth century research in the development of military vehicles was directed towards experiments with agricultural tractors and steam traction engines—the most noteworthy being the propositions by Zagryazhskiy and Blinov.[1]

Two automobiles were tested by the Russian Army for the first time during the 1897 Belostok manoeuvres, but although they appeared promising for use with the Army, the War Ministry rejected a proposition to purchase automobiles for further evaluation. This was due mainly to the lack of similar work abroad.

In November 1899 the Imperial Artillery Committee examined a project put forward by an engineer named Dvinitsky.[2] Resulting from the apparent success of a number of automobile competitions and demonstrations held about this time, where automobiles showed high degrees of reliability, Dvinitsky proposed mounting a small calibre quick-firing gun on an automobile. The project was presented before two committees: one under Engineer-Chairman Lieutenant-General Sluchevsky, and the other under Lieutenant-General Takhtarev, but neither commitee showed much interest in the project and it was turned down. A further project, put forward by Dvinitsky during 1900, for a large armoured steam-powered wheeled vehicle (referred to as the Dvinitsky Armoured Car) was provisionally accepted, and construction of this vehicle was undertaken under the supervision of the Imperial Artillery Committee. Protected by plate armour it was found to be underpowered and too heavy, and was therefore abandoned.

During December 1900 the Artillery Committee considered another proposal, put forward by Lutski. This was for 'the construction by the Russian War Department of a fighting vehicle armed with machine-guns.'[3] Lutski produced the drawings for his proposed combat vehicle, which he intended to build on the basis of a then current transport lorry for which he recommended the most suitable model. As before, however, the Imperial Artillery Committee rejected this proposal with the following statement:

It is not considered favourable at this time, nor is it official policy, to employ automobiles for military purposes. . . .[4]

Mendeleev's projects. A remarkable project for an armoured and armed tracklaying vehicle was proposed by Vasiliy Dmitriev Mendeleev (1886–1922), son of the famous Russian scientist Mendeleev.[5] Over the period 1903 to 1906 Mendeleev studied in the Shipbuilding Department of the Kronshtad Marine Engineering College, and during his studies on Russian military ship design, he became interested in the design and construction of an 'Armoured Land Cruiser'. Between 1908 and 1916, whilst working at the St Petersburg Shipbuilding Yard, he became involved in the design and construction of a new 1,000 hp engine which was to be employed in a new submarine being built under the directive of the Marine Technical Committee. Realizing the potential of such an engine for propelling a heavy land vehicle, Mendeleev spent the five years from 1911 to 1915 designing his fighting vehicle.[6] His first proposal was for a 170-ton machine to be armed with a 120 mm naval gun (mounted in the front of the armoured hull), as well as machine-guns mounted in a rotating turret. Ammunition stowage for the 120 mm gun was to be 51 rounds, whilst the armour thickness of the hull was to be 150 mm on the front and 100 mm on the sides. The crew was to consist of 8 men, and Mendeleev estimated the maximum speed of this vehicle to be 14 mph. His vast knowledge and experience in ship design allowed him to undertake this very ambitious project, in which he incorporated several original and far-sighted ideas for that time. The uncompleted drawings and technical description are contained in his notes at the Archives of the Academy of Science.

The powerful internal-combustion engine was located within the armoured hull, together with the rigid transmission, ammunition compartments, crew arrangements, steering system and various other special features. The petrol tanks were located at the rear of the vehicle on the floor, in a specially insulated compartment. The gearbox was also displayed with four gears for forward motion and one for reverse; to change from forward to reverse direction, the rotation of the crankshaft could be reversed. Of particular interest was his pneumatic suspension system: each suspension unit consisted of a cylinder rigidly attached to the tank hull and closed by a piston connected to a large roller. Air to each cylinder was controlled by a special compressor, so that between each bogie wheel and the tank hull an air cushion was established, upon which the hull could rest. The air in the suspension acted in the same manner as in the normal motor-car tyre: it softened the blows absorbed by the track during the motion of the tank, and passed them on to the hull. In order to fire the gun, the tank would stop and the air in the suspension released (by means of a throttle connected to a header-pipe) so that the hull would lower to the ground—forming a block-house. Provision for pneumatically lowering the hull enabled the vehicle to move with half-exposed running gear. This idea, to completely or partly lower the hull on to the ground, enabled the protection from enemy fire of the most vulnerable part of the vehicle—the suspension. In addition, by lowering the hull on to the ground, it would be possible to divert the powerful recoil loads from the suspension to the complete hull so that a firm firing platform could be established, and most of the tank's movement due to recoil could be eliminated.

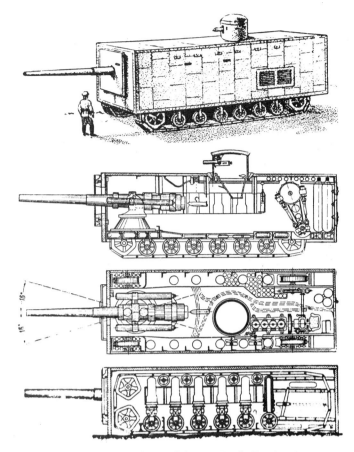

3. *General drawings of Mendeleev's Tank Project.*

Taking into account the excessive weight of his proposed vehicle, and the relative restriction of trains in a load-carrying capacity, Mendeleev incorporated a special arrangement to enable the vehicle to be mounted on railway bogies, and be propelled along with the aid of a steam engine.

To steer the vehicle, Mendeleev proposed a pneumatic-servo drive, acting through clutches, gearbox and steering mechanism. In case of a failure in this servo-drive system, an auxiliary control mechanism was provided. By means of either system, ammunition could also be applied to the gun, which would significantly increase its rate of fire. A machine-gun turret, able to rotate 360°, was to be mounted on the hull roof, and be lowered inside the hull by the aid of a pneumatic device. Pneumatics were also considered for regulating the track tension. A special compressor was to supply the necessary compressed air for operating the various pneumatic systems. It is interesting to note that Mendeleev also provided for four-post steering, allowing the vehicle to be controlled by any of the crew members should the driver be incapacitated, or his steering controls damaged by fire. Although not incorporated in his original drawings, Mendeleev contemplated employing inclined armour for increased immunity to shell penetration. However, owing to the industrial conditions at that time, no attempt was made to build a prototype of Mendeleev's tank project.

A second armoured vehicle project undertaken by Mendeleev (on which little data is available) differed in that the gun calibre was increased to 127 mm, two machine-gun turrets replaced the single one of the earlier type and the

side armour thickness was meanwhile decreased to 50 mm.
Nakashidze's armoured car. In keeping with the other armies
of the time, the horse provided transport for all arms in the
Tsarist Army, although as early as 1905 attempts were being
made to provide the cavalry with armoured cars for use in
the war against Japan. Shortly after the outbreak of the
war the Cossack body of the Manchurian Army in Siberia,
under Nakashidze, completed the design of an armoured
car project, but in spite of the support given by the Commander of the Manchurian Army, General Linevich, the
War Department refused to undertake the project in Russia.
Nakashidze's drawings were, however, despatched to
France, where the construction of his armoured car was
undertaken by the firm of Charron Girardot et Voigt.[7]
The initial order for 36 vehicles was, reluctantly, reduced to
one, and in 1905 the completed vehicle was delivered to the
Russians.[8] Designed from experiences in combat in Manchuria, the vehicle proved to be of exceptionally good
design. It had a large ground clearance and the wheels were
protected by armoured discs as opposed to the contemporary use of wooden spoked wheels. A portable bridging
device facilitated overcoming obstacles, such as trenches,
up to 3 metres in width. A machine-gun was mounted in a
revolving turret, and another stowed within the vehicle. The
armour was 4·5 mm thick, giving the car a combat weight
of 3 tons. Its maximum speed was 50 kph.[9]

In 1905, Nakashidze submitted an official report to the
War Department wherein he requested an official trial for
evaluating the possible future value of armoured cars in the
Russian Army. Following this, in 1906, a trial was carried
out with experimental armoured cars, moving along all
types of road and across dry, arable land, on a route from
St Petersburg via Oranienbaum (now Lomonosov) to
Venki.[10] Experimental machine-gun firing was carried out
at the Imperial Officer School firing range. Both stationary
and mobile firing trials were conducted at the school under
the supervision of Filatov, the Chief Range Officer at the
Oranienbaum School.[11] The results of these firing trials
were very favourable, and an armoured car was subsequently entered in the Krasnoseliskikh manoeuvres during
July 1906. The commission who tested the car stated that
it was of great value for reconnaissance in the rear and
flanking areas of the enemy, for liaison between fronts, for
disordering attacking enemy cavalry, for partisan work and
in the pursuit. The Commission stated that:

> The armoured car has a wide future as a supporting
> means of combat.[12]

Following this evaluation, it was proposed to redesign and
improve the armoured car at the Izhorski Zavod, but
although supported by the General Staff, the proposal was
turned down by the War Department.[13]

The early industrial position. The Tsarist régime, however,
failed to develop the vital industries, particularly in the field
of automobile and tractor manufacture. As a result of this,
the first Russian motor plant, the Russo-Baltic Company,
was only established at Riga in 1908. The poor conditions
of motor transport is exemplified by the number of vehicles
available: even in 1913 there were only 1,500 motor trucks
in the whole of Russia, and in 1914, at the start of hostilities,
there were only 11,000 vehicles in Russia, of which only

*4. The Russo-Baltic Armoured Car; 5. A Russo-Baltic-
Kégresse Half-Track; 6. The wooden working prototype of
Vezdekhod. The designer, A. A. Porokovskikov, is on the
right of the photograph; 7. Sectional view of Vezdekhod as
it was to be when completed.*

4

5

6

7

2,000 were lorries. During the period 1908–14 the Russo-Baltic Company manufactured only 450 automobiles, and even these were assembled from imported components. At the turn of the century there had been some attempts to establish small automobile factories, but these were never completed, this was also the position in other fields of industry; only a few wheeled tractors were turned out, including that in 1910 by Maminim.[14] The fact that Russia had no auto-tractor industry seriously hampered the manufacture of armoured fighting vehicles.

The Russo-Baltic armoured car. The first Russian-built armoured car was released from the Russo-Baltic Zavod during 1913, and this was followed by several more for the newly-founded Automobile Corps at the outbreak of World War I. This corps was mostly composed of imported foreign trucks and passenger car chassis, armed and armoured in Russia.[15] For various reasons, production of automobiles at the Russo-Baltic firm was stopped in 1914. On these armoured cars were placed dual controls, allowing them to be steered not only by the driver, but also by any other crew member. Duplicate controls were mounted at the rear of the hull and some parts of the rear chassis were reinforced to take the extra weight.[16]

Kégresse half-track cars. An interesting outcome of this period was the work carried out by the French engineer, Adolphé Kégresse, who ran the Tsar's Garage at Petrograd. In 1910 he adapted the American Holt Tractor principle into a flexible laminated rubber-metal track, which was used in the conversion of a light automobile to the first half-track. This invention was then completed at the Russo-Baltic Factory which, at the beginning of 1913, produced the 'Avtosani' (Auto-Sledge), a half-tracked car. During the Winter of 1913–14 a half-track produced by the Russo-Baltic firm was tested in Winter conditions (moving along icy roads, deep snow and so on), the results being very favourable to its adoption by the Army. On 21 February 1914 'Avtosani' completed a march from the Tsar's Garage to Pavlovsk and back. During this march, the vehicle travelled not only by road, but also through deep snow, over pits and bumps and snow drifts. It successfully negotiated all obstacles in its path. On good hard-surfaced roads it developed a speed of 56 verst[17] per hour. During this same Winter 'avtosani' completed a similar trek from the Tsar's Garage to Luga and back.[18]

The employment of the automobile in the Army, its tactical use and organization was meanwhile studied by a Colonel Dobrzhanskiy, and in 1913 he presented to the War Department a special report on the role of the armoured car in future war. He also took an active part in the design of an armoured car during 1913–14. Under the circumstances, his was a good summary of the methods of exploiting armoured cars; this report was presented to Lieutenant-Colonel Chemerzin,[19] and it outlined one of the first attempts to define the tactics of various forms of armoured units under combat conditions.

World War I tank projects. With the outbreak of the First World War, various projects began to take form simultaneously. On 14 July 1914 (old calendar) the Government proclaimed a general mobilization, and five days later Germany declared war on a Tsarist Russia that was not ready for war; Russian industry lagged far behind that of other European countries, and consisted predominantly of out-of-date mills and factories with antiquated machinery. Her agriculture could not provide a solid economic base for a prolonged war, with the result that the Tsarist Army suffered defeat after defeat. The German artillery deluged the Tsarist troops with shells, whilst the Russian Army lacked guns, ammunition and even rifles—sometimes three soldiers had to share one rifle. Whilst the war was in progress it was discovered that Sukhomlinov, the Minister of War, was in league with the German espionage service and actively discouraging the supply of munitions so as to leave the front without guns and rifles, whilst some of the Tsarist ministers and generals were surreptitiously assisting the success of the German Army in other ways.[20] This, if true, certainly explains the failure of the Tsarist Army to take up some of the proposed fighting vehicles put forward at the start of the War.

Bibergan wrote:

During the First World War 1914–18 we find the Czarist Army with surprisingly poor techniques. The War Ministry possessed only a small number of armoured cars, the combat role of which was rather obscure. The first month of the War showed the operational use of the armoured car to be greatly limited and that it was unable to meet the requirements demanded by modern war. The circumstances soon arose whereby warfare adopted a positional nature, and many specialists considered the idea of creating a vehicle which could destroy barbed-wire obstacles, cross trenches and shell-holes and accompany attacking infantry across the battle-field. At a very early stage . . . vehicles with high mobility were already being considered in Russia. . . .[21]

Vezdekhod. In August 1914, a Russian engineer by the name of Porokovskikov approached the Russian War Department with a project for an armoured and armed fully-tracklaying combat vehicle. (This project deserves particular attention since it could well be classed as a tank—representing an idea which would be exploited later in Britain through the efforts of Carden and Martell.) Porokovskikov wrote:

To the factor of mobility I took a fresh approach. Whilst observing a soldier crossing the line, it suddenly occurred to me that it is no joke running in to attack an enemy armed with machine-guns. And so, why could we not send to storm a trench, not only infantry, but also men protected against heavy lead, provided with an engine, covered in armour and armed with machine-guns? . . . The design problems I contemplated to be in the production of an endless-band, tracked running gear of the tractor type. The problem of steering with tracks also arose. An idea came to me: steering could be carried out on the spot by skidding, in braking one of the tracks. During the following days I thought of new considerations. In heavy conditions my vehicle should run on tracks, and along good roads it should run on wheels.[22]

Porokoskikov was a master machinist at a factory in Riga, and in August 1914 he presented his vehicle design to the authorities, the project being considered by the Deputy Chairman of the Air Fleet. This was for a fast-moving fighting vehicle, capable of moving not only by road, but also across country. By virtue of its mobility it was called 'Vezdekhod' ('Go Anywhere'). The inventor considered two possible types of running gear: in the first scheme it was proposed to have one wide, endless track mounted under the hull floor. For the second scheme it was proposed to employ two tracks on the American Holt principle. Porokovskikov wrote:

All these factors I incorporated in its design, and during mid August 1914, I handed this over to the HQ of the Supreme C-in-C. . . . An expert colonel gave the conclusion that my vehicle was not feasible. . . .[23]

The Main Military Technical Department did not approve the various drawings, documents, and estimated construction costs. On 21 December 1914, however, this material was submitted to the Chief Engineer Officer of the Army of the North-Western Front, who after studying the project, compiled a special report for the Army Commander. In this report he expressed the necessity of constructing a Vezdekhod-type vehicle and outlined how useful it would be in combat. At the Headquarters of the Supreme Commander-in-Chief, it was thought that the vehicle had great possibilities.

An official despatch dated 24 December (No. 6686) commissioned the Chief Engineer Officer of the Army of the North-Western Front to construct a prototype of this new combat vehicle. Since in the design and construction of the prototype it would prove simpler to undertake the first scheme with one wide track, this version was approved. For a prototype, on which to test the inventor's principles, it was not considered necessary at this stage to evaluate other than the running gear and automotive components, there being little doubt about the feasibility of the project, and resistance to the construction and testing of the vehicle being but very small.

On 13 January 1915 preparations were made for the construction of Vezdekhod. A workshop was hastily constructed in Riga, at the front of the Nizhegorod Regimental Barracks, and on 1 February work was begun on the construction of the first Russian tank. The workshops were provided with special equipment for carrying out this task, and actual manufacture was undertaken by highly-skilled military technicians—especially appointed to this task by the Chief Engineer Officer of the Army of the North-Western Front. In order not to delay tests of the automotive components, the hull of the first prototype was produced of wood, with neither turret nor armament. The exceptional skill and enthusiasm of the personnel resulted in minimum building time, and the work was completed on 15 March 1915.

In parallel with the assembly of the experimental chassis, work was also undertaken on the construction of an armoured hull. Experiments were carried out with temper-hardened stainless-steel leaf, between which was sandwiched soft-tempered mild steel (for absorbing the impact of bullets). Initial ballistic trials were carried out with separate plates of leaf armour, but later an armoured hull was constructed and attached to the chassis of a Russo-Baltic lorry for testing its ballistic immunity. The vulnerable suspension was to be protected by armoured sides. It was planned to mount two machine-guns located in a fully rotating turret.

The experimental chassis, utilising automobile components, consisted of a welded framework, on which were mounted four metal cylinders supported on ball-bearings. On the external surface of each cylinder was attached three sprocket rings, in which engaged the guide-horns of the track. At the front of the frame was a tension regulator which permitted the front axle, together with its cylinder, to move up and down in two forks. A similar arrangement for regulating the tension of the rear roller was also fitted. With the aid of these two tension regulators it was possible to control the tension of the single track under the hull floor. For steering the vehicle it was necessary to turn two steering wheels, placed one on each side of the vehicle. By means of a tiller-bar, acting through a normal automobile steering system, the driver could turn the forks on which these wheels were mounted and thereby steer the vehicle. In

the rear part of the hull was located the 20hp petrol engine which drove the rear cylinder via a planetary transmission and Carden shafts. The attitude of the track at the front of the vehicle aided in ascending obstacles, the track being raised slightly above the ground. The rear part of the track passed under the driving roller and rested on the ground. On good, hard roads the vehicle was supported at the front by the steering wheels, and the rear part of the track lay on the ground. When travelling across soft ground the steering wheels would submerge in the soil and all the weight-bearing surface of the track came into contact with the ground, the wide track provided a low ground pressure. In the latter case the steering wheels could create sufficient torque to alter the vehicle's direction. When moving along roads, therefore, the vehicle was practically wheeled, and across soft ground, tracked.

During the first preliminary automotive tests on 18 March 1915, it was found that the track shed during motion of the tank. Porokovskikov wrote:

To start the engine, I engaged the lever. The vehicle shook. I pressed the lever, to engage the clutch, and after a few turns—I heard a shout: 'The track has broken!'[24]

After a month of investigation the cause of track-shedding was detected and overcome by the installation of cylinders with sprockets in place of those which were formerly smooth. On 20 June 1915, Vezdekhod was once more sent for trials, this time in the presence of an official committee. A series of trenches, pot-holes, and other obstacles were laid out in the Regimental Barracks Square, across which Vezdekhod performed well. The vehicle also gave a display of turns, easily making rapid manoeuvres in a figure-eight pattern, and very quickly gathering speed. The results of the test commission were outlined in Report No. 4563:

It appears that Vezdekhod is a sound and practical idea; it can achieve a speed of 25 Verst/hour. In addition, Vezdekhod can ascend a slope of 40 degrees inclination, cross a trench three metres wide, and a vertical obstacle of $\frac{3}{4}$ metre. All significant holes and rough surfaces were crossed wherever tests were carried out. Vezdekhod steers easily during fast motion, and turns very satisfactorily. In all, Vezdekhod crosses terrain and obstacles impassable to conventional motor vehicles.

On 29 December 1915, during winter tests at Petrograd, Vezdekhod attained a speed of 40 Verst per hour, and generally performed very well. In order to deduce the speed which would be attainable by an armoured Vezdekhod, the prototype was ballasted to simulate the weight of the armoured hull—total weight about $3\frac{1}{2}$–4 tons. It was further intended to adapt this vehicle to swim, but this part of the work was not completed. The peculiar feature of Vezdekhod was its wide, single track, occupying practically the entire width of the vehicle. Its large supporting surface provided good mobility due to the small ground-pressure. It also had a high angle of approach for good obstacle ability.

It appears that a great deal of potential was exhibited by Vezdekhod during its final trials, and it should have attracted considerable attention in higher military circles. But this was not so: the Army expressed no interest in continuing work on the project. Even if they had the poor conditions of Russian industry at this time would have made manufacture of this vehicle in any quantity, impossible. Out of 18,000 Roubles allotted for work on this project by the Government, only 9,660 Roubles were actually spent on the vehicle—the remainder was kept by

8. *The experimental half-track by Colonel Gulikevich.*

the inventor. The famous Soviet tank historian Mostovenko has since stated:

> The original drawings of Vezdekhod have not yet been found [1958], but comparatively recently a document was discovered which contained basic drawings for its construction and also a photograph of the vehicle taken at the time of the tests. . . . In spite of the successful results of the trials, work on improving Vezdekhod was discontinued. The Main Military Technical Department did all it could to discourage experimental work, and to frustrate the organization of the industrial production of tanks in Russia. To various suggestions for further developing Vezdekhod, the Chief of the Main Military Technical Department replied with the following typical statement: 'Why should we meddle in this business? What is it to us?' From December 1915 to October 1916 all further work on Vezdekhod was forbidden. . . .[25]

Vasiliev's armoured vehicle project. At the beginning of 1915 Aleksandr Vasiliev completed design work and manufactured a prototype fighting vehicle.[26] His armoured and armed concept was described as a 'large armoured automobile'. It was stated to be able to overcome a vertical obstacle equal to one-quarter its own height, and a trench to one-third its own length. The Technical Committee of the Main Military Technical Department examined this proposal on 17 March 1915, together with a further proposal for introducing tracked vehicles into the Army, but declined to support the inventor. In January 1917 Vasiliev, after being acquainted with a photograph of English tanks in the press, bitterly wrote to the War Department:

> Pardon my enquiry into this affair, but why does this invention remain without progress in Russia when its manufacture abroad causes a sensation?[27]

Kazanskiy's project. A further project for a wheeled tank was taken up again in 1915, this time by Kazanskiy, a member of the Technical Committee of the Main Military Technical Department.[28] In an official report (No. 267) dated 6/4/15, the following statement was published:

> V. A. Kazanskiy has put forward a proposal for an armoured tractor. He suggests an armed and armoured three-wheeled tractor. He stated that the speed of this tractor could be around 15–20 Verst/hour—although this is not of great importance since the vehicle is intended primarily for penetrating the Front and exploiting beyond to locate and destroy enemy infantry.

The vehicle was intended for destroying barbed-wire obstacles, and was to be armoured so as to provide im-

munity to field-artillery shells and machine-gun fire, whilst itself being armed with several machine-guns. It was the inventor's opinion that it would be necessary to employ wide, large-diameter wheels. This project was also turned down.

Gulikevich's armoured vehicle. In July 1915 Colonel Gulikevich handed over to the Main Artillery Department a report, in which he stressed the necessity for making an armoured tracked fighting vehicle, armed with a light gun and several machine-guns:

> The armoured car, which at the moment is the only vehicle used to mount machine-guns, is deficient in that it is unable to negotiate every type of highway—and furthermore, it is easily stopped by barbed-wire obstacles; however, we could have . . . [a] 'tracked tractor', which is especially designed for moving over all forms of terrain—even ploughed fields. Its special construction . . . incorporates one more important feature; that is, it can break and trample over a barbed-wire obstacle. . . .[29]

Gulikevich called his proposed fighting vehicle 'Samodvigately' (Self-Propelled). In recommending the commencement of the necessary design work, he wrote:

> If experiments give reasonable results, it would be vital to begin its mass-production immediately. By estimation, I suggest that not less than 40 of these vehicles (armoured and armed 'Samodvigately') should be built together, since if we supply the Army in the field with only one or two vehicles the enemy would be able to use and manufacture it in larger numbers and size, than us.[30]

In his report the inventor not only demonstrated the urgency of making the tank and outlined its characteristics, but also indicated the conditions necessary for its successful tactical employment—in mass, without warning, and also how it should be deployed—not less than 40 vehicles in a unit.

Realizing the impossibility of organizing the complicated construction of such a vehicle in Tsarist Russia, Gulikevich planned to armour already existing tracked tractors. In order to carry out tests, the inventor was unable to obtain such a tractor so he was compelled to limiting his ideas to a half-tracked armoured car. The main features of Gulikevich's armoured half-track car were the use of metallic track, with power taken not only to the track but also to the front wheels.[31]

Porokovskikov's 'land cruiser'. During August 1915 the Technical Committee of the Main Military Technical Department considered a project for a 'Land Cruiser', by A. A. Porokovskikov. It was to consist of 5 or 6 units with large diameter rollers, on which was to be mounted an armoured hull. Between the first two or three rollers it was intended to mount the engine and driving compartments, and between the remaining rollers an armoured hull containing the armament, ammunition and gun crew.[32]

Bikovets' armoured tractor. In December 1915 Lieutenant-Instructor Bikovets put forward a proposed vehicle for destroying barbed-wire obstacles—a heavy armoured tractor with eight driven wheels. This weighed about 10 tons and was powered by a 65 hp engine. The tractor was tested on a specially built barbed-wire obstacle which it destroyed. Mostovenko remarked:

> Typical of the lackadaisical and routine attitude facing Russian inventors at that time, was the conclusion given by the Committee conducting the trials: . . . 'As a means of destroying barbed-wire, the employment of a large quantity of expensive metal on such a tractor would, of course, be refused. . . . Such a heavy tractor might well be

9

able to demolish a barbed-wire obstacle, but to make such a tractor withstand projectiles from enemy artillery whilst moving across a ploughed field . . . at a speed of 6–8 Verst/hour would be extremely difficult—if at all possible. . . .' Bikovets' proposal was turned down by the Technical Committee. At one sitting the Main Military Technical Department 'agreed to take it under consideration,' but nothing further was done. . . .[33]

The 'Tsar Tank'. A three-wheeled combat vehicle, which was intended for breaking through the German Front, was built and tested during 1915. The Russian War Minister, Lebedenko planned to make this vehicle one of the main secret projects of the War. He approached the Tsar with his project, presenting him with a small wooden model which he demonstrated on the Tsar's writing desk. The Tsar approved the project, and authorised Lebedenko to supervise the construction of a full-scale prototype. Involved in the design of this vehicle was Alexsi Mikulin (later a famous aircraft engine designer). Mikulin was called before Lebedenko who said:

You have been recommended to me by Nikolai Egrovich Khukovski as being an able and talented engineer. Would you agree to undertaking the drawings of my invention? With the aid of such a vehicle we might accomplish a breakthrough of the German Front, and Russia would win the War.[34]

After Mikulin had given his consent, Lebedenko explained his idea in detail, and asked:

Can you produce a wheel of ten metres diameter? If so, then we may build a vehicle in the form of a tricycle with two large, ten metre diameter wheels at the front, and a roller of twenty centimetres at the rear. In this way

9. A rare photograph showing the Tsar Tank on test; **10.** *The Reno-Russkiy Tank Project (1915);* **11.** *The Austin-Kégresse Armoured Half-Track (turrets in diagonal arrangement).*

the vehicle could cross over any trenches and buildings, and would weigh about 60 tons. . . .[35]

In the design of the vehicle Lebedenko was also assisted by Zhukovskiy (who later became a pioneer of Soviet aviation) and Professor Steckin (later member of the USSR Academy of Science). Zhukovskiy directed the design of the enormous wheels and Professor Steckin made the remaining calculations. Initial construction of the prototype vehicle was carried out in deep secrecy in Khamovnikakh Square, in Moscow, but the final assembly of the vehicle took place in a clearing in the dense forest surrounding the Orudiev Marshalling Yards near the town of Dmitrova. The vehicle was completed during August 1915 and when trial run weighed 40 tons. The completed vehicle, which resembled a large field-artillery gun carriage, consisted of two large spoked wheels 9 metres in diameter with a smaller roller at the rear for steering. The hull was comprised of a lattice framework on which was mounted the turret. The 'tank' was powered by two 250 hp Sunbeam engines—one driving each wheel and also assisting the steering. From the engine on each wheel shafts drove two automobile wheels which, in turn, drove a large spoked wheel.

In the construction of this vehicle Lebedenko spent a very large sum of money for that time—210,000 Roubles. The work was financed by 'Souzom Gorodov' (The National Treasury), and directed by the Main Military Technical Department. The vehicle became famous as the

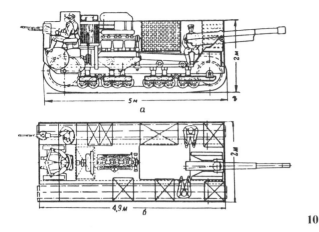

10

11

'Tsar Tank', being larger than any other fighting vehicle ever produced.

During the first trial the vehicle moved slowly forward, knocked down a stand in front of a huge tree, and ended up with the rear roller embedded in the mud. It was suggested that a larger roller be installed to decrease the ground pressure, but the Technical Commission (supervising the construction of the vehicle) would not grant permission for continuing the project, since it was apparent that it was very vulnerable to enemy fire. The vehicle was abandoned in the Orudiev Railway Yard until it was recovered for scrap in 1923. Later on, Mikulin wrote that he had been disappointed with this vehicle project, which he considered superior to a vehicle with tracks.

Reno Russkiy projects. In 1915 a tank project was undertaken having the following characteristics:[36] weight—20 tons; crew—4; armament—107 mm gun and large-calibre machine-guns; armour—10 to 12 mm; maximum speed—7 kph; engine—200 hp. The vehicle was to have had a sprung suspension. When presented to the Main Military Technical Department on 10 August 1916, this project—as with all the other proposals—failed to receive the necessary support. According to Watyn-Watyniecki,[37] this vehicle (which resembled more an SP gun carriage than a tank) was designed and investigated by the 'Russkiy-Renault' establishment at Rybinski.

Another project put forward about this time for a 'Large Powered Armoured Tractor',[38] was intended to have had a weight of 12 tons, a speed of 12 kph, and be armed with a 75 mm gun and machine-guns.

Early armoured car employment. Meanwhile the first Russian armoured car action took place during the War in

East Prussia, and another followed later in Poland in the vicinity of Lodz. The success of these operations was outlined in the official reports:

> The armoured car proved itself to be of great value and to have much potential for supporting actions, especially in the attack. . . .[39]

A further report from the 2nd Army Staff, North-Western Front (dated 3/1/15) stated:

> In the battle of Lodz the effect of machine-gun fire from armoured cars dispersed enemy columns advancing along roads.[40]

The First Army Staff gave the following account of combat actions of the first armoured troops:

> The combat record of the automobile during November showed that—when used in reasonable numbers—a place for this new arm is certainly justified.[41]

There were, however, certain disadvantages in using armoured cars: reliance upon good roads made such a vehicle completely unsuitable for use in winter conditions, owing to the poor state of tracks. There was an urgent necessity for creating a new type of combat vehicle having good mobility in terrain where roads were nonexistent or unnegotiable.[42] The winter of 1914–15 revealed conclusively the unsuitability of armoured cars for operations under winter conditions.

Army adoption of half-track vehicles. After the outbreak of World War I half-tracked tractors began to be employed for towing artillery. Experience with these vehicles displayed the advantage of the tracked vehicle over the wheeled one for mobility and tractive effort, and motivated the application of this concept to an armoured fighting vehicle capable of advancing across-country under difficult conditions. As a result it was officially declared in 1915 that, in order to use automobiles in snow, it would be desirable to employ a vehicle like the Russo-Baltic half-tracked car, and the Putilov Firm (later renamed Kirov), which was the largest of the St Petersburg plants, was ordered to produce armoured and transporter half-tracks for the Russian Army. Three-hundred half-track assemblies of the Kégresse type, were ordered for installation on armoured cars during 1916.

During tests in August 1916, near Petrograd, a half-tracked armoured car developed a speed of 40 kph. It easily travelled across open country and swamps. In the same year a half-tracked armoured car was test run for 1,500 km, and proved to be very successful. On poor road conditions it averaged a speed of 9–10 kph, whilst on good roads 20–22 kph. This half-track weighed about 5·3 tons. The armament consisted of two machine-guns, and the armour (designed to provide immunity to conventional small-arms bullets at ranges above 50 paces) was on a 7 mm basis. The vehicle was manned by 5 men. In order to increase the mobility of half-tracked cars, they were provided with additional wheels and skis for overcoming ditches and travelling through loose snow.

In October 1916 the Putilov firm built a new turret for armoured cars, mounting a machine-gun such that it could direct fire both on to the ground and at aerial targets. Turrets of this type were ordered for mounting on 30 half-tracked armoured cars (two turrets per vehicle) during autumn 1916. These half-tracks, based on the British Austin armoured cars, were completed by the October Revolution, and several were employed in the defence of Petrograd during autumn 1919. Mostovenko wrote:

> It is of interest to note that in some official documents released during the period 1919–20, half-tracked ar-

moured cars became referred to as 'Russian Type Tanks'. Actually, during this period armoured half-tracked cars carried out the role of light tanks more successfully than, for example, French light tanks—which proved to be considerably inferior to these Russian vehicles in mobility. . . .[43]

The success of the half-tracked armoured cars resulted in a directive in the autumn of 1916, to equip all basic models of armoured cars with half-track assemblies, but owing to confusion and devastation during the rising this undertaking was not completed. In addition to producing half-tracked armoured cars, however, work was also carried out on improving the mobility of conventional armoured cars, particularly with respect to overcoming barbed-wire obstacles.

Abortive projects, 1916–17. On 23 November 1916 the committee for armoured automobiles considered a model and drawings of a fighting vehicle weighing around 10 tons proposed by engineer Yakovlev. The main feature of his design was the employment of 12 wheels, all driven. The armour basis of the sheet metal hull was to be 9 mm, and the armament to consist of 6 machine-guns, whilst the vehicle was to be able to cross rough terrain and overcome various obstacles. In considering the project, however, the commission declined from giving any decision.[44]

About the same time another fighting vehicle project was considered, which was to weigh about 50 tons. Its running gear was to consist of 10 large-diameter wheels, 6 to be driven and the remaining 4 to be steered. Provision was made for a 'two-storey' arrangement: the upper storey to comprise the fighting compartment, and the lower to accommodate the engine and transmission. Protected by 9 mm armour, the vehicle was intended to mount 6 guns and several machine-guns.[45]

Also in 1916 an inventor named Chaykovskiy presented to the Main Ship Building Department a proposal for building an amphibious armoured car. After examining this project, the following statement was given:

An automobile, capable of moving in water, is not required by the Navy Department.[46]

A further project was proposed for a 'Super Tortoise', to weigh around 200 tons, and to be armed with two 8 inch howitzers, several guns of smaller calibre and 10 machine-guns. The armour basis was to be between 20 and 30 mm; the vehicle was to be powered by a 300 hp engine and to run on rollers 2·5 and 6·6 metres in diameter.[47]

In October 1917 a Cossack Officer, by the name of Kirichenko, put forward a suggestion for a self-propelled combat vehicle incorporating a very novel mechanism for moving along, but unfortunately practically no details of his project are preserved.[48]

A project for an armoured transporter ('Armoured Autocar'), based on a lorry chassis, was proposed by engineer-mechanic Sestroretsky, an employee at the armament firm of Vasiliy Konovalov. The inventor wrote:

A modern force, deployed on a wide front, naturally requires modern means of transportation. As a rapid means of transporting such a force . . . [it is] proposed to use, on a wide scale, autocars of three and five tons capacity . . . provided with armour protection on all sides with a thickness of 4 and 6 mm. Each such car should be provided with one machine-gun, mounted in a turret at the front having a good arc of fire, as well as side-slit openings with strong shields for use by riflemen. Inside the armoured hull could be seated 20 men. . . . [The] wheels of the autocar should be adapted for our country

roads, the rear wheels, protected by steel discs, being fitted with hard-wearing double tyres. The front wheels should also be protected by armour plate. . . .[49]

Sestroretsky also proposed that these autocars should be used for transporting ammunition, and for the evacuation of wounded from the battlefield, and numerous other tasks. He put forward a greatly detailed account of his projected vehicle, and produced detailed drawings of it; but no interest was shown in this project by the authorities.

At the beginning of 1917 the Main Military Technical Department considered a detailed report put forward for moving Russian artillery by tractors. In this report also presented was a theoretical basis for the widespread introduction of tracked prime-movers for artillery. The object of the study was to determine the required type of tractor and also to consider the feasibility of introducing a self-propelled gun carriage with tracks. Being outside of the industrial and economic capacity of Russia at that time, however, the project was turned down.[50]

Over the period 1914–16 Russian inventors also put forward suggestions generally relating to tank technology. In 1914 Bazhanov manufactured and successfully tested a wheel with internal shock absorbers, intended for use in armoured cars and artillery carriages, but this did not receive the attention it deserved. In the same year Chemerzin used a periscopic device for armoured cars.[51]

On 1 June 1915 engineer Vasiliy Rebikov proposed a two-storey turret arrangement for armoured cars. On the main revolving turret he proposed mounting a further turret armed with a machine-gun, the latter to be provided with a means of turning independently of the former. The inventor carried out several tests in mounting armament in armoured cars, but none of these were accepted. The location of armament was held by Rebikov to be one of the prime considerations in combat vehicle design;[52] but the problem of increasing the accuracy of fire from armoured vehicles also took the attention of Russian inventors. When firing on the move the prime factor becomes the unfavourable effect of the vehicle's motion. This effect, due to vibration, may be considerably—or even totally—damped by stabilising the armament. During 1916 a Petrograd firm proposed an electrogyroscopic stabiliser for the armament of armoured cars, in order to increase the accuracy of fire on the move. This the War Department turned down on the grounds that it was too cumbersome.[53] Mostovenko wrote:

The vital support for all these ideas and even the improvement of existing equipment, was not given by the Tsarist officials. It is generally known that it is necessary to ventilate the fighting compartment of armoured cars (i.e., clear it of cordite fumes), or else the rate of fire of the armament is considerably limited. For a successful solution to this problem Russian engineers once more endeavoured during 1915. As the result a ventilator was built at the Armoured Department Military Automobile School for the turret of an Armoured car. Examination of this suggestion by the Commission of Armoured Cars (on 22 December 1916) resulted in the following statement: 'a special device for ventilation is not required; by slightly opening the hatch in the turret roof this problem could be overcome.[54]

At the beginning of 1916 Kuziminim designed an improved armoured car having 6 driven wheels, and somewhat later, Przhevaliskiy proposed a device for destroying barbed-wire obstacles, which he intended to be mounted on an armoured car. None of these projects were accepted.[55]

Official negligence in this respect could not go unnoticed

12. *Vezdekhod No. 2 (or 16r)*.

by the general public. Mostovenko wrote:

    During September 1916 appeared the first reference in Russia to the use of a new English weapon—the 'Land Ship'. This appeared in the gazette *Modern Times* (No. 14568), dated 25 September 1916 (old calendar), and also in the *Petrograd Gazette* (No. 253). A further report appeared in *Modern Times* (No. 14572), dated 29 September 1916 (old calendar), entitled 'Land Fleet—Russian invention', which disclosed the failure on the part of the Main Military Technical Department to support Russian work on building the first of this new weapon—the high mobility combat vehicle. . . .[56]

Even though the Russian claim to having built the first 'tank' may be well founded, this does not necessarily mean that they invented the tank. The tank, as an individual machine, is only part of the problem. Its evolution was the result of a great number of individual efforts in various countries, and in various spheres. The important consideration is the eventual realization of the practicability of the tank, the solution of all the technical problems involved, and then the farsightedness and concentrated efforts on the part of the British in producing it in mass and employing it tactically. It is not only the man who invents something who should be praised, but also the one who realises its potential, resolves a method of using it, and modifies it accordingly— and then uses it effectively!

Vezdekhod No. 2. Shortly after this article there followed an imperial enquiry into the failure to provide the Russian Army with tanks. To humour public opinion, the Chief of the Main Technical Department sanctioned the design of an improved Vezdekhod, again by Porokovskikov—Vezdekhod No. 2, or, as another means of distinguishing it from its predecessors, Vezdekhod 16r. The project was soon completed, and on 19 January 1917 the vehicle was despatched to the new Armoured Department Automobile Unit of the Main Military Technical Department. Its examination was considerably delayed by a period of more than 10 months.[57]

The running gear of Vezdekhod No. 2 combined elements of those from the automobile and tracked tractor. The rubber endless track, located under the hull floor, revolved on four sprung drums. The rear drum drove the track through a transmission. On the two extreme drums were mounted four automobile wheels, with larger diameters than the drums. The front drum was sprung to improve its obstacle ability. The front pair of wheels were steered as in a conventional automobile.

When running on firm roads Vezdekhod No. 2 ran on the wheels alone (as with the original vehicles) and operated as a normal automobile; the track rotated free of the ground. On loose soil, as before, the wheels submerged in the ground, and the track—now in contact with the ground —drove the vehicle along. Turning was carried out with the front wheels as on the road. The armour was 8 mm thick, and the armament consisted of from three to four machine-guns. Two to three machine-guns could be placed in the turret, which allowed each machine-gun to be deployed independently of the other. The transmission steering mechanism and automotive components were located in the rear of the hull; at the front of the vehicle was located the driver's compartment, and in the centre lay the fighting compartment. A special partition was provided between the engine and fighting compartments, with a hatch for servicing the engine.

Tanks from abroad. In 1916 Russia was lagging greatly behind her allies in war production, and what little existed of the poorly-equipped automobile industry had no facilities for the production of vehicles in large quantities. The employment of tanks on the battlefields of Europe by Britain and France caused a general requirement for this new weapon from all the Allies, Tsarist Russia being no exception. Although Britain and France were obliged to America for a large order for tanks, the political situation necessitated the compliance with Russia's request. Both Britain and France supplied the Russians with tanks; 25 heavy Mk V tanks and 8 Whippet tanks were shipped from England and several (believed to be 100) lighter Renault FT tanks from France. The majority of these were eventually issued to the forces under the White commanders Denekin and Wrangel.

2 The Foundations of the Soviet Tank Industry

The birth of Soviet armour. In order to consolidate Soviet power, the old State machinery was shattered and a new Soviet staff machine set up in its place. This included nationalization of the land and all large-scale industry, and the speedy conclusion of the War, for this was hampering the consolidation of the Soviet powers more than anything else. All these measures were to be carried out between the end of 1917 and mid-1918.[58] During World War I the Communist Party paid much attention to encouraging interest in new arms amongst army personnel—particularly the 'Avtobronie' section of the Russian Army. This was successful in that the majority of the armoured troops, mainly composed of workers, came over to the Soviet side. An overwhelming number of armoured troops, deployed in Petrograd during the October Revolution defected to the side of the Revolution. The value of this Petrograd Avtobronie division during the October Revolution was outlined in *Pravda* on the First Anniversary of the event:

> The passing of armoured sections on to the side of the Military Revolutionary Council (late in the night of October 24) greatly accelerated the ultimate victory of the revolutionaries.

Prior to the outbreak of the Civil War, a Russian banker by the name of Ryabushinski, had obtained a concession from Italy to build Fiat light tanks (an Italian copy of the French Renault FT), at a charge of 1,000,000 Roubles. The Russian War Department had granted him an 8,000,000 Rouble loan to commence this undertaking, but his progress had been slight. His plant was comprised of a series of ill-equipped and disconnected workshops, although there were facilities for a forge, foundry and machine-shop. This plant was taken over by the Soviets during the Civil War, who expanded it and employed it to overhaul captured vehicles (cars and trucks which had been used by the Tsarist Army). In the course of the First World War another small plant was set up at Puzynev.[59]

The Communists established the Supreme Council of National Economy to administer the industry of the country, and decreed the formation of the Red Army and Navy. From the very start the new Red Army appreciated the value of the tank in its new military strategy, and made great efforts to construct tanks and armoured cars by its own efforts. The Revolution, and the War, had seriously impaired what little Russian industry there was: the factories and plants which had been responsible for the repair and conversion of tanks, armoured cars, and other automotive equipment were mainly centralised in and around Petrograd and Moscow, and in the Ukranian industrial regions. Those situated in the Ukraine were virtually

destroyed by the war, and the Russo-Baltic plant had been evacuated to Petrograd during the course of the war.

On 31 January 1918 the People's Commissariat issued a special directive covering the formation of the first Central Command Organization for armoured sections—resulting in the foundation of the Armoured Department Council (Centrobron). The function of Centrobron was to organize armoured sections within the Army, and also to provide a basic training and education nucleus.[60] The first armoured sections were comprised exclusively of armoured cars and armoured trains. The construction of armoured trains and armoured cars was undertaken at firms such as Putilov, Izhorski, Obukhovskiy, and several others.

In August 1918 Centrobron was placed under the command of the Director of Military Engineering, and by November the new armoured force was in possession of 23 armoured trains and 38 armoured car detachments, with a total of 150 armoured cars. With subsequent defeats of White forces this number gradually increased. During 1919, special departments were formed to control and develop the use of armoured vehicles, and efforts were made to provide more schools and State technical institutes necessary for training technicians and cavalry officers. The Red Army had no tanks actually in service before 1919.[61]

During 1919, the Putilov firm released a batch of half-tracked armoured cars, which were successfully employed in winning the battle against Udenich. Having fairly good mobility, half-tracked armoured cars were employed in minor interactions with infantry and cavalry. performing the tactical role of tanks. During the battle with Udenich, in October 1919, 5 half-tracked armoured cars were attached to the 2nd Rifle Division, 7th Army, and took part in the battle around Petrograd. These vehicles supported the offensive with covering machine-gun fire. The unexpected attack caused the enemy to retreat in panic to Tsarsky Selu (later Pushkin). Half-tracked armoured cars were also employed successfully during the counter-offensive to take Karlino.[62]

From the defeated Tsarist forces the Soviets captured several tanks. In the Ukraine, during the spring of 1919, Soviet troops captured a group of the English Mk V heavy tanks (called 'Ricardos' by the Russians, from the make of the engines used to power them). A further 20 of these were captured from Denekin in the autumn. Later, more tanks were captured in Northern Russia from Wrangel with the liberation of Rostov-on-Don, and 20 French Renaults,

together with several Whippet tanks, were taken at Odessa. In addition, the Soviets collected some 10,000 motor vehicles from the Tsarist forces. One of the Renault tanks captured during the Spring of 1919 by the 2nd Ukrainian Soviet Army Group was sent to Moscow as a present to Lenin. Bibergan wrote:

A detailed knowledge of tanks began only at the end of 1918 and the beginning of 1919, when the White guards were provided with vehicles of all types for fighting the Red Army. Most of these vehicles were captured by our Red Army. By the end of 1920 the tank trophy park exceeded 100. The basic 'providers' of tanks to the Red Army were Denekin, Wrangel, Udenich, and Chaykovskiy, together with General Miller and the White Polish. . . .[63]

The first Soviet tank. By mid 1919 the Soviet Regime had become reasonably stable, and the various conditions necessary for the development of the armed forces were beginning to take form. The basis of Soviet tank construction was laid towards the end of 1919. The Higher National Economic Council (VSNch) formed a special central organ for directing the war industry during September 1919 called the Military Industrial Council (SVP); under the Chairmanship of VSNch president P. A. Bogdanov, a directive was passed to begin building tanks. A high priority was placed upon this task by Lenin. Bibergan wrote:

Towards the end of the Civil War, in order to increase our combat tank park, it was decided to begin our own production of this type of vehicle. The most convenient model for our industry at that time appeared to be the French Renault tank. The main difficulty was in producing the engine and transmission. No modern engine was available. We then decided to employ the engine of the 1½-ton Fiat automobiles. A special construction bureau was formed, whose fundamental task was to reconstruct this engine for tank use. In the construction of this engine 60 per cent new parts were employed. . . .[64]

Following this, the Council commenced the development of a light tank on the basis of the French Renault FT type as captured at Odessa and on the Petrograd Front. Samples of this vehicle had been shipped back to the Krasno-Sormovo factory, at Bryansk (Nizhni-Novgorod) for repair. Throughout the period 1918–19 this factory had carried out the manufacture of armoured trains and the maintenance of the Volga Fleet. In autumn 1919 the Council were instructed to form a special tank construction group, which

13. *British Lanchester Model 1914 Armoured Cars in the hands of Soviet troops, 1915;* **14.** *Painting by Soviet artist I. A. Vladimirov, entitled 'The capture of Mk V Tanks from Wrangel at Krymie';* **15.** *Mk V 'Ricardo' tanks in Soviet service.*

14

15

was successfully accomplished. This group, placed under the direction of Khrulev, consisted of experienced designers such as Krimov, Saltanov, Moskovkin and others. It was instructed by Lenin personally to provide the Red Army with tanks as soon as possible. Investigations were undertaken for a new light tank design in which Lenin took a great interest. Simultaneously with the preparation of the drawings. Nefedov organized the production side, establishing suitable workshops for building tank components. The actual construction work was supervised by Chepurhov, Volkov and Yastrebov. Mostovenko wrote:

> Manufacture of tanks under the poor conditions of the Civil War was carried out with great difficulty; one factory alone was not capable of manufacturing all the various components of such a complicated vehicle, and therefore this was distributed between three factories....

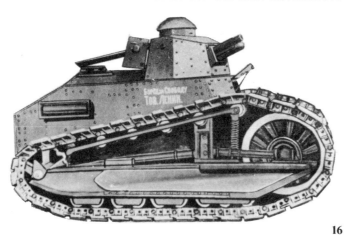

16

Many intricate problems were overcome during the production. Not only was experience obtained in building a complicated combat vehicle, but also in building the special components—for example, the gearbox, splinedshafts, etc. Major problems in the manufacture and assembly of the armoured hull were also overcome. To organize the production of tanks in such a short period of time was a great achievement. The feats of work achieved by the Group at Krasno-Sormovo, under the difficult conditions of the Civil War, enabled the solution of difficult problems, formerly beyond the capability of Russia.[65]

The armoured hull and turret (consisting of 8 and 16 mm plates) were to be built at the Izhorski factory at Kolpino, South of Petrograd; the engine and transmission at AMO (Moscow Automobile Factory—later AZIL, Automobiliniy Zavod Imeni Likhachev); and final assembly of the tank was to be carried out at the Army Sormovo Workshops. Towards the end of the following January, after two months of preliminary design work, construction of the first prototype Soviet tank was commenced. The KS (Krasno-Sormovo) light tank, as it later became known, was completed by 31 August 1920—seven months after the start of the programme. Bach draws attention to foreign influence:

> The inability at that time to create a tank industry led to a decision to make do with captured and modified French tanks. Thus, in 1923 arose the 'Russkiy-Renault M-23', which was produced in the Sormovosky Factory under the guidance of Swedish and American engineers, and proved to be an able tank. In a short time it was placed in series production. The optics came from

Germany, the gear-box from the USA and the engine, a commercial water-cooled 4-cylinder Fiat of 45 hp, came from Italy.[66]

This tank was shipped from the factories to the proving grounds at Kiev to undergo acceptance trials with the Army. After trials had been completed, on 1 December, the Military Industrial Council reported the completion of the first Soviet tank to Lenin. This first tank, which also became known as the 'Russkiy-Renault', was given the impressive title 'Borets za Svobodu Tov. Lenin' (Freedom Fighter Comrade Lenin). On the same day Lenin issued a directive for the manufacture of a further 15 tanks to be completed by the following spring; it was planned to build 5 platoons each of 3 tanks—2 of these armed with machine-guns, and 1 armed with a 37 mm gun. The Soviets were now in a position to commence home tank construction. Following

17

this first tank, by 1922 a further 14 of this type were built—including: 'Parizhskay Kommuna' (Paris Commune), 'Proletariat', 'Burya' (Tempest), 'Pobeda' (Victory), 'Krasno Borets' (Red Champion) and 'Ilya Muromets'. The tanks used a clutch designed by Porokovskikov for his original light tank. These factories also repaired captured tanks for redistribution to Soviet units. Mostovenko wrote:

> By virtue of its combat characteristics, the Sormovo tank was not inferior to contemporary foreign tank models of this type, and certain design features were excellent....[67]

In January 1920 some 100 tanks which had been captured from the White Armies had been reworked and distributed amongst the armoured car detachments, which, by this time, had received some basic training in their use. The availability of several tanks, captured in fairly good condition, enabled the formation in January 1920 of a Soviet Army 'Avtotanki' unit. Each Avtotanki unit (on establishment) had 3 tanks, 2–3 light automobiles, 3–4 lorries, and 2–3 motorcycles, but the first 'Avtotanki' unit became the 1st Tank Detachment, and was equipped with the English Mk V tanks. The Military Revolutionary Council set up the Inspectorate of Armoured Units and instructions were issued to employ tanks in the RKKA (Raboche-Krestiyanskoy Krasnoy Armii—Workers-Peasant Red Army). The commanders of all armoured units along the front were placed under this new organization. Up until then the governing body had not been resolved.

Early Soviet designs. Whilst official tank development proceeded on the basis of the Renault FT light tank, there were other attempts at producing armoured vehicles by Soviet engineers. In 1919 Maksimov produced a small one-man ultra-light tank called 'Zhitonoski' (Shield Bearer). This tankette, which weighed only 2¼ tons, was of conventional design although the driver was prone in order to reduce the overall height. It was about 7 ft long and mounted a 7·62 mm Maxim machine-gun at the extreme front, in a sponson with limited traverse (some 15 degrees). The armour was on a 10 mm basis, and the tankette was powered by a 40 hp Fiat engine (made under licence by AMO) giving it a speed of 15 mph. The vehicle was limited to a great extent owing to the discomfort of the driver, lack of vision and restriction in using the armament, and was consequently rejected by the Military-Industrial Council. It was too much to expect one man to steer the vehicle and shoot at the same time. Although doomed to failure, it was nevertheless an interesting project. 16 trial vehicles were produced by Sormovo during the period 1920–22.

1916 on the South-Western Front, breaking through the enemy front simultaneously in several sectors. The result of these attacks on a broad front diverted the enemy reserve forces and enabled a breakthrough up to a depth of 45 miles.[68]

The new theoretical strategies used during the Civil War have been attributed to Lenin. In order to develop military strategy it was first necessary to unite the people, provide an industrial state and an abundance of technical and skilled workers. The first significant attempts at bringing all this about were made in mid 1918; Trotsky tried to get Allied military aid for re-organizing the Soviet armed forces, and asked for British and French instructors to train the Red Army; but since the Allies did not recognise the new Soviet Government there was no compliance with these requests.[69]

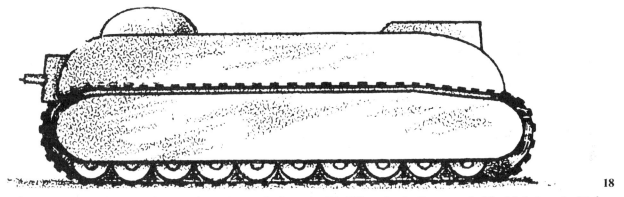

18

16. *The original Soviet KS tank, 'Freedom Fighter Comrade Lenin'; **17.** KS tanks in Petrograd; **18.** Maksimov's Light Tank 'Zhitonoski'.*

Tactical ideas. Throughout 1920 great efforts were made to speed-up the organization of technical units—particularly armour, artillery, aviation and engineering; the Tenth Party Congress was basically responsible for the introduction of the new economic policy, and concerned itself with the streamlining of these formations. Armoured units were assigned to co-operate with infantry and cavalry units, and were to carry out attacks on the flanks and rear of the enemy. It was envisaged using tanks for breaking through fortified enemy positions, destroying barbed-wire and other obstacles, providing fire-support to troops, causing havoc in the rear areas of the enemy, capturing and holding positions in the line of approach of Soviet troops and so on. The advance of the tanks was to be supported by artillery. The basic role of the tank was therefore considered to be in direct support of the infantry, but it was also intended that the tank should be used in defence and in counter-attacks.

The forerunners of tank forces in Russia became the armoured car and armoured train units which played an important part throughout the Civil War. During this struggle the Soviet Army gained experience of strategic offensive operations, defensive tactics based on the employment of rear defence lines, and counter-attacks by several armies on adjacent fronts. In addition, the Red Army carried out such interesting manoeuvres as enveloping the enemy by rapid flanking tactics, turning movements, and deep penetration into the enemy's rear areas by cavalry units. Flanking attacks were apparent in the routing of the armies under Kolchak, Denekin and Wrangel. New techniques of obtaining a breakthrough on a positional front were devised and often applied by Soviet commanders, as in

The first tank combat that the Soviet Army fought took place on 4 July 1920 at Zyabki Railway Station. In addition to the 2nd Tank Detachment, it involved Armoured Train No. 8 and Armoured Car Detachment No. 14. The battle demonstrated the combined use of tanks, armoured cars and armoured trains in an attack supported by the 33rd Infantry Division.

The enemy fortified position laying between Svyada and Dolgoe consisted of three lines of trenches protected by barbed-wire obstacles, and was strongly defended. The position was penetrated in a carefully prepared attack, with the aid of the 2nd Detachment equipped with three heavy tanks. Mostovenko describes the action:

On the moonlit night of the 1st/2nd July the tank detachment carried out a reconnaissance of the surrounding country right up to the front line of enemy trenches. They reconnoitred suitable crossing points along the river, toured the perimeter of the enemy defences, and planned the attack routes for each individual tank. The task for the tanks was difficult; they were required to advance to the enemy trenches across open country. In order to divert the attention of the enemy, therefore, armoured trains were employed. Prior to the tank action, the positions were prepared by artillery. Two hours after beginning the assault the tanks broke through the defences. The breakthrough achieved by the tanks was then exploited by cavalry, infantry and Avtobroni detachments. The enemy was completely routed and fled in disorder. Armoured cars supported the thrust and pursued the retreating enemy troops. Many prisoners were taken in this battle—together with 8 guns, some 20 machine-guns, and numerous other trophies.[70]

This was a good demonstration of co-operation between tanks, infantry and armoured trains. The latter were also used in the battle to distract artillery fire and thereby ease the task of the tanks. Armoured trains supported troops with artillery and machine-gun fire in the Soviet defence of the railway track, Zyabki Station and terminus. They were manned by boarding parties to assist in carrying out tactical tasks.

On 1 August 1920, after partial demobilisation, the Red Armoured Force was composed of 10 tank detachments, 44 armoured car detachments, 2 brigades and 7 independent division. These units totalled about 100 tanks, 103 armoured trains and 150 armoured cars.

The Soviet Army later used tanks in the 'liberation' of Tiflis, in the Caucusus, on 25 February 1921, and at Volochai. (Even though the European war had come to an end the Soviet Army was still fighting the Poles on the South-Eastern Front.) Re-worked Renaults were employed during the actions in Poland, the Ukraine and the Caucusus. The main strength of the newly-formed detachments consisted of Mk Vs and Renault light tanks, but soon the KS tanks began to appear. Production of this model continued at Sormovo throughout the war, but was suspended in 1922 after the completion of only 15. The KS tank compared well with the original Renault in both firepower and armour protection, but although the authorities seemed satisfied with the tank, its service use demonstrated the requirement for a more compact, lighter tank with better armament. Bach wrote:

The Russians, early on, recognized the advantage to a modern army of the radius of action and mobility facilitated through the total mechanization of all troop arms. On the basis of practical experience gained during the Russo-Polish War, the Russians immediately began to experiment for years without success, with new ideas and equipment in order to attain the lead in European tank technology, with which—at that time—they could not compete. . . .[71]

The Teplochod AM project. In late 1919, therefore, the tank construction group sought the design of a completely new tank, and on 2 November 1919 the magazine *Izvestia Narodnovo Komissara po Voyenniem Dielam*, No. 244, published the conditions for a competition sponsored by the Council for the best tank design. Of the many submitted, first prize (totalling 250,000 Roubles) was awarded to an amphibious tank solution, designated Teplochod (Motor Ship) Type AM submitted by the Izhorski Factory. The design was carried out at the factory under the direction of ship engineer G. V. Kondratev. During 1921 the construction of two such tanks was begun. These tanks were amphibious, weighed about 10 tons and were armed with a 76·2 mm gun, mounted in a fully-rotating turret. The crew consisted of three men, and the power unit was a 90 hp engine transversely mounted. When in water the tank was propelled by a 3-bladed propeller.

A second competition proclaimed during 1922, now sponsored by the Central Armoured Force Command of the RKKA (which had been formed in May 1921), resulted in a further 7 different tank designs, but none of these were completed owing to the dissolution of the Central Command during 1923, and the construction progress of the two original amphibious tanks was interrupted. Bibergan wrote:

The reason for this was, in the first place, that with the dismissal of the Armoured Command there was no single co-ordinating centre for directing this work. All were controlled by AU, which overloaded its own work. Secondly, in industry itself there was no co-ordinated technical centre, able to direct all the spheres of tank design and construction; the production of armament, armour, engines and transmission, suspensions and minor equipment. . . . As regards armour and armament we were in a good position, but in the field of engines and transmissions our industry in 1922 was ill-prepared, and the design and production of tractors was only in the embryo stage.[72]

In designing tanks during the early 1920s, various new types of transmission and suspension were designed and tested. Over the period 1920–21 experimental work was carried out on tractors at factories such as Zaprorzhe (formerly the Alexandrovski Steel Works), and Kolmna Locomotive Works, south-east of Moscow. In 1920 the Bolshevik Plant in Leningrad built a prime-mover with automotive aid from AMO but major tractor production during this early period was undertaken by the tractor division of the Putilov Plant.

Peace. In July 1920 peace treaties were signed with Latvia and Lithuania and in October with Finland. The fighting against Wrangel, Pellura, Bulak-Balakovitch and Makhno in Southern Russia likewise came to an end in November of that year. Even so, fighting continued on a small scale until 1922 when the Russian Far East fell under complete Soviet domination. During 1922, armoured units were reorganized into three basic types for the new peace-time conditions: armoured car detachments (each with 10 armoured cars, 14 lorries and 108 men), a tank/armoured car detachment Type B (with 4 tanks, a few armoured cars, 15 personnel carriers and 104 men), and a detachment Type M (with 4 tanks, a few armoured cars and 77 men).

Soviet-German co-operation. Since further military and technical development in Russia, during the period 1920–30, was to be greatly influenced by that in Germany, it would be as well to consider the condition of the German Army at the end of World War I and its growth thereafter. Indeed it may be assumed that the start of military planning began in Germany on the day following the conclusion of the Armistice in November 1918. The effect of the war produced a psychological resistance to surrender and disarmament; the limitations imposed on Germany by the Versailles Treaty had not only forbidden the production of heavy armaments such as tanks, artillery and aircraft, but also restricted the overall strength of the forces to some 100,000 men (including some 4,000 officers). No provision was allowed for a General Staff or a military academy to centralise the studies of military organization, leadership, strategic doctrine or tactical instruction. This restriction upon the armed forces caused a great despondency on the part of the German military. In 1920 the 'Chef der Heeresleitung', General Hans von Seeckt,[73] attempted to obtain an extension of the Army to 200,000 men, but this was denied, making it obvious that there were to be no concessions on the part of the Allies. Even so the new Reichswehr constituted an excellent experimental nucleus in which the problems of future armies were ceaselessly studied and discussed. Unwittingly, the Entente had really brought about the establishment of a perfect military laboratory within the German Army, in which professional soldiers became very highly trained during the 12 years permitted them in active service. The greatest obstacle to the development of German military theory was that for many years new concepts and ideas had to remain on paper—the men and machines necessary for experiments in modern war were not available. The only logical solution was to attempt a military concordat with Soviet Russia where, outside the limits of Allied control, the organization of war industries, the development of mechanized warfare, the effects of new firepower, the tactical co-operation of different arms and services and many other associated topics could be studied and developed. From the Russian point of view, the refusal of the Allied governments to recognize the new Soviet régime, made any attempts at securing either British, French or American aid to develop Soviet industry and technology, pointless. Collaboration with the Germans appeared to be the only possible solution. Both Lenin and Trotsky gave their support to this pact, and agreed to co-operate wherever possible.

Throughout 1920, both Germany and Russia achieved a closer relationship; both countries realized that modern

informed Trotsky that he was negotiating with firms such as Krupp and Blohm & Voss who appeared willing to co-operate, and an organization called GEFU (Gesellschaft zur Förderung Gewerblicher Unternehmungen—Armament Development Company) was established to control the manufacture of arms by German firms in Russia. The head offices of GEFU (which was described as a trade enterprises development company) were established in both Berlin and Moscow in late 1921, and the company was assigned an initial capital of 75,000,000 German Marks to finance the development of war materials such as aircraft, engines, chemical warfare agents, tanks and ammunition in Soviet industrial centres under the supervision of German technicians.[75] Under the supervision of GEFU several armaments projects were started.

With the signing of the Rapallo Agreement on 16 April

19. *Later model KS tanks (with both 37 mm gun and machine-gun) in the May Day Parade of 1922;* **20.** *Final model of the KS tank used by the 'Ossoaviakhim', with a long-barreled 37 mm gun.*

military organization must be firmly based on an industrial organization capable of rapid transformation to the requirements of modern war. In addition to this, Poland was a mutual enemy to both powers, so that the immediate advantage to the Russians of a Russo-German collaboration was abundantly clear. Although Seeckt was opposed to the Communist régime, he appreciated that rapprochment with the Russians would provide a means of escape for Germany from the limitations of the Versailles Diktat. A military/technical collaboration with the Russians would enable the reformation of the German war industry, and provide a proving ground for German military theories and equipment without the knowledge of the Entente. In the winter of 1920–21, therefore, General Seeckt organized a group of officers selected from the Reichswehrministerium into a special committee for investigating the proposed military/industrial collaboration between Russia and Germany.[74] In order not to arouse suspicion abroad, this group was formed in great secrecy (designated Sondergruppe R). The new organization was placed under the command of Colonel Nicolai, who undertook secret negotiations between Soviet Russia and German industry. Seeckt's right-hand man, Colonel Otto Hasse (who in 1922 became the 'Chief of the Truppenamt') was responsible for the negotiations and contacts with the Russians. In 1921 the Soviet representative in Berlin (Kopp) met the People's Commissar for Military Affairs (Trotsky) to discuss the provision of a military-industrial aid programme by Germany for rebuilding the Red Army. On 7 April, Kopp

1922, the German armaments firm of Krupps obtained a concession for the establishment of an experimental tractor station at Rostov-on-Don, by the River Manysk in Southern Russia. This station (later known as the Rostselmash Agricultural Machine Works) was actually under construction in January, and when completed incorporated 32 machine shops. Under cover of a commercial development scheme, the experiments on heavy tractors were very closely associated with those on tanks—in fact the first German tank models were designated leichter or gross traktoren (light or heavy tractors). Mikhail Frunze, who succeeded Trotsky in the War Office during 1923, was naturally quite impressed by the progress being made in this 'tractor' industry.

Refinements to the KS tank. By the end of 1922, the Russians had produced a further 15 of the KS tanks as ordered—the later models being provided with both a 37 mm gun and a machine-gun in the turret (a decision resulting from experiences during combat). These tanks were supplied to the new 7th Detachment, and on 23 February 1922 (the 4th anniversary of establishment of the Red Army) they took part in the march past in Moscow. Mostovenko wrote:

> The appearance of both gun and machine-gun armament did not take place on even experimental light tanks abroad until 1926–30. Such a light tank—for the first time combining both a gun and machine-gun—was designed and produced at the 'Krasno-Sormovo' Factory.[76]

In 1923 the Soviets prepared to recommence the manufacture of automobiles on Russian soil; the AMO work shops were reorganized and greatly expanded, and although the production of automobiles progressed fairly satisfactorily, the production of tractors was still in a serious position; only 33 were produced throughout 1924.

The formation of the GUVP. During 1923 the problems associated with the design and construction of tanks were now studied by the GUVP (Glavno Upravleniy Voennoy Promishlennosti—the Main Department of War Industry). This department laid down the following programme:

    a. To carry out all systematic trials possible in the economically undeveloped Soviet Union.

    b. To produce equipment for training tank personnel.

    c. To study tank technology.

    d. To design and test new experimental tank models.

In undertaking this programme, the GUVP was also responsible for organizing the necessary equipment for the industries concerned, as well as the training of personnel for tank units. Within the framework of the GUVP, on 6 May 1924, a tank-technical bureau was set up to carry out an analysis of the tank warfare employed during World War I. Preparations were made to train a cadre of tank men, and plans were drawn up for a new tank model.[77] Bibergan wrote:

> This resolution led to hasty progress. A proportion of material was provided to the tank units for courses of instruction, and the remainder dispatched to the factories. By this time a technical bureau was established, which worked in conjunction with the GUVP.[78]

Arising from the earlier political reorganization, all existing tank units were modified during 1923. Separate light and heavy tank squadrons were formed, and the Armoured Force Central Command was set up under the direction of the RKKA, which provided two tank training brigades. Higher commanders were trained in two schools: the Armoured Vehicle and Tractor Command School and the Senior School of Motorization in Leningrad. Independent light and heavy tank battalions were formed (up to 30 tanks in each), and regiments, each consisting of two battalions, were to be established to take the place of squadrons.[79]

From 1924 onwards, the reformation of the Red Army was seriously undertaken, and it became a requisite that at least 50 per cent of the armoured personnel be of proletarian origin, for the party to secure the local support of the cavalry arm.[80] This reformation was hampered greatly by the difficulties which confronted the Government in the restoration of essential war industries. The output of munitions had increased considerably by comparison with the 1921 level, but new conceptions of mechanized war now necessitated the organization of several new branches of war industry.

Foreign influence on the Soviet armaments industries. In 1924 Frunze publicly expressed the requirement for the development of internal combustion engines for military application; he emphasised that the poor state of Soviet industry made it impossible to achieve any rapid progress towards equality with the Western powers. He made great efforts to overcome the attitudes of the majority of Soviet military officers who held contempt for Western technical progress —a philosophy which had resulted as an aftermath of Communist indoctrination during the Civil War. In spite of this, however, foreign specialists were welcomed during this phase; the Americans helped to organize the mass production of motor vehicles while the Germans were very active in the field of aircraft production and tanks. The most significant example of foreign assistance was that given by the Ford Motor Company whereby the USSR obtained machines, technical personnel, and even more important, the benefit of nearly 20 years of Ford's experience. By 7 November 1924, AMO was able to select ten of its own trucks—the F-15 Model—to take part in the parade in the Red Square. This date is significant in that it marked the birth of the Soviet motor industry. Also in 1924, the Military Industrial Council undertook the manufacture of a tracked lorry and the Kommunar tractor at the Kharkov Locomotive Works; these were later used to develop the automotive components of tanks.

The first reorganization of armoured units. In October 1924 the 7th Tank Detachment was disbanded, and an independent tank regiment, consisting of two tank battalions, was created; these were cadre and training units respectively. In 1925 separate light and heavy tank battalions were formed, each with 3 companies comprising 10 tanks. On 7 April 1925, the first full scale conference was held to ascertain the future role and composition of Soviet cavalry formations. Present at this conference were some 300 senior cavalry commanders,[81] including Budenny (who opened the proceedings), Frunze, Tukhachevsky and Voroshilov. The conference concerned itself with a series of important questions such as organization and tactics. It also considered the complex questions in regard to cavalry, and its preparations for war; as a result of this, in October 1925, the cavalry were divided into newly organized divisions. Although the cavalry arm had been given a new lease of life, a great deal of work had yet to be carried out in determining the most efficient way of employing it in future war, the best form of organization, and means of exploiting the increase in fire-power now available through the production of modern weapons. The future of armoured fighting vehicles and the way in which they were to be used, had yet to be investigated. In 1925 Frunze stated that the capitalist countries had a considerable lead in industry over the Soviet Union, and until industry could be established, the Red Army would be deficient in equipment at the start of any future war (but added that Russia had a considerable source of strength in the sheer vastness of her territory).

One of the main goals in the Army reformation of 1924–5 was the transformation of the entire structural organization of the Red Army as well as raising its combat value through providing troops with the necessary technical means, particularly tanks. Up to now in the organization of the Red Armoured Force one could find many types of units—such as divisions, detachments, brigades, squadrons and regiments. The final organizational form adopted during October 1925 eliminated many of these and in their place set up tank regiments (of 2 battalions each), independent light tank battalions and heavy tank battalions (both with thirty tanks), and also armoured train regiments (3 light armoured trains, 1 heavy and 2 armoured batteries). The armoured force was not integrated with general military units but was subject directly to the commander-in-chief, who often employed them for supporting infantry or cavalry.

GUVP design investigations. Throughout this period, the GUVP had undertaken a project for a new tank based on the analysis of World War I experiences. By May 1925 an 80 ton tank was in the process of construction at AMO (in the Tank and Armoured Car Department). This vehicle had overall tracks similar to the British Mk V 'Ricardo', but with a large turret and no sponsons. The tank was to carry 10 men and to be armed with two 75 mm guns and four machine-guns. The armour varied between 12 and 40 mm. Bibergan wrote:

The basic design was orientated around the 'Ricardo' engine, which was fairly cheap and available abroad. This engine was fitted in all Mk V tanks. However, it made the vehicle configuration too high. Added to this, it did not satisfy the basic requirement—power, for example, of 1 hp for every 12 kg. The profile of the tracks resembled an ellipse. Not entirely adequate was the comfort of the crew. The authorities seemed to have been carried away by foreign technical trends. . . . A cupola stroboscope was evaluated, with vertical slits in the sides. This cupola was rotated by a special motor, allowing constant vision. Experience, however, showed it to be inadequate. In building this tank we were primarily concerned with the problems of decreasing noise.[82]

Being based upon the Great War tank designs, this vehicle was suited purely for the trench-war concept, and therefore did not coincide with the new Soviet strategic role for cavalry. It was abandoned before completion.[83] Another similar tank project was under consideration and a prototype is believed to have been completed. Designated TG–5 (T–42), the tank was basically a mobile fortress and is stated to have weighed 100 tons.[84] It was armed with either a 105 mm or a 6 inch howitzer, two 37 mm guns, and several machine-guns (including two for anti-aircraft use). With an armour basis of nearly 3 inches, it was manned by a crew of from 8 to 10 men and could achieve a speed of 25 mph. Due to a decision to halt the development of tank types used during the World War no further work on super-heavy tank types was undertaken.

The birth of the automobile industry. By 1926 the production of vehicles at AMO had increased to 265 vehicles per year. In 1927 factories more suitable for the construction of tanks and armoured cars were founded at Chelyabinsk and Stalingrad. The US aid helped to establish factories at Bryansk—based on the Ford Baton Rouge plant (later named Molotov), the Spartak (ZIS) factory in Moscow (later named ZIL), and the YaAZ factory at Yaroslavl, north-east of Moscow. Gradually Russia was creating a powerful defence industry.

The GUVP tank programme. The exact policy adopted by the Technical Bureau of the GUVP was laid down during the session of the bureau at the beginning of 1925:[85]

i. Note, that the tank provides a powerful means of supporting infantry and of obtaining a breakthrough, with the necessary support of artillery, and also that, in addition to its firepower, it provides a means of destruction, laying a road in the path of its advance. It is vital then, to fill the gap immediately and provide our army with this means of combat.

ii. The tank represents a special combat machine, and so the organization of tank design and construction should be undertaken as an independent task.

iii. The next consideration, for the system of manufacture, appears to be the design, construction and testing of the principal components in modern tank technology, such as: engines, armament, suspension, armour, and methods of gas protection.

iv. In order to carry out these tasks the GUVP should form a 'Tank-Staff' Group. . . .

v. In parallel with the study of the design of basic components, there should be undertaken a special study of supervision, liaison and command. On these bases should be considered: the necessity for the GUVP to speed up development work and the organization of tank design . . . with the selection of a permanent tank-staff group within the construction bureau and the scientific-technical council

of the GUVP, for continuing the design and development of tank technology and ensuring subsequent production . . . all investigations and solutions being carried out in this country.

Bibergan wrote:

Such was the policy which guided our home tank industry during 1924–5. Owing to incorrect assumptions, and the abundance of tank projects, our tank development was delayed for a long time. Up until 1929, our basic tank was one designed in 1920—the 'Russkiy Renault'. Only in 1929, when we began to carry out the First Five-Year Plan and our industry matured—not by days, but by hours—did we have a basic home tank industry. The leader of the nation, Comrade Stalin, became personally involved in the problems of tank design and put us on the right road. . . .[86]

3 The First Five-Year Plan

During the First Five-Year Plan discussions of 1927, Voroshilov (who succeeded Frunze as the People's Commissar for Military Affairs in 1926) urged the need for the creation of a large tank force within the Soviet Army, an undertaking which would only be made possible by the establishment of a suitable industrial basis. His military aims were sound and far-sighted: to maintain the numerical strength of the Soviet armed forces, at the same time increasing the quality and quantity of equipment and adapting training procedures to the level of technical requirements. His ultimate aim was to bring the Soviet Army to qualitative and quantitative equality with (if not superiority to) Western forces in equipment and manpower. It was not until training had reached such a point that Russia could contemplate the production of tanks to any considerable degree; in 1927 the output of trucks was only 505, and tractors 937. It was equally vital to provide skilled engineers and technicians to handle the new plants as well as design, develop and build the new machinery for war. Svietshin wrote:

> Modern weapons must be thrown into battle immediately and in great numbers. They represent a power which must not be expended in driblets. In this sense there must be no 'economy' and no experiments in battle.[87]

Due to the inadequacy of the heavy tank projects which had been under consideration until now, there still remained a requirement for a tank to fit into the new tactical role of the cavalry arm. Bibergan wrote:

> In the technical bureau 'specialists' were appointed to govern all the research departments and lead the way. The bureau considered that the tank should be employed purely in infantry regiments and even battalions. Thus its programme was as follows: to build rapidly a small regimental tank (Polkovoy Tank). This trend evidently reflected the opinion of French commanders in the role of tanks. Even these 'specialists' considered that no tank could sustain a speed of 30–45 kph. It was unnecessary for the speed to exceed 20 kph. One of these 'authorities' wrote: 'If you asked me which vehicle is better; that which could move at 20 kph or that which could move at 30 kph, then it is only necessary to consider the question of Achilles and the Tortoise, to say then, that the superior of these two machines would be that having a speed of 20 kph'.... It appears curious, now, when tanks of our manufacture rush past the Red Square at speeds between 45 and 50 kph, that these 'authoritive' engineers based their problems upon the outcome of 'Achilles and the Tortoise'.... It is of course true that foreign regiments had small tanks with a speed of 20 kph. This attitude went to other extremes; the design of a land ironclad weighing 1,000 tons, armed with 6 in guns, of which, it was estimated, only one such tank would be necessary to disrupt the enemy.[88]

Garret Underhill wrote:

> At this time elements of the Red military believed that tanks were capable of obtaining a decision by deep and massive action, largely independent of other arms. It was a belief which persisted until the mid-1930s. In its most hypertrophied form it was represented by the project of a super-super-super heavy tank, literally a land battleship. The idea was that a very limited number of these giants would be stationed at a point behind the frontiers. Special roads would radiate from each base, so that upon approach of a hostile force the tank guarding the threatened sector would sally forth and utterly destroy

the invader. This fantasy was projected about the time of the 6 ton T–18 tank, when Red industry was hardly in a position to carry out such a project should it be deemed practical. A German automotive engineer working on the T–18 actually did some work on the project, which never got off paper.[89]

The MS light tank. The first GUVP design brought to the prototype stage was the experimental 5 ton infantry-support tank T–16. Over the period 7–15 June 1927 a special commission under the direction of P. G. Dibenko carried out general vehicle trials. On 13 June, G. K. Ordzhonikidze and K. E. Voroshilov attended the trials. The commission found the vehicle to be unreliable, with the result that the design was altered and in November the project finalized as the MS–1 tank (Maliy Soprovozdieniya —Little Accompanying Tank) which, after improvement in the suspension, was adopted by the Army as the T–18. This tank was designed primarily for infantry support. In this vehicle the engine was a flat, air-cooled, opposed-piston model (to reduce the size of the tank) incorporated with the transmission in a single compact housing. It had a final drive with internal gear pinion. For the first time support rollers were employed for the track. The compactness of the various components was achieved by transversely mounting the engine. In the modified steering system an ordinary differential was employed. Mostovenko wrote:

> The employment of more compact components, together with the economic use of the hull space, allowed a decrease in weight of the MS–1 tank to 5·5 tons, at the same time retaining the same armour protection, armament and crew as in the Sormovo tank. The maximum speed of the original tank was 17 kph, but after these improvements in running gear the speed was increased to 22 kph. With respect to the basic configuration (e.g. armour, hull and turret, provision of a tail, form of track guards, etc.) the MS–1 tank retained certain features of the Sormovo light tank.[90]

The performance and mobility of the T–18 were better than those of the KS tank, and in 1928 production was undertaken at the Leningrad Armament Plant (later renamed Bolshevik 232). During May 1929 workers of this combine provided the Red Army with the first series of 30 tanks, and up to 1931 produced about 960 machines of this type in several versions. The final versions, extensively modernized, were designated MS–2 and MS–3. These tanks weighed between 5·5 and 5·9 tons and developed a maximum speed of 11 mph. Production of this tank continued through until 1931.

The Kazan Tank School. During 1927 the Russians and the Germans negotiated to establish a German tank school at Kazan, on the Volga, where eventually, it was hoped, the technical knowledge and experience of the Germans would contribute to the advancement of the Soviet war industry. Over the period 1924–27 Soviet industry was beginning to become firmly established, thereby providing a basis for tank development for both Germany and Russia. Although there had been collaboration as early as 1922, the lack of a firm industrial basis in the Soviet Union had delayed the formation of any definite co-operation regarding tanks. At the end of July 1927 the Germans had reported that the Russians were beginning to 'drag their feet' over the Kazan project (now being referred to as the 'Heavy Vehicle Experimental and Test Station').[91] The Soviet Foreign

21. *Projected 1,000 ton tank;* **22.** *The MS–1 Light Tank;* **23.** *The MS–2 Light Tank;* **24.** *The MS–3 Light Tank.*

Minister, Litvinov, suggested that the school be registered as a limited company to avoid suspicion abroad. He also approached the German Foreign Office (Auswrtiges Amt) for their approval of the project, and suggested that the Soviet representative in Berlin, Krestinsky, should be assured by the Germans that no political considerations would be raised against the proposed establishment. The establishment of the school was delayed considerably from the start; not all the Soviet General Staff were in favour of the proposal and it was Voroshilov who eventually sealed the agreement.[92] The Commissar for Defence, Voroshilov, had postulated the inevitability of war between Germany and the Soviet Union, in which efficient use of technical equipment of advanced design was to be of prime importance. He recognized tanks to be a fundamental weapon, upon which he placed the greatest emphasis. He stressed the necessity for the establishment of a broad economic base to provide for emergency war conversion, and to enable the manufacture of the many items which would not necessarily be foreseen at any stage of technical evolution. Voroshilov was greatly disturbed by the state of Soviet industry prior to the First Five-Year Plan. To provide the necessary material he demanded the creation of a far greater armaments industry than envisaged by other Party Members. Discussing the period 1924–28, Voroshilov said:

> In the field of war technology this period was characterized by the solution of the problems in providing weapons to the RKKA. During these years much work of a theoretical nature was done, allowing us to plan a further technical reconstruction of the Red Army with respect to all the requirements of modern warfare.[93]

Mostovenko wrote:

> The nature of the international situation in 1927 inspired preparations against intervention by imperialists and the threat of war to the USSR. As a result, the Communist Party strived to prepare the defence capability of the Homeland. . . . Reconstruction under the guidance of the Communist Party successfully reinstated Russian industry, which had been destroyed during the Imperialist War, the Civil War, and by foreign intervention, and also created great possibilities for providing the Red Army with the necessary war technology.[94]

During September 1928, the Kazan Tank School, which was situated to the east of Kazan, was included in a tour of military establishments by General Blomberg, Chief of the German General Staff. At this time the construction work was almost complete, and Blomberg was greatly impressed by both the organization and amenities offered by the local terrain for the instruction and development of tactics and equipment. He was not, however, satisfied with the training of the instruction staff, and remarked that the supply and distribution of tanks should be speeded up and given the highest priority. The German tanks presented a problem, but Blomberg affirmed that it was hoped to ship some prototypes during the spring of 1929, at which time operations at the school could be commenced.[95]

Pending the arrival of the German models, the Russians continued development along their own lines. With the completion of the T–18 vehicle it became evident to the High Command that new models were required to bring the Soviets in line with foreign development. In conformity with the ideas prevailing in the twenties, in addition to infantry-accompanying tanks such as the T–18, the Army also required tanks able to execute independent roles as 'manoeuvre' groups working with the infantry in greater depth. Such 'manoeuvre' tanks were stipulated to have

powerful armament, thick armour and greater speed than the T–18, and hence over the period 1928–9, in the design bureau of the Kharkov Locomotive Works the new T–12 tank was designed. Its designers were A. A. Morozov, V. Doroshenko, A. Bondarenko, M. Tarshinov, P. Goryun and N. Kutserenko. This tank was submitted for trials early in February 1930. It weighed about 19·5 tons, was armed with a 45 mm gun and 3 machine-guns, and had a speed of 14 mph. The trials showed this vehicle also to be unreliable mechanically. About the same time a testbed is believed to have been produced for the later T–20 tank (based on the MS–3). At the Kiev exercises in 1928, Blomberg had criticised the Soviet MS–1 for its lack of speed;[96] he had seemed more impressed by the BA–27 armoured car, incorporating the same turret and armament as the MS–1. In spite of its shortcomings, and with

25

25. *The experimental T–12 Tank;* **26.** *BA–27 armoured cars on parade in the Red Square.*

little likelihood of an immediate replacement, production of the T–18 tank was continued during 1928 by Bolshevik in Leningrad and Molotov in Gorki. In 1928 the total output of cars and lorries from all factories was only 835; the total number of motor vehicles in the USSR being only 18,000—most of which were imported.

In 1929 mechanized units began to be formed which were intended for independent operations. A mechanized regiment was set up—the First Mechanized Regiment, with a tank battalion (equipped with the new MS–1 tanks), an Avtobronie division, a motor-rifle battalion and an artillery battery. The total armoured strength up until 1929 consisted of 200 tanks and armoured cars—most of which were obsolete. This regiment was placed under the command of Colonel Kalinovski. With the foundation of the Special Far Eastern Army (ODVA) in August 1929, a company of MS tanks were assigned to the Trans-Baikal Force. The MS tank remained in service until 1932 having progressed through four marks—MS–1, 2, 3 and 3A. Minor changes were introduced in turret design, suspension and armour; a smoke-projector and a gas-filter were later added. The MS tanks were used during 1929 to suppress the fighting along the Kiev-Voronezh and Chinese Eastern Railway (KVZhD).

Military aspects of the First Five-Year Plan. It was resolved by the highest members of the Party and the Government of the USSR, during 1927, together with the General Staff of the RKKA (under the direction of M. N. Tukhachevsky), to begin formulating the Five-Year Plan for the development of the Soviet armed forces. The initial plan was laid down to 'determine factors in future armed conflicts, such as infantry and powerful artillery operations, cavalry and aircraft'. (Armoured forces and tanks were not considered in detail at that time since industry had barely begun producing the first tank models, and the entire Red Armoured Force was composed of only 1 regiment of tanks and 6 divisions of armoured cars. In the equipment of these units was to be found about 100 operational tanks—45 English Mk Vs, 12 Whippets (also known as 'Taylors'), 33 Renault tanks and Renault derivatives produced by the Sormovo combine. The number of armoured cars totalled 54.) In a succeeding variant of the plan, approved by a ruling of 30 July 1928, it was intended by the end of the First Five-Year Plan to be in possession of 1,075 tanks and to form 3 new regiments together with various independent tank battalions. These alterations were compiled in the final draft for the Five-Year Plan to develop the national economy of the USSR. During the First Five-Year Plan

26

discussions of 1929, the Communist Council passed a resolution 'On the State of the Defences of the USSR', in which it was declared:

The large-scale work that has been undertaken to strengthen and improve the technical equipment of the Army is considered correct and opportune.

The Revolutionary Military Council is instructed to speed up the rate of the technical improvement of the Army.

Along with the modernization of existing armaments, steps must be taken to secure, in the course of the next two years, the manufacture of experimental models of modern types of artillery, all modern types of tanks, armoured cars and so forth, and then supply them to the Army.[97]

The main targets in the technical reconstruction of the Soviet armed forces included:

a. The formation of new fighting services and arms (aviation, armoured troops, chemical, engineering, and other special troops) and the enhancement of their number and significance in the Armed Forces in conformity with the requirements of modern warfare.

b. The motorization and reorganization of the 'old' arms (infantry, artillery and cavalry) in conformity with modern military requirements.

c. The modernization and fundamental improvement of obsolete equipment still in use with the Red Army.

d. Mass training of technical cadres, and teaching the entire personnel of the armed forces to handle modern equipment.

The policy laid down in the *Preliminary Correct Line for the War Doctrine of Tanks* followed the contemporary French pattern, modified to a certain extent by the philosophy of General Fuller. It laid down two main roles for the tank: firstly, to lead the assault wave, and to penetrate the enemy's artillery and reserve zone, and secondly to provide direct support to infantry formations. The first of these roles was to be carried out by independent army troops, and the second by infantry.

It seemed of vital importance that, whilst capitalist governments were divided among themselves, and whilst they had still not recovered from the losses of the Great War, the USSR should make itself substantially independent of the outer World in all the means of waging war, and all the indispensable commodities. Hence the exceptional concentration of the First Five-Year Plan on the opening of new mines, oilfields, hydro-electric plants, iron and steel works, and generally on a rapid expansion of the 'heavy industries', by which munitions could be manufactured, or troops be transported, instead of seeking directly to increase the manufacture of the household commodities desired by the people.[98] The establishment of the tank industry, in particular, was only possible through the establishment of a highly-developed complex of metallurgical, motor-building, electric motor building, automobile, tractor, optical equipment, armament building, ammunition, fuel industries and so on. Werner wrote:

The chief factor which makes the war economy of the Soviet Union so extraordinarily powerful is the possession of oil in abundance, because oil is the fuel of all modern weapons of offence, the aeroplane, the tank and motorized transport. The recognized theoretician of the tank and motorization, General Eimannsberger, states:[99] 'A stream—no, a river of oil must flow constantly into the country which wages modern warfare.' The Soviet Union is the only big European power which possesses oil in abundance. . . .[100]

After eighteen months of discussion the plan was launched on 3 April 1929, but at the start of the 'restoration' period some of these industries were not highly developed, and many did not exist at all. In the First Five-Year Plan discussions, the Soviet Government issued a directive for the establishment of the two giant automobile factories—Gorki Zavod (with an annual production of 100,000 lorries and light automobiles), and the Moscow Zavod (with an annual production of 25,000 lorries and automobiles). Tractor building was to be concentrated at the Putilov Works at Leningrad (up to 10,000 per annum) and at a new plant at Stalingrad (up to 40,000 per annum). The optimal version of the plan provided for the establishment of another large tractor building plant beginning in 1929–30. Automobile construction was to be increased up to 130,000 per annum, and of these up to 100,000 were to be produced at the new plant at Nizhny-Novgorod. During the final confirmation of the plan, 6 May 1929, the number of tanks envisaged for equipping the Army was now put at 3,500 of all possible types, i.e., more than three times that considered earlier. The task of technically equipping the Red Army was taken up by the newly-formed organization headed by Chief of Armaments of the RKKA, I. P Uborevits, a post which after 1931 was taken over by M. N. Tukhachevsky. A month later, on 15 July 1929, the highest ranks of the Red Army and the armaments industry passed a special directive covering the production of tanks, and approved the 'Minimum' programme for tank production. The party and the government ordered engineers to direct their attention towards a wide net of experimental work. Established by the General Staff, under the direction of

V. K. Triandafillov and N. M. Rogovsky, the 'Programme for Armoured-Automobile Supply to the Red Army' emphasized the requirement for creating mechanized units as well as the total mechanization of the Armed Forces. By the end of the First Five-Year Plan the Army was intended to have: 3 mechanized brigades, 30 mixed tank battalions (with 32 light and 34 medium tanks), 4 heavy tank battalions of the Reserve High Command (with 35 tanks), 13 mechanized regiments of cavalry (each composed of tank and armoured car divisions). Each infantry division was intended to have an armoured car company.

Although the infantry and artillery arms still held precedence, a great deal of discussion took place over the future exploitation of the tank. Soviet military science strived to form the most effective organization of armoured tank and mechanized units for that time. The question of the tactical use of tanks was given adequate consideration. The official opinion in this field was reflected in the regulations and instructions released towards the end of the 1920s. In the second edition of the *Infantry Combat Regulations* (1927) a detailed account was given of the employment of tanks in close co-operation with infantry. Mostovenko wrote:

The mechanical immaturity of the tank at that time forbade its use in solving independent operational problems. In the Provisional Instructions for the Combat Use of Tanks, released towards the end of 1928, two main roles for the tank were outlined: for close co-operation with infantry, and for carrying out independent tasks in the rear of the enemy (e.g., engaging artillery, severing supply-lines, liaison and command roles). . . .[101]

About this time, a number of articles were published on the topic, of which the most interesting were written by Colonel K. B. Kalinovski, a distinguished Soviet Army commander. In his articles, 'The Use of Tanks and Their Co-operation with Infantry' (1927), 'Tanks in Defence' (1927), 'Tanks in Offensive War' (1928) and 'High-Speed Tanks in Meeting Engagements' (1929), he also considered the problems of anti-tank defence.[102] Wheldon wrote:

In the USSR, the idea of 'Tanks with Motorized Troops' gained rapid support from 1928 onwards, its strongest advocate being Colonel Kalinovski, who later commanded the first Soviet 'Mechanized Experimental Force'.[103]

In 1929 an independent force was set up, consisting of armoured and mechanized units, as well as a command organ for the motorization and mechanization of the Red Army. In addition to tank units for supporting infantry, mechanized units were considered for independent operations. Marshal M. Tukhachevsky pioneered the combined use of all arms, which became a fundamental of the new Soviet military doctrine. The tank was allocated to the direct support of the infantry storm group, which when faced with larger numbers of enemy tanks would be formed into independent echelons of long-range groups (Tankovye Gruppy DD). These DD groups would be used mainly for engaging enemy artillery attempting to hold up the advance of the infantry tanks.

On 30 August 1929, a joint Soviet-German conference was held to discuss the future of the Kazan Tank School;[104] representing the German Reichswehr were Colonel Lätz, Lieutenant-Colonel Malbrandt (the tank school commandant), Major Pirner (head of the test section) and other

27. *The T–17 Tankette;* **28.** *The T–20 Light Tank;* **29.** *The T–23 Light Tank;* **30.** *The 'TG' Heavy Tank;* **31.** *The T–24 Medium Tank.*

German military staff, Soviet tank commanders Polyakov and Yeroshenko representing the Red Army. The school clearly demonstrated the ability of the Russians and the Germans to work together in a military and technical capacity, and pupils of both armies were simultaneously taught the theory of cavalry tactics, weapons employment, communications, and given a general technical and mechanical course. All these facilities were sponsored by the Inspektion der Kraftfahrtruppen (Inspectorate of Mechanized Troops) in Berlin, the instruction staff being mainly composed of experienced German Army officers.

The school was also responsible for the test and evaluation of German prototypes and foreign models, as well as providing a tactical training nucleus for officers. Here, the Germans experimented with some of their prototype vehicles in secrecy, continuing the work which had previously been undertaken by the Krupp establishment at Rostov-on-Don. Amongst others, there were departments allocated to training, testing, technical evaluation and logistics. At the school, German officers were in the great majority; having been technically dismissed from their service (for political reasons), they were in theory attending as tourists. The course ran as long as three years and only German vehicles were used for training.

The 16th Party Congress commenced on 26 June 1930, and concerned itself particularly with the complete technological reformation of the Army. The Congress charted a programme for the full-scale building of Socialism, and emphasized the importance of speeding up the development of industries enhancing the defence might of the Soviet Union. One of the main tasks even of the First Five-Year Plan was to build up the strongest possible war industry, and to model industry as a whole in such a way that it could be rapidly adapted to the requirements of economic war mobilization, in a state of emergency. The initial task was to create the economic conditions necessary for the mass-production of armaments. Voroshilov stated:

> The basis for the arming of our country lies in the accelerated development of our economic system, in the increase in metalurgical production, in the development of our chemical industries, in the production of motor cars and tractors, and in general in the development of our engineering industries. . . .[105]

The Central Committee of the Communist Party of the Soviet Union and the Soviet Government gave these questions much attention. Up until 1927 the Committee was in control of work in the Soviet tank industry, but in 1930 a faculty for mechanization and motorization was established at the Military Technical Academy in Leningrad. During the same year, the Auto-Tractor Institute 'Lomonosov' in Moscow set up a military-technical-industrial faculty with design and production departments for tanks.

New GUVP tank models. The shortcomings of the MS series demonstrated the lack of experience on the part of its designers, and the GUVP decided to undertake the development of a less complicated scheme so that designers, engineers and technicians might gain more experience in this field. Referring to the old KS and MS tanks, Bach wrote:

> Tanks of a similar fighting quality may be found even today in the armies of medium and small states and are considered as being considerably valuable weapons, whilst Russia on the other hand in 1930 possessed a total stock (about 3,000*) and regards them as being obsolete, assigning them to the semi-military youth organization

(Ossoaviachim) as training equipment.[106]
*(It would appear, in fact, that the quantity quoted by Bach is erroneous; most sources put the figure at about 100–300.)

The new Soviet Board of Tank Construction was composed of Morozov, Doroshenko, Bondarenko, Tarshinov, Goryun and Kucherenko.

Between 1929 and 1931, Soviet engineers tried out eight types of tank, designed for various purposes. With respect to their combat and technical characteristics, they differed little from the MS–1. In 1929 the development of a light one-man tankette was commenced; the T–17, as it became known, was fairly reliable but it was found a great disadvantage for the driver to operate the armament (a 7·62 mm machine-gun) and command the tank as well as drive. Its most noteworthy features were its rubber-metal tracks and air-cooled two-cylinder engine developing 18 hp. Other vehicles followed with many refinements, as well as an increase in crew number. These included light tank T–19, light tank T–20 (having a more powerful engine of 60 hp, clutch and brake steering and an improved suspension), which was based on the French Renault NC–27, and light tank T–21 in 1929; the T–23 (a two-man tankette of 3½ tons developed from the T–18 vehicle, with reduced weight and having a speed of 28 mph), and the Direnkov medium tank —in 1930; and finally a heavy tank TG (Tank Grotte) was built in 1931. The TG was armed with a 76 mm gun and four machine-guns and weighed only 25 tons. It was manned by a crew of 5 men and the 300 hp engine gave the vehicle a speed of 20–25 mph, which was a vast improvement on some of the earlier designs. It is of interest to note that the TG had a pneumatic-servo steering system, operating through a mechanical gearbox. A prominent feature of the TG was the faired hull configuration. The transmission in general proved troublesome. Consideration was given to the construction of a 1,000 ton tank, some 110 feet long, but neither this nor any of the earlier developments were taken any further. Nevertheless, this work provided a means of gaining vital tank design and manufacture experience. The most outstanding tank development of this period was the T–24 medium tank produced during 1929. This tank was based on the unsuccessful T1–12 tank, but was a larger (18½ ton) infantry-accompanying tank using the same coil-spring suspension with hydraulic buffers as the T–18. It was characterized by its three-storey distribution of armament: 45 mm gun and two machine-guns in the main turret, one machine-gun in a special cupola and one in the hull front. The cupola rotated on the main turret, allowing direct fire and observation independent of the latter. The T–24 was powered by a more powerful M–6 engine, developing 300 hp, giving it a speed of 14 mph. The transmission was planetary, and the armour was proof against large-calibre machine-gun rounds at all ranges. Twenty-five of these tanks were completed during 1930 by the Kharkov Locomotive Works, but due to construction faults and poor mechanical reliability, no further production was undertaken.

German tanks at Kazan. In the meantime, Blomberg's endeavours to speed the production of the German prototypes at Krupps and Rheinmettal eventually proved successful and tank prototypes were secretly shipped in sections to be reassembled at the Tank School. These consisted of German 18 ton tanks (batches of 5 each from Krupp, and Rheinmetall) developed during 1928. Guderian wrote:

> Since 1926 a testing station had been in existence 'abroad' where new German tanks could be tried out. The Army Ordnance Office had given contracts to firms

for the production of two types of medium and three of light tanks—as they were then classified. Two specimens of each were produced, so that there was a total of 10 tanks in existence. The mediums were armed with a 75 mm, the light tanks with a 37 mm gun. These specimens were not built of armour plate, but of mild steel. The maximum speed of all these types was approximately 12 mph. The officer responsible for the production, Captain (later Major) Pirner, had taken pains to include a number of modern requirements in the new models, including gas-proofing, a good engine efficiency rate, an all-round field of fire both for the turret gun and for the machine-guns, a sufficiently high ground-clearance, and excellent manoeuvrability. He had, to a great extent, succeeded in achieving all this . . . wireless equipment was not yet available.[107]

Two other vehicles were sent to Kazan—an unsuccessful wheel/track tank chassis built in Austria, and five German Leichter tractors from Krupps and Rheinmetall, weighing between 8 and 9 tons. These vehicles were experimentally fitted with 37 mm guns. Magirus, Daimler-Benz and Büssing-NAG also sent out their 1927 experimental 7–8 ton wheeled armoured car chassis; the Büssing-NAG Company included one example of a 6-wheeled amphibious armoured car, a report concerning the testing of which stated that it sank on its maiden voyage and was abandoned by the Russians—leaving the vehicle to rot in the water, complete with its Russian crew. This incident greatly disturbed the German observers at the time, and it was left up to them to rescue the Soviet crew from their unfortunate plight. It is interesting to note that the Germans did not dispatch any of the armoured vehicles which really interested them, such as the early test-bed tractors for the Maybach transmissions. Quite an important factor when one considers that the most advanced and complicated aspects of tank technology are that of steering and gear-changing, both of which depend on the transmission system. It was a long time before the Russians were able to develop a satisfactory transmission for tanks.

Soviet purchases abroad. Apart from the German vehicles, the Soviet Government had taken steps to obtain other tanks abroad; during 1927 a Kolo-Housenka 50 wheel/track tank was purchased from the Skoda Works at Pilsen, in Czechoslovakia, and a Fiat 3000B light tank from Italy. No effort was made, however, to obtain any tank models from the Landsverk firm in Sweden, which was one of the foremost armoured vehicle contractors during the 1930s, although the Russians did later adopt many of the design features of Swedish tanks. In spite of these developments, it became evident that no immediate supply of tanks in quantity was to be forthcoming—either from Soviet industry or the Germans and consequently it was decided to purchase tanks from Great Britain.

This was to be an interim measure pending the development of a successful model in the Soviet Union. On 30 December 1929 a special commission, headed by the Director of Mechanization and Motorization of the RKKA, I. A. Khalepski together with 'defence industrial worker' D. F. Budniak, went abroad. They visited both the USA and Great Britain, inspecting suitable armoured vehicles then under design or in the process of testing. Soviet political and military representatives contacted the British Government, and a purchasing order was granted by the Board of Trade on 21 March 1930. Since Vickers-Armstrong were at this time the most advanced contractor of armoured vehicles in Great Britain all the tanks were purchased from

them. These consisted of: 15 Medium Tanks Mk II (called the 'English Workman' in Russia), 26 Carden-Loyd Mk VI machine-gun carriers, 8 Carden-Loyd amphibious tanks, 15 Vickers-Armstrong 6 ton tanks and 12 tractor-trucks. Concessions were granted to manufacture most of these models under licence in the USSR, and they formed part of a subsequent exchange of tank equipment between the Red Army and the Reichswehr. The Russians also acquired the licence to build the German Munich Bayerischen Motoren Werk M–6 six-cylinder BMW engine, which was later developed into the M–17 and used to power the BT and T–28 tanks.[108]

By the beginning of 1930 the Kazan Tank School was reaching its climax. On 3 January General Ludwig expressed his opinions to Trautman on the Soviet plans for developing their armaments industry.[109] One point emphasized by Ludwig was that the 30 Russian made tanks at the School did not work; neither did the German vehicles at this time. This was largely because the Germans had avoided involving big firms with overseas branches in the Rapallo Agreement; such firms as Opel might have informed their American branches of the German violation of the Versailles Diktat. As a result, the Russians were unable to gain any first-hand knowledge of up-to-date mass production techniques as applied to tank design and manufacture.[110] Realizing that there was very little to be gained from the Kazan project, the Russians established another tank development centre at Voronezh, where they later evaluated foreign tank models purchased in Great Britain and the USA.

The first Mechanized Brigade. During the period of the First Five-Year Plan the size of the Red Army did not numerically increase. There were 71 infantry and $16\frac{1}{2}$ cavalry

32. *One of the Vickers Medium Tanks specially adapted for Russian use. These tanks were known by the Russians as 'English Workmen'.*

divisions, with a small number of artillery and technical units. Twenty-nine of the infantry and $12\frac{1}{2}$ of the cavalry divisions were incorporated in the standing Army, whilst 42 infantry and 4 cavalry divisions comprised the Territorial Militia. The infantry divisions were formed into 21 rifle corps, while the cavalry divisions were organized into 4 cavalry corps. A few infantry divisions and several cavalry brigades were separate from the corps formations.

The first mechanized brigade was founded in May 1930. It was set up in the Moscow Military District under the command of K.V. Kalinovski In its composition there were included 2 tank battalions, 2 motor-rifle battalions, a reconnaissance battalion, an artillery division and other specialized units. The brigade was equipped with MS tanks, BA–27 armoured cars, and also Russian-built automobiles and tractors, and was called 'Brigade Kalinovski'. The total vehicle establishment consisted of 60 tanks, 32 tankettes, 17 armoured cars, 264 lorries and 12 tractors. This brigade successfully took part in exercises carried out in the Belorussian Military District. These exercises provided much valuable experience and a year later, after reorganization and expansion, the brigade comprised: reconnaissance groups in regimental strength (tankette battalions, armoured car divisions, motorized battalions and artillery divisions), assault groups also at regimental strength (two tank battalions, two SP divisions, and a motorized infantry battalion) as well as an artillery support group composed of 3 divisions with 76·2 mm guns and 122 mm howitzers, and an anti-aircraft artillery division. In total, this brigade now contained 4,700 men, 119 tanks, 100 tankettes, 15 armoured cars, 63 SP anti-aircraft machine-guns, 32 SP 76·2 mm guns, 16 122 mm howitzers, 32 SP anti-aircraft 37 mm guns, 12 SP anti-aircraft 76·2 mm guns, 270 lorries and 100 tractors. Experimental trials and large manoeuvres, carried out between 1929 and 1930, together with experiments in combining mechanized and tank units with other arms, enabled the rapid development of the theoretical use of armoured troops.

In spite of the efforts of the First Five-Year Plan, no reasonable quantity of tanks was supplied to the Red Army before 1932; this was mainly due to the lack of a basic automobile or tractor industry geared to mass-production. The absence of a firm industrial basis had certainly forbidden the introduction of mechanized forces on a large scale, and at the beginning of 1931 the Red Army possessed only 300 MS tanks and 100 BA–27 armoured cars; the Russians claimed to have produced 740 tanks during 1930 but this is doubtful. Even so, the actual known quantity was larger than that extant in any other army at this time (with the possible exception of the French), but apparently not sufficient by Soviet standards. Operational and tactical research into the combat use of the tank, carried out during 1930–31, showed a requirement for material other than the MS tanks and BA–27 armoured cars. Erikson wrote:

The fact that even the experimental models failed to produce any significant improvement upon the types of tanks used during the First World War has since been admitted by the Russians. These tanks suffered from many defects, such as frequent track breakage, unreliability of the engine and transmission components, too great an amplitude of the suspension—giving rise to bad vibration which hindered both road and cross-country performance, and a poor reliability resulting from bad maintenance and handling. . .[111]

The Germans have stated that they found the Russian tanks extremely difficult to drive and control. Technical difficulties did not, however, discourage the Russians from continuing to produce tanks, and the successful fulfilment of the First Five-Year Plan laid the foundation for the manufacture of tanks of more advanced form, conforming to roles envisaged by the Soviet Army at that time. The First Five-Year Plan also brought into being new schools and courses for tank commanders and drivers. In 1930 the Main Military Staff College created a department of mechanization and motorization, which co-operated with the Moscow Automotive and tractor Institute (NATI). Tactical studies were advanced through the creation of experimental tank and armoured car units. These special schools worked in conjunction with students at the Leningrad Polytechnic Institute, which turned out such famous tank designers as Koshkin (who later designed the T–34 cruiser tank), Dukhov, Astrov, Sichev, and many others. The Motorization and Mechanization Directorates carried out a great deal of useful research during experimental exercises at Kiev, the first of which took place in May 1930 and involved the First Mechanized Regiment with a special brigade of MS tanks and BA–27 armoured cars.

In July 1931 General Adam of the Truppenamt, who was making his annual visit to the Red Army, attended a meeting at the Kazan Tank School with Chalepski (Head of the Faculty for Mechanization and Motorization of the Red Army in Stalingrad) together with Lebadev, his adjutant, and Tygunov (Head of the Faculty of Mechanization and Motorization of the Leningrad Academy). One aspect of the meeting was to discuss the exchange of tank equipment between the Germans and the Russians, which was successfully accomplished![112] Several exercises were held in the area of Kazan, mainly by the Germans using Soviet equipment (Tankarteilungen), but Russian armoured units participated at certain times. (The Russians, of course, were by now directing their main efforts on tank technology and tactics in the direction of the other establishment at Voronezh.)

Tukhachevsky and the expansion of the armaments industries.
In 1931 Mikhail Frunze tried to improve the state of Soviet industry and its relation to the Red Army, and Tukhachevsky was appointed Inspector of Armaments. Under the industrial expansion programme outlined in the First Five-Year Plan, new industries became established which were greatly to influence the armaments industry. A new large industrial area was established in the Ural Mountains and Western Siberia, of which Sverdlovsk and Chelyabinsk became the major industrial centres, and a coal and iron centre was set up in the Kuznetsk Basin to serve the West Siberian industrial base. Great new tractor plants were set up at Stalingrad and Kharkov, and Dnepropetrovsk became the base for a large new automobile industry. The AMO plant in Moscow was greatly enlarged and named after Stalin, whilst the YaAZ (Yaroslavl) plant was rebuilt in larger form. In 1930 the Volgorod Tractor Plant was set up, and by the mid 1930s became one of the largest producers of agricultural tractors and spare parts in the world. The Gorki Motor Vehicle Plant (GAZ), which had been founded in 1929, started production during 1932, while in 1931 the Soviets satisfactorily concluded negotiations with the American Ford Motor Company for a large plant at Nizhni-Novgorod, east of Moscow. This plant was named after Molotov, and the city itself renamed Gorki. Originally equipped to produce the Ford GAZ-AA four-cylinder Model A truck (which became the standard truck in the Soviet Army), the Molotov plant was destined to play an important role in the development of Soviet tanks. In addition, 1931 saw the expansion of the ZIS plant. The completion of the industrial programme of the First Five-Year Plan opened the way for the production of tanks in quantity. The journal of the Polish Army stated:

Since 1929 the Red Army has been in the process of motorization and mechanization as a result of the Five-Year Plan and the increase in war production. One must compliment the Bolshevists on the thorough fashion in which they are carrying out the motorization and mechanization of the Red Army, and on the determined efforts they are making in this field![113]

The light vehicle types selected for production in the new

automobile plants were not intended to prepare these factories for the construction of heavy armoured vehicles. The demands of war would still call for the construction of large quantities of trucks and staff cars, so that the added task of a heavy tank programme might be outside of the large, but still immature, automobile industry's capability. Since the Soviets also required tractors for both agricultural and military purposes, the design of which was closely analogous to that of tanks, it was decided to select this industry as the one to design, develop and produce tanks and tracked artillery prime-movers. This was to be the industry upon which the Soviets were to rely for heavy tracked vehicles in both peace and war.

From the experience gained during the experimental period at Kazan, and at the other tank establishment at Voronezh, it was possible to constitute a family of fairly high-quality armoured vehicles for the Army. The various foreign models which had been purchased and trial run, together with the German prototypes, formed the basis of a new series of tanks, the specifications for which were outlined in the 1931/32 Tank Programme.

The 1931/32 Tank Programme. When Voroshilov was in the process of formulating the defence aspects of the First Five-Year Plan, he gathered around him all the experienced tank engineers and armour commanders. These were given the task of defining the new tactical and technical characteristics of tanks, and determining their place in modern warfare. Zacharoff wrote:

> Soviet military authorities long ago came to the realization that the interminable plains of Eastern Europe were lacking in strategic strongpoints and lent themselves admirably to the broadest manoeuvres of mechanized forces. The strategists set to work to guard against this danger by building a tank corps of their own![14]

The result was the 1931/32 Tank Programme. The armoured equipment considered under this programme was placed under four main categories:

a. The obsolete wartime equipment still in use with the army.

b. The modern equipment for direct infantry support.

c. The modern equipment for remote infantry support.

d. The modern equipment for distant action.

The specifications for the newer equipment were dominated by their tactical roles; it was considered that direct infantry support would require particularly light, fast, powerful tanks; remote infantry support, particularly heavy tanks; and distant action, primarily 'fast tanks'. Four basic factors were taken into consideration:

a. The expression of the tactical mission contained in the vehicle design.

b. The military characteristics which would enable the fulfilment of this mission (speed on roads and across country, radius of action, trafficability of various types of terrain, crossing fords and trenches, armour, armament and weight).

c. The mechanical components which would enable these capabilities (the engine, transmission, suspension, etc.).

d. The personnel responsible for the technical organization, the crews, their inboard facilities, means of vision, of sighting, of communication with other tanks, and the various specialized techniques which would facilitate the servicing of equipment or which would increase their effectiveness.

As a result, the following classifications of tank types were specified:

1. Reconnaissance Tanks. These were to be ultra-light tanks (tankettes) with high speed and manoeuvrability and difficult to detect. No unduly powerful armament was specified. Some were to be amphibious.

2. Destroyer and Pursuit Tanks. The function of these vehicles would be to combat enemy tanks and armoured cars, and to suppress enemy machine-guns, artillery and flame-throwers. They were to be able to advance quickly over normally impassable terrain, and be long enough to cross ditches, trenches, and other obstacles. They were not to be deterred by artificial field obstructions. These tanks were to have stronger armour than their reconnaissance counterparts and more powerful armament for destroying enemy tanks. They were to be larger, more substantial machines. The lightest models were to weigh around 12 tons, the mediums to weigh about 25 tons. When deprived of opportunities for frequent refuelling, their reserve capabilities were to enable them to carry out long-range missions just the same.

3. Breakthrough Tanks. Soviet tank tacticians anticipated situations where the enemy might heavily fortify himself, dig-in, erect strong defensive fortifications and anti-tank devices. Pursuit tanks were considered inadequate for breaking through such defences as the Mannerheim Line, for example, and so a requirement existed for a heavy tank. This was to have very powerful armament and armour protection against small-calibre shells, with high obstacle penetrability and large fuel reserves.

4. Tanks for Special Application. This group embraced all those machines which were to have a narrowly circumscribed function, such as artillery tanks carrying larger calibre guns than usual (which were to halt before opening fire, or to fire from covered positions). Engineer tanks were envisaged for engaging in such tasks as bridgelaying, chemical warfare, smokescreening and flame-throwing. It was considered desirable that such special-purpose tanks should be convertible from tanks of the other categories. Special mention was made of tanks specially designed for laying barbed-wire obstructions and mines.

5. Armoured Cars. The mobile cover provided by armoured cars was considered to be of particular value to the infantry and cavalry, but they were to be used principally for communication and reconnaissance work in advanced positions. The main advantage of the armoured car was considered to be its mobility, which would make it possible for the infantry and cavalry to keep up with the tanks and to support them, developing well co-ordinated operations in defence or attack. The medium and heavy models were to have an operational range of from 125 to 190 miles, enabling them to operate to a depth of 95 miles from their base, and return for more fuel or for maintenance, although with intermediate bases on route, longer ranges would be possible. On a good road an armoured car was expected to achieve an average speed of 25 mph, though speeds of 40 mph and more would be of great advantage. In order to increase the manoeuvrability of armoured cars (when used in conjunction with tanks), the tank experts insisted that these should be equipped with removable tracks for the rear wheels. This would, to a certain extent, make them independent of firm terrain and able to traverse fields, snow, sand and ploughed land. (These experts did not appear willing to adopt the half-track which they had found cumbersome during the war, and which had proved expensive to manufacture and difficult to maintain.) The armoured cars were to utilise commercially produced car and lorry chassis, and were to be fitted with removable flanged wheels to enable them to travel on rails. The normal wheels were to be provided with tough, resilient rubber tyres or multi-chambered pneumatic tyres, and sometimes tyres containing a liquid which would harden over bullet-holes. All armoured cars were to be immune to shell fragments, and small arms bullets at ranges above 200 metres. The armament was to consist of machine-guns on lighter cars and 37 or 45 mm anti-tank guns on the heavier models, located in fully rotating turrets. The interiors were to be electrically lighted, and ammunition stowed in readily-accessible containers, while tools were to be carried for lighter repairs. Observation slits were to be provided in the turrets and other areas of armoured cars (and tanks) occupied by crew members. The 'programme' also foresaw the production of SP guns for the preparation and support of tank attacks, combating enemy tanks and arming mechanized artillery units, SP anti-aircraft guns for engaging bomber and fighter/ground attack aircraft (with a dual role in engaging tanks), and SP anti-aircraft machine-gun mountings for protecting mechanized units from fighter/ground attack. Command tanks were intended to have long-range radio equipment for maintaining communication between armoured and mechanized units. There were also envisaged smoke-producing tanks and completely armoured tracked transporters for carrying infantry.

It was stated by Khalepski that the design of all these vehicles, in order that they could enter mass-production during 1931–2, must be concluded by autumn 1930. By this time the testing and rectification of experimental models should also be carried out. With the necessity of founding the heavy industries, however, this deadline could not be met. The only technical and basic industrial experience of producing tanks had been gained from the T–18 programme. During the economic year 1930 industry had turned out a total of 325 T–18 tanks, 30 T–12 medium tanks and 10 experimental tankettes. It was considered necessary to produce a sufficient quantity of light tanks for collective experimentation before embarking on large-scale production of Russian models, and at the same time to determine the necessary tactical tasks of the new forms of tank units.

The mass production of tanks was now necessitated by the immediate political situation regarding Japan. In 1932 the considerations of high policy connected with national defence led the Soviet Government to make an important deviation from the First Five-Year Plan, in order to avert the danger of a Japanese invasion. Even at the cost of creating a serious shortage of foodstuffs, the Government established stores of grain and military equipment along the line to the Far East, and devoted much labour force to the building of additional aeroplanes and tanks—all of which were given calculated publicity. On 18 September 1931 Japan invaded Manchuria; Mostovenko wrote:

. . . . 1931–2 brought to notice the serious international situation—the threat of war against the USSR by Japan. During 1931 Japanese troops entered Manchuria with the objective of gaining a springboard to Northern China and the USSR. As a result of the Japanese military intervention in the Far East there arose the First Home War, and later the seizure of control by German Fascists in Central Europe after 1933 gave rise to the Second Home War. Hence, one of the fundamental tasks during the First Five-Year Plan was the technical re-equipping of the Soviet Army, which was subsequently carried out in a very short period of time. This was now possible owing to the creation of a vital industrial basis. Having at the beginning of 1931

only 300 MS–1 tanks and about 100 BA–27 armoured cars, these were neither qualitatively nor quantitatively capable of satisfying the requirements of the Red Army. The urgency of the situation necessitated the conversion of several factories to the production of armaments which were vitally needed by the Soviet Army at that time. The measures taken to strengthen the defensive capability of the USSR included the organization for the production of new forms of armaments including that number of tanks required for equipping the Army. Up until the First Five-Year Plan this country had virtually no automobile or tractor industry. The successful completion by the nation of the First Five-Year Plan created the conditions for organizing the mass-production of various types of tank for the Soviet Army. The Central Committee of the Communist Party and the Soviet Government took all the necessary measures so that the Soviet Army received the most modern tank models for that time![115]

On 13 February 1931 the Revolutionary War Council of the USSR passed a directive accepting the Vickers and Christie models for production. During the fourth quarter of 1931 the Army received 17 twin-turreted T–26 tanks (in total, 120 of this version were built), 348 T–27 tankettes and 3 fast wheel-track BT tanks, which together with other vehicles took part in the 7 November 1931 parade in Red Square. The T–19 and T–20 light tanks, which had become serious rivals to the T–26, were found to be extremely complicated and did not lend themselves to mass-production. Overwatching the production of tanks was People's Commissar for Heavy Industry, G. K. Ordzhonikidze. Directly assisting design and production were S. M. Kirov, S. V. Kosior and A. A. Zdanov.

The Stalin Military Academy. In 1932 the Stalin Military Academy for the Mechanization and Motorization of the Army was founded, Stalin himself celebrating the opening with a speech in which he emphasized the importance of the school and the Soviet tank arm:

This country, initially weak and unable to defend itself, has become a country which is powerful in determination and defensive capability, a country prepared for any incident, a country capable of mass-producing all the contemporary ordnance and defensive requirements necessary for crushing any attack from outside![116]

In terms of numbers, he went on to say, the most significant arms production carried out during the First Five-Year Plan was in tanks (there having been about 3,300 tanks produced during 1932). The full title of the academy was 'The Military Academy of Motorization and Mechanization of the Workers' and Peasants' Red Army in Honour of Stalin', abbreviated, from the initial letters of its Russian name, to 'VAMM'. The reason for founding the Academy was to gather into one nucleus the principal agencies of experiment, test, and exploitation of the motorized and mechanized instruments of warfare; to arrive at correct principles of tactics and strategy in the use of motorized vehicles and mechanized equipment in warfare; to train a sufficient number of student officers in these principles so that the new methods of warfare might be thoroughly understood throughout the Red Army; and to train a sufficient number of specialists in the requirements of the Army to enable them to be sent back into industry to assure the success of procurement programmes for motorized and mechanized equipment. The academy was located in the eastern suburbs of Moscow near the Yauza River, a small tributary of the Moscow River. It was also near the main line of the Kursk Railroad. A special proving ground 60 kilometres from Moscow was assigned to the Academy for testing purposes. This proving ground was located in broken country which permitted adequate tests over various obstacles on various slopes and in sand, mud, and snow.

Course of instruction at the Academy lasted four years. Amongst the many other facilities at the school the hydraulic laboratory had special apparatus for carrying out experiments with amphibious tanks. Within the academy was set up another military industrial faculty called 'Lomonosov', where the RKKA Academy for Mechanization and Motorization was to produce a new line of commanders and tank engineers. Students attended extensive courses on armoured warfare; those who graduated included General Chernyakhov, Colonel Poluboyarov, General-Lieutenant Kotin, and Ermolaev. This institution was supported by the faculties of mechanization in Leningrad and other important cities. Mostovenko wrote:

> In the preparation of tank design personnel an important part was played by the resolution TsK VKP (b) which, in 1933, directed a group of students at the Leningrad Polytechnic Institute in one of its tank-building workshops for carrying out design projects. This group included later-famous tank designer M. I. Koshkin. Into the tank industry came engineers from other Soviet high-education departments, such as I. L. Dukhov, N. A. Astrov, L. S. Troyanov, and L. E. Sichev. The requirement for tank and mechanized troops intermediate commanders and technical officers necessitated the formation during 1932–4, of other new tank technology schools and colleges. . . [117]

Pupils were taught that the tank, when used in conjunction with other arms, was the fundamental factor in the offensive. As far as the tank designs were concerned, the Russians were wise in their initial choice; having selected the best models available they could afford to concentrate on quantity production, and by the mid 1930s, hundreds of tanks were recorded at parades, manoeuvres and tank parks. The tank production of the thirties was carried out in a total of 30 factories. The magazine of the Japanese Admiralty wrote:

> It is not merely the great number of tanks which is important, but the fact that an enormous number of them are of the most modern type. The mechanization of the Red Army astonishes all the foreign attachés who were present at its parades! [118]

Armoured tactics. The goal for which the Soviet Government had been striving since the Civil War was now near at hand; that is, providing the Army with a basic, powerful, mobile armoured arm evolved around the tank. The exploitation of the fast American Christie tanks, which had been purchased during 1931 and evaluated at Voronezh, brought into being large quantities of the fast, effective BT tanks—developed primarily for long-range independent operation. Their high speed was considered useful in enveloping operations, and the Russians also envisaged them in the assault role aiding the infantry. Attempts to develop an operationally effective combination of artillery, aviation, motorized infantry and armour were demonstrated in the manoeuvres carried out during 1931–3, resulting from the idea of the mechanized unit under evaluation in Great Britain. A mechanized brigade was formed in 1931 which consisted of the new T–28 medium and T–35 heavy tanks. The formation and tactical use of tank units was based directly upon the British experimental armoured force being investigated on Salisbury Plain. At the beginning of

August 1931 approval was given for a plan to build a force over the period 1931–3, and the Council for Labour and Defence was established to realize 'The Great Tank Programme', based on the assumption that:

> The achievements of technology and industry in the USSR in this sphere laid a definite basis for successive changes in the general operational-tactical doctrine in the use of tanks, particularly changes in the organization of armoured and mechanized troops enabling the creation of superior forms of mechanized units able to execute tasks not only on the field of battle but also in the entire operational depth of the front. New fast armoured equipment formed the basis for projecting entirely new combat and operational theory.

A special commission responsible for the development of armoured troops passed a directive on 9 March 1932 recommending the creation of the following large units: mechanized corps comprised of mechanized brigades, tank brigades of the Supreme Command Reserve, mechanized regiments for cavalry and tank battalions for infantry divisions.

The Soviet armoured force was classified into three fundamental sections: the Independent Mechanized units (dating effectively from 1932), the Supreme Command Tank Reserve (TRGK), and the various tank units distributed among the infantry and cavalry. In mid 1932 four tank regiments were formed under the Supreme Command Reserve—firstly in Smolensk, secondly in Leningrad; the third existed already in Moscow, and the fourth in Kharkov —each composed of 3 tank battalions. There also existed 3 independent territorial tank battalions and 2 mechanized regiments of cavalry. In 1932 the mechanized brigade was extended into a mechanized corps, under the command of Kalinovsky, with about 500 tanks and 200 armoured cars. This corps consisted of: 2–3 mechanized brigades, 1 motorized infantry brigade, and 1 independent artillery regiment. (By 1 May 1933 the Army possessed 2 such corps together with 6 independent brigades.) The corps was called 'Mechanized Corps Kalinovski'. Infantry and cavalry units absorbed support tanks, each infantry battalion receiving an organic battalion of light tanks, and each cavalry division—a mechanized regiment. The Tank Reserve of the Supreme Command (TRGK) was organized into tank regiments, battalions and companies. Tank regiments had 2–3 battalions of up to 3 companies for the breakthrough and support of main operations. The tank units were allotted general support roles and were also required to co-operate with the cavalry; they consisted of independent tank and tankette battalions, and tankette and armoured car companies. The first definite principles for the tactical use of tanks were outlined in the *Combat Regulations for Mechanized Forces* released during 1932–3, and the regulations therein proposed three fundamental ways of employing tanks: [119]

1. In close co-operation with infantry or in the support of cavalry (Tank Group NPP—Nieposredstviennoy Poddierzhki Piechoty—also referred to as TPP).

2. In tactical co-operation with infantry (Tank Group DPP—Dalshey Poddierzhki) or cavalry units for long-range support (Tank Groups DD—Dalnogo Dieystviya).

3. In operational co-operation with large units composed of independent mechanized units.

4 The Second Five-Year Plan

During August 1933 a plan was considered for the development of the Soviet armed forces during the period of the Second Five-Year Plan. A directive of the Council for Labour and Defence stated that in the period of the Second Five-Year Plan: 'It is necessary to reach such a level of Army mechanization, that will enable troop arms to carry out mechanized warfare decisively, and on a large scale during military operations'.

The industrialization of Soviet Russia under the First Five-Year Plan enabled the passage from theory to practice of mechanized war a real possibility. The transformation was achieved none too soon in view of the radical change in the German political sphere which acute Soviet observers were able to anticipate several years before the change took actual form in 1933. Mostovenko wrote:

> The threat of a new war grew more imminent; of this it was impossible to be unaware, particularly with the arrival to power of the Nazis and the creation of the German war machine. In order to prepare the country for the repulsion of any aggressor, the Communist Party of the Soviet Union took the necessary steps in ensuring that the Soviet Army would be armed with up-to-date weapons. This was included in the contents of the Second Five-Year Plan of 1933. . . .[120]

From 1933 to 1934 the military budget of the Soviet Union increased from 1·5 to 5 thousand millions of roubles, and budgetry expenditure on armaments serve as a reliable measure of armament level. Under the Second Five-Year Plan a directive of the Communist Party and the Soviet Government was released to bring the output of motor vehicles up to 630,000 per year, in two stages: in the first stage the existing plants were to be enlarged and the new heavy truck plant at Yaroslavl put into operation, and in the second stage two new plants were to manufacture 3 ton trucks, and one further plant to produce 5 ton trucks. It was intended to begin the production of vehicles with high piston displacement engines and closed rigid bodies. The heavier vehicles were to change from carburettor engines to high speed diesels. Under the Plan, the Putilov Plant (which had formerly made everything from artillery to locomotives and armour plate) lost its tractor facilities; these were expanded and made independent. The large new plant at Stalingrad, the Dzerzinski Factory, was commissioned to produce tracked vehicles as well as the great factory at Chelyabinsk.

With the maturity of the Soviet Tank Industry, development after 1932 branched out in many directions, with the eventual establishment of the light, medium and heavy tank programmes which will be covered more fully in other chapters. Voroshilov said:

> As the result of the work performed during the period 1924–28 the Red Army was given a strong modern structure. Its supply of effectives was thoroughly organized, the periods of service laid down, and modern Field Service Regulations introduced. The rank and file were thoroughly trained, the officer corps reorganized, and a network of military training schools and academies established. By 1928 the Red Army had developed from an organizationally backward army into a modern one incorporating in its organization and training all the lessons of the World War. . . . We have modernized our entire artillery park, and brought it to the level of foreign armies by increasing the number of howitzers. For the first time in our country we have created our own heavy artillery. We have organized and carried out the production of our own anti-aircraft, anti-tank and

tank guns. And finally we have created our own small-calibre artillery, which is necessary today for smaller infantry units. . . . We may consider the task of the equipping of the Red Army with tanks satisfactorily underway. We not only have these combat vehicles in our units, but we also have various types of tanks for carrying out different combat roles. . . . We must place more attention on providing the Army with tanks; the Central Party Committee and the Red senior staff must take over all control, and direct every resource towards achieving this aim of the Red Army![121]

During the Second Five-Year Plan all the vital factories intended for the production of automobiles and tractors were completed:

a. The Gorki Automobile Plant (renamed Molotov) expanded to produce 300,000 cars annually.

b. The Stalin Automobile Plant in Moscow expanded to produce 80,000 cars annually.

c. The Yaroslavl Plant was expanded to produce up to 25,000 5 ton trucks annually.

d. The Ufa Plant was established to produce 100,000 3 ton trucks.

e. The Stalingrad Automobile Plant was established to produce 100,000 3 ton trucks and was in production by the summer of 1933. In 1933 this plant was re-equipped to produce caterpillar tractors—scheduled to turn out 22,500 tractors by 1937; this figure was modified in 1937 to 40,000 annually.

f. The Samara Plant was set up to produce 25,000 5 ton trucks annually.

g. The Ural Railroad Car Plant was set up to handle 54,000 cars.

h. The West-Siberian Automobile Plant was set up to handle 100,000 3 ton trucks.

i. The Chelyabinsk Heavy Tractor plant started operations in June 1933 and was given the task of producing tracked tractors, production beginning with the 48 hp Stalinets S–60 Model. The output from this factory was intended to cater for the large military prime-mover requirement. Scheduled to produce 20,000 by 1937, this figure was modified in 1937 to 40,000.

j.' The Kharkov Plant manufacturing 15 hp tractors, reached capacity by 1934; by 1937 it was producing 36,000 annually.

k. The Red Putilov Plant, where first tractor production began in 1934, was producing 10,000 by 1937.

All tractor production from these factories was directed from the Kharkov Factory, and production organized from the Red Putilov Plant.

Foreign interest in Soviet developments. The development of industry in the Soviet Union gave her an advantage over Germany since she possessed a greater manpower reserve and better raw material resources. In fact, the carrying out of the Five-Year Plans completely altered the relation of military strength in Europe. In considering the mechanization of the Red Army, Werner wrote:

The triumphal advance of the motor has altered the structure of armies. Mechanization and motorization have produced new military units. Mechanization is the use of the motor as part of the weapon itself, as for instance with tanks, motorized artillery, etc. Motorization is the use of mechanical transport for the movement of troops. Moto-mechanization (an expression which has grown up in practice and been adopted in Soviet Russian military literature) is a combination of mechanized weapons supplemented by motorized troops. These

moto-mechanized units are already many and varied in their composition. There are tank squadrons accompanied only by motorized artillery, and there are the moto-mechanized units proper, organized in light and heavy divisions according to their tasks and the type of tank used, in which the tank formations are supplemented by motorized infantry or cavalry, and there are also specially mobile divisions in which the tanks are accompanied by motor-cycle units, cyclists or cavalry squadrons![122]

The 1931–2 Tank Programme furnished the army with large numbers of tanks of varied types—mainly based on the Vickers and Christie models purchased earlier. Mostovenko wrote:

The foreign press has often emphasized the fact that, in 1931 the Soviets were purchasing from abroad 6 ton Vickers tanks, Christie wheel/track tanks and Carden-Loyd tankettes, on the basis of which tanks T–26, BT–2 and tankette T–27 were designed and standardized for army use. This was put forward as significant evidence of the dependence of Soviet tank designers upon models created abroad. There is little to be gained in disputing this statement, since the results of our tank building industry, in creating before the Second World War the

33. *F–15 trucks being produced by the A.M.O. factory in Moscow.*

best tanks in the World, present a very convincing reply to such fantasy; bear in mind the following points:

1. None of these tanks abroad, which here received due recognition and acceptance for production, were adopted by foreign military authorities. The 6 ton Vickers tank and the Carden-Loyd tankette were not accepted for general use by the British Army, and the Christie tank was not approved by the US Army.

2. Such tanks were able to be designed in our country, but only after a large expense in time, since in our country it was necessary to train designers and engineers. Consider also the international situation at this time, compelling our industry to produce the best available tank equipment in the shortest possible time.

3. The design of all these tanks, and especially the Christie tank, were fundamentally altered. They were provided with newly designed turrets and armament mountings, steering systems, clutches and other components.

Note that in the field of tank armament mountings we were leading the Americans![123]

The Russians displayed great admiration for Christie, with the proviso: 'that it is unfortunate that he was born in the imperialist camp and hence not given the chance to exploit his ideas to the full!' Tukhachevsky had approached Stalin on at least one occasion with a proposal for contacting Christie and offering him a substantial sum of money to aid the development of tanks in the USSR, but was criticized 'for succumbing to western bourgeois teachings and ideas'. Needless to say nothing came of the proposal. (This latter incident may have contributed to Tukhachevsky's eventual downfall.)

After 1932 several self-propelled artillery mountings and tracked vehicles for specialized roles were developed on the basis of the T–26 tank. During the 1930s light tanks T–26 and BT were basically the most numerous tank types in the Soviet Army. Werner wrote:

The high quality of Soviet war production is no more miraculous than its huge volume. For almost a decade now the Soviet Union has purchased the best models and the best types from all the highly-developed industrial countries of the World, and introduced them into her own war industries. The highest achievements of international military techniques meet in the technical equipment of the Red Army: the famous American Christie

34. *Stalinets artillery tractors leaving the production line for delivery to Soviet artillery units.*

tank, the British Vickers and Carden-Loyd and the French Renault tank. . . . Thus whilst the USA and Great Britain have each no more than a few hundred of their best tanks, the Red Army has thousands of the same models. Naturally, the war industries of the Soviet Union are not content merely to take over these foreign models and copy them pedantically; on the contrary, the native military technique of the Soviet Union is also highly developed, often along lines which are unknown in other countries, for instance, super-heavy bombers, super-heavy aero-engines and certain types of light tanks. . .[124]

Soviet tank technology during the thirties. About 30 factories began mass-producing tanks and other types of armoured vehicles on their chassis—SPs, armoured carriers, etc. Approval was also given for providing vehicles of other classes; the design bureaux of the experimental departments at the establishments in Kirov and Leningrad, directed by N. V. Barikov, S. A. Ginzburg and O. M. Ivanov, investigated projects and prototypes of light amphibious tanks, medium tanks and heavy tanks. They

also experimented with the medium tank series TG, as a theoretical study in the feasability of a project for a super-heavy tank weighing 100 tons. In early 1932 Russia had in service about 480 tanks in working order, but this number rapidly grew as industry became more and more keyed to tank production. The rate of production of military trucks, for example, increased from year to year (25,000 in 1932, 50,000 in 1933 reaching 200,000 in 1937). At the beginning of 1933 the Soviet Army had 2 motorized corps, 6 separate motorized brigades, 4 separate tank regiments and other tank units. According to German estimates of machines sighted at parades and tank parks, by 1933 there were some 2,000 tanks in service with the Soviet Army. In actual fact, the total number of tanks available by the end of 1933 were some 7,000 but how many of these were battleworthy is not known. In any case, the Five-Year Plans had obviously begun to produce results in terms of tanks by the end of 1933. Over the period 1931 to 1933, the Soviet Army received the T–27 tankette, the light tank T–26, the fast, light, wheel/track tank BT, the medium T–28 and the heavy tank T–35. These models replacing the single MS type, provided the Soviet Army of 1933 with five different types of tank weighing from 2·8 to 50 tons. The combat characteristics of Soviet tanks during the 1930s were well in keeping with the then current Soviet military operational-tactical philosophy in their use. The basic requirements of tanks, taken into service during 1931–6, became firepower and mobility. Gun calibre, ranged up to 76 mm, while the armour of tanks was required to be bullet-proof only, to protect them against normal calibre bullets and shell fragments, and sometimes against large calibre machine-gun bullets. The decision to employ bullet-proof armour resulted from the absence, at that time, of anti-tank artillery in any likely enemy army. In comparison with the tanks of the Great War, Russian tanks during the 1930s, and those abroad, could attain a high speed and range as well as increased reliability, maximum speed ranging from 10–50 mph. Light tanks were provided with coaxially mounted gun and machine-gun. After 1937 coaxial armament mountings also became standardized for medium and heavy tanks, together with machine-guns located in several places. For rotating the armament in T–28 and T–35 heavy tanks, the turrets were electrically operated. In a number of tanks successful use was made of vertically-stabilized armament. Bach mentions a photo-electric stabilizer/aiming-device which was employed on certain Russian tanks (in particular the T–26B) to facilitate firing on the move.

In the production of armoured hulls electric-arc welding became the basic method of joining armour components, by the mid 1930s. Engines were petrol types only; in contrast to the 40 hp engine of the MS tank, the new tanks were powered by engines of up to 500 hp. In the BT, T–28 and T–35 tanks, liquid-cooled aircraft engines were employed, and for the T–26 a special horizontally-opposed air-cooled engine was developed. For the smaller tanks use was made of conventional automobile petrol engines. After 1938 BT tanks were successfully powered by a new special tank diesel engine. Of the new tanks supplied to the Soviet Army, of particular value was the fast wheel/track BT tank, then the most popular Soviet tank. The T–28 and T–35 tanks became among the most powerful tanks in the World for that time, and possessed high degrees of mobility—their maximum speeds being around 20 to 30 mph. For light, medium and heavy tanks a mechanical step-up gearbox was employed, in which the gears were shifted by a sliding pinion. In the smaller tanks an automobile gearbox was used. Steering was carried out by final drives, although the T–27 and T–37 light tanks used a simple differential. The variety in types of suspension, on the other hand, clearly showed this aspect to need further consideration. In connexion with this, tests were carried out on independent suspension systems to determine the most suitable for tank use.

The standard army trucks became the ZIS and GAZ models; the ZIS factory is known to have produced 80,000 military trucks during 1933 (70,000 ZIS–5/6s, and 10,000 ZIS–7s). The 6 cylinder ZIS–5 truck, which began to come off the production lines in 1933, was still in production in 1946. Another truck produced in great quantity for the Army was the 5 ton Ya–5, produced by YaAZ during the period of the Second Five-Year Plan.

During 1933, the People's Commissar for Defence, Marshal Voroshilov, said that the First and Second Five-Year Plans had laid excellent foundations on which to build all the technical appliances for modern warfare. It has been claimed that the motorization and mechanization of the Red Army throughout this period came about as a result of a political agreement between Stalin and Tukhachevsky, the Chief of Ordnance, and that Stalin made available the funds for realizing the ideas of Tukhachevsky and his followers. Tukhachevsky pioneered the use of the tank in the Soviet Army—not to be used on its own but as the basis of the shock army in the form of the motor-mechanized unity. In the opinion of the Red General Staff the tank was not a weapon to be used on its own, and the British tank theory was therefore strictly rejected. In the Red Army the tank was to be used in co-operation with all the technical resources of the Army, and in direct co-operation with other arms. Werner wrote:

The expression 'Moto-mechanized Unit' has developed in Soviet military literature. It means the combination of tanks, i.e. mechanized units, with motorized infantry units which follow the tanks and co-operate with them. Tank detachments are also trained to co-operate closely with cavalry. . . . Soviet-Russian military literature criticizes the plans for motorized shock armies put forward by the British and French Army reformers Fuller and De Gaulle. It declares that such formations must be inflexible in their organizational structure, and that the various arms involved are too closely dependent on each other and that therefore there is little elasticity and mobility. It indicates too, how such defects can be avoided: by the formation of a tank reserve at the disposal of the Supreme Army Command to be sent into action where and when required; by the organizational introduction of tanks into infantry and cavalry units; and finally by creating the possibility of changing the combination of arms rapidly at need. . . . According to Soviet doctrine, the decisive phase of the battle, the development and carrying through of a breakthrough, can be performed only by motorized units. High-speed tanks will be followed at once by motorized infantry units which will occupy enemy positions immediately and carry the fighting far into his territory until the reserves themselves have been defeated![125]

Reaction to German militarism. By October 1934 the Russians came to the conclusion that the German attitude towards Russia was becoming increasingly hostile, and on 31 October the Kazan Tank School was closed down![126] (With its amenities and advantages as a tank training and development centre, however, Kazan continued in use by the Red Army at least until the beginning of World War II, if not later.) Considerable attention to strengthening the military and economic might of the USSR was devoted by the 17th Party Congress of 1934; it noted that:[127] 'political parties seeking war and revenge had returned to the forefront of the Imperialist Camp, and that matters were closely moving towards another Imperialist war. In the face of these developments, Stalin pointed out in a report of the CC CPSU (B) that the Soviet Union had to take measures to safeguard itself against surprise attack and to be ready to ward off aggression'. General Baratier wrote:

In the event of mobilization the Red Army will prove a powerful weapon for victory. The Red Army possesses an even greater number of mechanized weapons than the best armies in the World![128]

In 1934 the standing Army was increased from 562,000 to 900,000 men. The army was developing a more and more industrialized character, and at the beginning of 1934 Voroshilov declared that 50 per cent of its effectives consisted of 'technical specialists of various degrees' serving machinery and mechanized weapons, not including machine-gunners. Youth Commissar Skonyevsko, in a speech at the presentation of old KS and MS tanks to the youth organization (Ossoaviachim) in Smolensk, May 1934, stated:

Study and master this machine! Become familiar with the rudiments of this trampling steel colossus; this demon of fury, backed by the power of your proletarian strength, will spread terror amongst the ranks of our enemies. Your task: to kill! Your goal: victory! Our aim: to be the master! Your reward: to someday carry the proletarian revolution into the heart of Europe![129]

During 1935 the 17th Party Meeting discussed a recent report concerning the state of the Army which resulted in a significant expansion of tank and tractor production. With a colossal increase in industrial output, the Soviet armoured formation expanded rapidly. Werner wrote:

Militarization in time of peace affects the economic system in two ways: it means first of all the creation of the biggest possible war industry, and secondly the preparation of industry as a whole and of the economic system in general for war mobilization. The adaption of the economic system to war production and war demands even in peace time. The organization necessary for complete war economy is already being built up today and held in readiness for the outbreak of war. As far as manpower is concerned, militarization means the thorough training of the greatest possible number of military reserves including in particular the highly skilled men for the technical troops: the air force, the tank corps, etc![130]

The strength of the Soviet tank arm. Russian tank strength in 1935 is not accurately known, although German Intelligence had estimated some 3,000 to 10,000 machines. A number of other contemporary German sources, including the *Handbuch der neuzeitlichen Wehrwissenschaft* and *Wissen und Wehr*, put the strength of the Soviet Tank Corps in 1935 at 10,000. This number was also quoted by Major-General Guderian. These estimates were made from tank parks, and the Germans put the number of mechanized brigades at 25. According to a Japanese source, the Soviet Army had 15 large tank formations and 50 smaller ones. The 17th Soviet Congress in January 1935 publicly stated that as a result of the Five-Year Plan tanks had increased by the following factors: tankettes 25 and medium tanks 7·5. It is known that by 1 January 1934 the Red Army had

35. *The Kiev manoeuvres; BT–7–2 tanks and Komintern artillery tractors leaving a tank park.*

at its disposal 2 mechanized corps, 6 mechanized brigades, 6 tank regiments, 23 tank battalions, and 37 independent tankette companies among infantry divisions. For the cavalry there were 14 mechanized regiments and 5 mechanized divisions. J. Watyn-Watyniecki wrote:

> The mechanized strength of the Red Army may be broken down as follows:

1,000 Armoured cars (mean hp=60)	60,000 hp
1,500 Specialized tractors (mean hp=80)	120,000 hp
100 Heavy tanks (mean hp=750)	75,000 hp
1,000 Medium tanks (mean hp=400)	400,000 hp
4,000 Light tanks (mean hp=80)	320,000 hp
6,000 Tankettes (mean hp=40)	240,000 hp.[131]

The Red Army had by this time an enormous transport park totalling over 10,000,000 hp; under the Five-Year Plans 1,904 tractor stations had been set up, making a total at the end of 1935 of 4,350. The Germans accounted for some 100,000 military lorries and 150,000 military tractors. Watyn-Watyniecki wrote:

> The rapidity with which the Department of Mechanization and Motorization in the Red Army makes its decisions with regard to the introduction of new tank types, and the equally great rapidity with which such decisions are then put into operation, i.e., the 'elasticity' of Soviet Russia's present day war industries in the matter of tank production, are very noteworthy indeed. The result of this is that today the Red Army is stronger in motorization and mechanization than any other army in Europe![132]

The respect and high regard which the Germans had for the Soviet Tank Arm at this time, is demonstrated by their criticism of a book published by a White-Russian emigrant, Colonel Saitzev, in Germany during 1934. In this book were outlined the alleged deficiencies of the Red Army, but it was severely criticized by the German military paper *Militär-Wochenblatt*,[133] which stated that Saitzev had grossly underestimated the effectiveness of the Red Army, that the shortage of machine-guns and artillery and the insufficient firepower of the cavalry arm had already been remedied under the determined leadership of Voroshilov, and remedied in a thoroughly efficient and modern way, and that the author had also drawn dangerously erroneous conclusions from alleged tank defects. Werner wrote:

> The tank arm forms the core of the offensive power of the Red Army on land, and it is supported by widespread motorization throughout the Army. The mobility of the Army as a whole is thus being approximated to that of the tank corps. Together with motorized infantry, mechanized artillery, modern cavalry and a modern air force, the Tank Corps forms the mobile sector of the Red Army, the actual shock army. . . .[134]

In 1935 General Guiderian wrote that he considered the Russians to have produced their best and most efficient armoured and motorized equipment in mass. He considered the training of their tank troops in handling such material excellent, as also their tactics and operational aims. He wrote as follows:

> The Russians have the best foreign models for ordinary commercial motors and also for tanks. They have bought Ford, Carden-Loyd, Vickers, Renault and Christie patents and adapted them to their own purposes. They

36

36. *A platoon commander's T–26B1(V) advancing during an exercise;* **37.** *A T–26B tank deployed under cover during the 1935 Kiev exercises;* **38.** *Engineers servicing BT tanks in a tank park (the tank at extreme right is a BT–5A).*

have produced their 'best and most modern motor vehicles in masses, they have trained their troops excellently in the use of them, and they have adapted their tactical aims excellently to the performance of these troops. The cavalry arm of Budenny of 1920 has developed into the Tank Corps of Voroshilov of 1935. . . . 10,000 tanks, 150,000 military tractors and over 100,000 military motor vehicles of various kinds put the Red Army at the head of Europe in the question of motorization. Great Britain and France have been left far behind. . . .[135]

After the Kiev manoeuvres in 1935 General Loizeau, the Chief of the French Military Mission which was present, declared in an interview:

> As far as tanks are concerned I think we shall have to put the Soviet Union in the first place. The Red Army has a whole arsenal of tanks of all sizes and types, starting with fast tankettes and ending with powerful armoured land cruisers. This opens up great possibilities for various operations, and for the co-operation of all possible arms. Your tank park is really splendid. Frankly, I wish we had one as good. . . .[136]

Logistic problems. Resulting from the tremendous increases in tanks being supplied to the Soviet Army, new problems arose in supply, maintenance and training. The manpower to keep one tank fully operational in the Soviet Army at this time was about 70 men (as against 35–40 in the British

and French armies)[137] With the colossal numbers of tanks quoted for the Army at this time the requirement for technicians must have been unimaginable. Apart from having these men actually available, it became necessary to form a vast organization in order to employ them to their full capability. This was clearly demonstrated during the autumn 1935 manoeuvres at Kiev. Even though a large quantity of drivers and vehicle mechanics were gradually being provided by the growth in industry and agriculture (the agricultural directives of the First Five-Year Plan having established a network of tractor stations throughout the USSR), this was still insufficient to cater for Army requirements. It became necessary for the Red Army to adapt itself to the role of a technical as well as tactical training nucleus; during 1936 it was announced that the Ossoaviachim had trained 900,000 drivers to meet the demands of a highly motorized army, and as a further reserve there was the technical personnel of mechanized agriculture, in particular the tractor drivers, amounting to several million men. At the Red Army Military Academy on 4 March 1935 Stalin said:

> In order to exploit the achievements of technology and the industrial expansion, it is necessary, comrades, to become expert in all forms of technology . . . necessary, comrades, to become experts in making the best possible use of this technology in all the principal arts of war. Technology, without expert technicians—useless! But technology in co-operation with specialists can achieve miracles. . . . One realizes, from our present situation— specialists can achieve everything. . . .[138]

The Russians had operated with large tanks units during the 1935 Kiev exercises, and the manoeuvres at Minsk

37

38

during 1936. During the autumn manoeuvres of the Belo-russian, Kiev and Moscow military districts combinations of different arms were demonstrated in forms which were either unknown altogether in other armies or known in theory only—for example the co-ordination of tank and aircraft manoeuvres on a large scale, the co-ordination of large cavalry groups with moto-mechanized units, and the co-ordination of all the elements of a powerful and mobile shock army, including the tank corps, the air arm, cavalry and motorized infantry. Werner wrote:

It is of primary importance to discover how the Red Army is able to operate with new types of weapons demanding a high degree of technical skill. Very favourable results were obtained with the introduction of modern weapons on a mass scale comparatively early on and several years before the western powers. . . . There are tank drivers who have been 2,500 hours at the controls. There are tanks which have travelled almost 4,000 miles, tanks which have travelled over 600 miles at a time without any mechanical defects, tanks which have travelled 300 miles through water. The highest degree of performance is demanded from both men and machines. The training of this arm is particularly important because it leads to the adaptation of modern motorization to the difficulties and peculiarities of the plains of Eastern Europe which are very poor in roads and ways. . . . The tank drivers of the Red Army are particularly experienced in driving through forests, and through all sorts of difficult and swampy country. The performances of the Soviet amphibious tank (T–37) are extraordinary. These tanks have been known to drive through tidal seas for 7 hours at a time. The technical training of the

tank crews is excellent, and the commanders of even the smallest units are trained in wireless communication. The battle training of the tank crew is equally good. The principle of sniping has been introduced into the Tank Corps. . . . Tanks in the Red Army are used in all situations and in co-operation with all arms. They carry out reconnoitring tasks: armoured scouts, amphibian tanks and tankettes. They give weight to infantry attacks, and they are organically attached to infantry units. In this case they are under the orders of the infantry commander, and their task is to go ahead and destroy enemy strong-points and machine-gun nests and attack his artillery, as well as break down wire or any other hindrance to the infantry advance. Normally 10 infantry tanks per kilometre are reckoned on, so that on the West Front the Soviet Union must have 6,000 such tanks at least. These are light and medium tanks. Cavalry detachments are supported by light and particularly fast tanks (BTs). The main weight of the Tank Corps, however, is concentrated in the tank units intended for long-distance operations (TDD), to turn the enemy flank and take him in the rear, or carry out a big breakthrough, that is, more or less independent operations on a big scale. The Christie tanks, which are particularly mobile, are designed for such purposes, these and very heavy tanks. The former commander of the Moto-Mechanized Units of the Red Army (I. Chalepski) has described these Christie tanks as 'operative' tanks![139]

Voroshilov stated that, thanks to the simplest contrivances, and above all to the experience of technicians and commanders, Soviet tank drivers had succeeded in taking their machines through swamps without much difficulty although, he added, they were never made for that. He stated that they had crossed rivers, lakes and even bays and that the Red Army had thousands of capable tank drivers who control their enormous machines 'like virtuosi'.

During the 1935 and 1936 exercises foreign observers noted how well the Russian tanks performed: there were hardly any breakdowns. The concluding review was climaxed by a parade of 1,000 tanks, again without a single breakdown—a performance which could not have been duplicated by any other army in the world at that time. Over 1,000 tanks and over 1,000 aircraft were in action during these manoeuvres and they were subjected to very gruelling tests over extremely long distances. These manoeuvres certainly proved the capacity of Soviet war material to stand up to great wear and tear.

Colonel Martell, a member of the British Military Mission which accompanied Major-General Wavell on a visit to the Minsk manoeuvres during September 1936 declared to Soviet correspondents:

The fact that only very few tanks were compelled to fall out on account of mechanical defects, and that there were no air accidents and no forced landings inspired us with respect for your tanks and aircraft. . . . The tank leadership I saw at the manoeuvres can only be described as brilliant![140]

In an immediate letter to the Director of Mechanization on 15 September he reported:

We have seen some 1,200 tanks of all kinds covering considerable distances during the four days of manoeuvres, and with practically no mechanical trouble. . . . On the fifth day over a thousand tanks marched past us on parade, and the worst we saw was a few engines missing fire a little at times. . . . The design of the fighting body is not very good (BT) but the performance of the machine is at least twice as good as the A–9. The suspension is excellent. The maximum speed is at least 30 mph, and it travels across average country at 20 mph easily. . . . We saw several machines pass at 30 mph over a prepared bank which had a vertical drop of 5 ft on the far side. The whole machine leapt through the air and cleared a 30 ft gap. There was no apparent damage to the suspension or the crew. The engine is an aircraft engine of some 300 hp output . . . and the great advantage of using a really powerful engine is very apparent. This lighter type of medium tank is developed from the Christie tank which the Russians bought from America and fitted their own engine and armament. It has one 37 mm gun and one machine-gun coaxial in the turret and I think 16 mm armour basis. I feel that we should buy a Russian Christie at once to study the suspension. . . . Unless we can improve the A–9 to a very considerable extent, I cannot help feeling dismay at the idea of our building any large number of these tanks which will be far inferior to existing Russian tanks![141]

(Immediately after this letter was received negotiations were made with J. W. Christie in the USA and a specimen vehicle purchased. This vehicle was developed into the A–13—the Crusader—and eventually the Cromwell). Other foreign military observers were equally impressed. General Loizeau stated:

Your tank crews have completely mastered the technique of handling their machines. They displayed the highest possible level of technical performance under all the conditions of modern battle![142]

In the same article, General Schweissguth was quoted:

We saw your tanks taking obstacles in a fashion that demonstrated the quality of their material construction and the ease with which they were operated. . . .[143]

Soviet armoured tactics reviewed. Apart from the unbelievable quantity of armour employed during these manoeuvres and the extraordinary high efficiency rate, observers were also impressed with the tactical handling of large tank formations. Tank formations were used to conduct independent offensives, and tank units operated over a wide radius together with moto-mechanized units of tanks followed-up by motorized infantry and artillery, as well as cavalry. Werner wrote:

Cavalry is one of the most important offensive weapons of the Red Army. One can say, in fact, that today the Red army has a monopoly of the mass use of cavalry under conditions of modern warfare. . . . Whereas in the West, in Great Britain and France, cavalry is well on the way to being completely unhorsed and turned into lightly motorized formations, massed cavalry remains in full existence in the Red Army and it retains its own special tasks. . . . In the Red Army cavalry represents a supplementary arm for use with motorized units. . . . Red cavalry has a double purpose: it is used as the core of the troops with which it operates![144]

Field Service Regulations 1934 declared:

Strategic cavalry with its considerable strength in arms and technical equipment (machine-guns, artillery, tanks, armoured cars and aircraft) is capable of carrying out various tasks in battle (attack, defence, reconnaissance, raids) independently. . . . In future wars cavalry will be given very responsible tasks to perform: cavalry formations strongly supported by aircraft, tanks and armoured cars will have operational-strategic roles to execute—wide encirclement of the enemy, and the capture of his most vital strategic, economic and political

centres, as well as tactical tasks: the final disorganization and destruction of retreating and defeated enemy troops. . . .[145]

Werner wrote:

During the autumn manoeuvres in West Russia in 1936 there was one phase of the struggle in which the cavalry appeared as the core of an army, supported by tank units and aircraft, and a new combination of arms for future warfare became evident. Together with tank units and motorized infantry, the Red Army has powerful cavalry formations, a highly mobile weapon for an offensive blow or for manoeuvring. At the same time cavalry in the Red Army is trained to co-operate closely with tanks, and it has its place in the decisive operations of the powerful moto-mechanized units. It is the task of the cavalry to follow-up tank attacks, to occupy captured territory and mop-up isolated enemy posts. It must never offer a good mark to the enemy, it must be highly mobile and be used against the manpower of the enemy whilst the tanks are destroying his fire concentration. In such a combination of arms the operation of pursuit can be carried out rapidly and with all energy, and the exploitation of successes can be carried out at top speed. . . .[146]

Krivoshein stated:

Just as for cavalry, the pursuit of a defeated enemy is one of the most fruitful tasks of mechanized troops. The great mobility of cavalry is supplemented by the impetus and manoeuvring capacity of the tanks, and therefore a mixed formation of cavalry and mechanized troops represents a very effective instrument of pursuit![147]

Despite the increasing productivity of the Soviet tank and tractor industries, interest in foreign tank models still continued, and even as late as 1935 some 400 Renault AMR light tanks were purchased in France and issued to units of the Soviet mechanized divisions. It is believed that this resulted from a political negotiation between Russia and France. Bach wrote:

Basically it can be seen that the structure and theory of the NPP units have been borrowed from Europe, particularly France. In this respect, we notice the transfer of two tank regiments to Russia, complete with instruction staff, for teaching the NPP groups. About 400 tanks were bought, of the light Renault AMR type. The effect of the Russian pact was clearly demonstrated by this fact![148]

It was about this time that the Russian experimental field, which had been available to the Germans since the Rapallo Agreement, was becoming gradually closed to German observation.

The tank role. Following a detailed and exacting analysis of the manoeuvres at Kiev in 1935, and at Minsk in 1936, the new Provisional Field Service Regulations (PU-36), (Vremennyi Polevoi Ustav) were issued on 30 December 1936, under Soviet Defence Commissariat Directive No. 245. These regulations outlined the new Soviet offensive role for cavalry and, as before, were modelled on British tactical ideas. The Soviet strategy had its own uniform guiding principles outlined in these regulations which were put into force during February 1937. It was a strategy of the knock-out blow aiming at the annihilation of the enemy. The new Field Service Regulations stated:

The military operations of the Red Army will be conducted with a view to destroying the enemy. The fundamental aim of the Soviet Union in any war which is forced upon it will be to secure a decisive victory and utterly overthrow its enemy. . . . The enemy must be caught throughout the whole depth of his positions and then encircled and destroyed. . . . It is impossible to be equally strong everywhere. To guarantee success troops and war material must be deployed in such a way that superiority is obtained at the decisive points. On sectors of secondary importance all that is necessary is the employment of sufficient forces to hold the enemy. . . . Only a decisive offensive at decisive points followed-up by ruthless pursuit can lead to the complete destruction of all enemy forces and resources. . . . Each arm must be used in battle with careful regard to its peculiarities and its strong points. Each arm must operate in the closest possible co-operation with all other arms and each arm must be used under the conditions most favourable for

39. *An NPP (TPP) Tank Group lined up for inspection. The photograph clearly demonstrates the small proportion of tanks fitted with radio equipment.*

developing its possibilities to the full. . . . Modern technical means permit the simultaneous defeat of the enemy along the whole of his battle front and throughout the whole depth of his position. The attack must encircle the enemy and totally destroy him. . . . Modern technical means of reducing the defensive (above all tanks, artillery, aircraft and mechanized units, when used on a mass scale) make it possible to organize a simultaneous attack on the enemy throughout the entire depth of his position, to isolate him, to encircle him completely and finally to destroy him.

Armoured units were administered by the Department of Mechanization and Armoured Forces of the Commissariat for Defence. The chief of this department was directly responsible to the Deputy Commissar for Defence who was in charge of supply of ordnance material of all kinds.

The Soviet Tank Corps journal stated:

The co-operation of troops, which is dependent upon the employment of the characteristics and advantages of each individual arm in combat, must be of particular concern to the commanders of all arms of the RKKA. Unco-ordination and the isolated use of different arms would give the advantage to the enemy: it would give him the opportunity to strike our troops piecemeal, cause futile losses and in due course bring defeat during a given stage of battle. . . . Regarding the co-operation of all arms, PU-36 states: 'The employment of each arm in combat should take into account its characteristics and

advantages. All arms should be used in close co-operation with each other where conditions allow. Infantry in close co-operation with artillery and tanks decide offensive operations and maintain the tactical defence during battle'.[149]

Mechanized units were to be composed of tanks, self-propelled artillery and lorry-borne infantry, and were assigned the role of executing independent operations disengaged from other types of troops or in co-operation with them. The Soviet infantry was strongly supported by mechanized weapons of all kinds. One third of the infantry was motorized, forming an organic part of army mechanization and being trained to work in the closest co-operation with the tank arm. The remainder of the infantry was provided with its own tank units. The tank was proposed for both infantry support and independent operations. It was taught that the greatest threat to infantry was not so much the tank as the infantry following in its wake. When facing a tank offensive, the battalion commander would adopt a circular defensive position, and the divisional commander would direct the divisional artillery on the brunt of the attacking enemy forces—in an attempt to separate the infantry from the tanks. Should a tank breakthrough occur, into the depths of the defended position, the divisional commander would employ his mobile anti-tank reserve, and his own tanks would mount a counter-attack. The Soviet infantry reached the highest known level of tank saturation for that time, and close co-operation with all mechanized arms became the basis of military training of all infantry units. The Soviet artillery was carefully trained to co-operate with the tank units and the air arm. The new technical instructions for the artillery provided for the concentration of large forces of heavy artillery in special groups for 'long-range effect'.

In the offensive it was taught that tanks must be employed only in large numbers, the divisional tank battalions being divided into infantry-support tanks (TPP—Tanki Poddierzhki Piechoty) and long-range tanks (TDD—Tank Dalnogo Dieystviya). The TPP were to be employed in offensive operations under the command of the corps or divisional commander. These moto-mechanized units of tanks (referred to in the new Field Service Regulations simply as mechanized units and even mechanized 'Landing Corps') were intended to breakthrough the retreating troops of the enemy, to attack them from the rear and cut them off from their base. For these tasks, tank battalions, rifle divisions and tank brigades of the RGK were formed. The TDD were to be employed for deep penetrations into enemy positions, as independent tank formations employed for extended manoeuvres and operations against the enemy's rear areas—in particular communications centres, reserves, HQs and artillery positions. Reserve Colonel Begishev wrote:

For the tactical success of operations it was necessary to introduce breakthrough mechanized corps, intended for use in co-operation with cavalry, and aviation and for clearing airborne units in the rear areas. As shown later, from the experience of the Great Patriotic War, these views turned out to be valid. On the basis of mobile warfare, Soviet theory concerned itself with further development and experimentation in the use of tanks in co-operation with infantry.[150]

Bach wrote:

The BA-27 is intended to provide security during the march of the NPP groups by covering, having its 37 mm gun available to check the sudden emergence of enemy

40. *A DD(TDD) Tank Group composed of BT–3s;* **41.** *A BA–20 armoured car, adapted to run along railway lines.*

tank units. The limited speed of the BA–27 arises from the idea that, in order to maintain the tactical co-ordination within the NPP groups under all circumstances to the end, because the BA–27 falling into danger has no possibility of high speed, it has to stand and fight—preserving the tactical unity of the NPP groups. Up to a certain degree one can consider also, the BA–27 as a lightly-armoured, tank-accompanying gun. (The particular tank-accompanying gun found in Russia is a cross-country 6-wheeled self-propelled mounting, having a top-speed of 80 kph, which is placed in separate units. These range in calibre from 77 to 150 mm, mounted on

open turntables, with gun shields—some long-barrelled, some howitzers. For cross-country work they are provided with overall tracks. In contrast to the French, all half-tracks in Russia are considered obsolete.) The NPP groups are incomplete without a reconnaissance vehicle. The nearest vehicle which falls into this category is an interesting ultra-light armoured car—the Bronieford, built around the commercial Ford chassis (under license). . . .[151]

The main fighting vehicles of the NPP groups were the T–27 tankette and the T–26 light tank (which formed the artillery backbone of the units). The NPP groups were originally equipped with T–26 Model A, but these were eventually replaced by Model B. The NPP groups were each composed of 100 vehicles, broken down as follows:

35 T–27 tankettes
35 T–26 light tanks Model B
20 BA–27 armoured cars
5 Bronieford armoured cars
5 BA–20 armoured cars

Bach wrote:

The DPP groups show in their tactics further modern operational views. Their task is to break through the main enemy line of resistance, to overrun anti-tank guns and to penetrate the enemy artillery positions, and afterwards—as far as possible—to employ the DD groups, predominantly consisting of fast combat vehicles, to successfully break through the remainder of the enemy front. These DD groups have an offensive role, based on the Fuller theory, in cutting the lifeline of the enemy army. In conjunction with the Air Arm, these units present extraordinary powerful armoured thrust brigades. . . .[152]

The DPP groups were provided with T–37 amphibious tanks, T–26 Model B light tanks, T–28 medium and T–35 heavy tanks, being based on the Fuller theory of armoured thrust brigades. The intended offensive speed of these units across country was placed at 60 kph, and along firm roads, or on hard ground at up to 110 kph. The main fighting vehicle of the DD groups was the BT tank. The groups were also equipped with large numbers of armoured cars (6-wheeled Ford BA–10s and amphibious BA–10s). The Russians intended the DD groups to work in conjunction with the air arm.

Bach wrote:

The average offensive breakthrough speed of the 'mixed' assault units is about 30 kph, assuming they keep on a uniform course and in uniform formation. It was demonstrated during the recent Russian manoeuvres, that these units are unique as tactical assault units go. Only the T–35 heavy tanks and the 6-ton tanks were established in the frontal assault, whilst the 3-ton amphibious tanks and the T–28 medium tanks were deployed at the expected location of enemy opposition, to break up the enemy front by deep penetration with an offensive speed of 45 kph. Following the success of such a breakthrough, the amphibious tanks now take over, proceeding with full speed (70–75 kph) forming the reconnaissance amenity of the DD units thrusting through the gap. This explains the necessity for high speed![153]

PU–36 also laid down four main fighting characteristics for tanks:[154]

1. High mobility.
2. Effective firepower.
3. Powerful striking force (obtained by movement and mass of tanks).

4. Immunity to conventional small-arms and machine-gun fire and light artillery fragments.

PU-36 was the result of some six years of operational research, although even at this stage it was appreciated that further investigation was called for. One point was assured, however: the necessity for providing artillery support for all forms of armoured attack. Long-range tanks with artillery support would be assigned to each tank battalion, consisting of 32 tanks, over a frontage of 300 to 1,000 metres. It is interesting to note the similarity between the new Soviet and later German theories of mechanized war; with the emphasis upon armour-protection, mobility, surprise and tactical flexibility, the Soviet offensive was visualized not so much as a lightning thrust, but as a series of successive blows, adding power to the offensive and exploited with careful preparation. Certain aspects of this strategy, such as the commitment of DD tanks, required a great tactical dexterity—which, as demonstrated by the 1936 Minsk manoeuvres, was not clearly evident in the Soviet Army at this time. Garrett Underhill wrote:

When armour was developing in the 1930s, the Soviets apparently thought that tanks—turreted tanks—should provide much of the artillery-type support for shock action and mobile operations. To this end, they fitted their first wave of armour with cannon especially powerful for the day. . . . The Red infantry-accompanying tanks at first mounted either a 37 mm (later 45 mm) gun or machine-guns; their mediums, a howitzer or light field artillery gun (calibre 76 mm). . . . They just put infantry battalion (machine-gun, and 37 or 45 mm anti-tank guns), or regimental (76 mm howitzer) weapons in armour. Nevertheless, it was thought that this armour would be able to drive through the 'entire depth' of enemy positions, and take out hostile field artillery as well as infantry weapons. The 45 mm gun was also the main armament of mobile warfare armour—of the BTs. . . . The job of the BTs was to sweep through or around the enemy's position, take out his artillery, his rear area installations—and, as part of the Soviet 'armoured division' of the day (the 'Moto-Mechanized Corps'), effect entrapments. Of course, the Soviets also thought that attack aircraft would be able to take over artillery roles in mobile warfare—a fallacy which the Germans were also guilty of at the time. . . [155]

In 1936 the output of Soviet tanks had increased considerably. According to German evidence at the beginning of 1936 the Red Army had 1,500 T-28 medium and T-35 heavy tanks![156] The Red Army was also the only army in the world which had amphibian tanks in large numbers and which used them in regular formations for carrying out special tactical tasks. Russian tanks were characterized, at that time, by their powerful armament (45-76 mm guns) and good performance. Armour protection was required to provide immunity to grenades and machine-gun fire as well as artillery shell fragments. During the Spanish Civil War, Soviet armour was found to be fairly soft, and shells passed straight through leaving clean holes; there was no internal scabbing or flaking. This effect was stated by the Russian armour technicians to be an advantage over the Germans, since tank personnel would only be injured by direct contact of the shot if they happened to be in the way (not the best philosophy to adopt by any means). Transmissions, engines and suspensions were particularly good for this time.

During 1936 engineer M. I. Koshkin became chief designer of the design group at the Kharkov Factory. This factory, one of the main producers of BT tanks during the thirties, carried out extensive work on modernizing this tank model. Among other developments, the new BD-2 diesel engine was tried out in a BT tank. This engine was later improved and became the basis for the V-2 used in the T-34 tank.

During 1936 the Stalingrad factory changed over to the production of tracked tractors, principally the STZ-3 model, a light 52 hp type for towing artillery. Neither this nor the KhTZ (Kharkov), ChTZ (Chelyabinsk) or Kirovets tractors at this time could be considered as suitable prime-movers for artillery; they could not keep pace with fast logistic or tank columns, and their size and general characteristics made them unsuitable carriages for self-propelled artillery. Even so, the national total in tractors reached 500,000 in 1937 compared with 100,000 in 1930.

The British 1940 *Notes on the Red Army* stated:

The great progress in mechanization generally and in the tractor industry in particular, coupled with the decrease in the number of horses available, has had considerable repercussions on artillery traction. . . . All army artillery and most of the corps artillery now appears to be mechanized. These are both tractor drawn. Certain field artillery regiments which have also been mechanized are either carried on lorries as 'Artillerie portee' or are drawn by lorries on which the gun teams ride. . . . The allotment and organization of artillery of mechanized and motorized formations is still in the experimental stage. The tendency was to allot 'Artillerie portee' to the motorized formations and artillery on self-propelled mountings to mechanized formations, but no finality has been reached, and there are some indications that no artillery is definitely allotted to mechanized formations. . . [157]

According to official figures published during 1937, every soldier of the Red Army was backed by 12 hp in mechanism. The entire motorized park of the Red Army, including motorization and mechanization, amounted to 15,000,000 hp. The tractors working in Soviet agriculture had a total of 7,000,000 hp. A heavy artillery tractor had 60-90 hp, a medium military lorry about 50 hp, and a medium tank between 150 and 250 hp. Werner wrote:

A motorized division employing no horse traction at all needs between 2,000 and 2,500 motor vehicles of various kinds. Thus the big motor park of the Red Army is sufficient to permit the formation of a powerful moto-mechanized first-line army, the motorization of a third of the infantry and of the greater part of the artillery, and in addition widespread motorization throughout the whole basis of operations in the rear. If the productive capacity of the Soviet tractor industry is taken into consideration it becomes clear that the possibilities of motorization in the Red Army are practically unlimited![158]

This same rate of development progressed in other fields of the national economy. Of particular importance was the growth in the iron and steel industry which provided a firm base at the Ural-Kuznetz complex, created under the control of the TKK (Central Communist Committee). And of no minor importance was the development of the oil industry.

5 Armoured Warfare in Practice

Over the period 1937–9 the organization of tank troops, and the principles for the tactical use of tanks in the Soviet Army underwent major alteration. By 1936–7 armoured formations had been formed into four main organizations:

1. *Moto-Mechanized Corps:* 7, each with about 500 tanks. These were distributed in separate battalions to infantry formations as infantry-support (NPP) tanks.

2. *Moto-Mechanized Brigade:* each with 2 tank battalions, 1 light tank battalion (with 16 T–37 tankettes and 22 T–26 light tanks), and 2 machine-gun battalions; up to a battalion of tank-borne infantry—7 men per tank.

3. *Mechanized Brigade:* each with 3 tank battalions (32 tanks in each) equipped with BT tanks; 1 light tank battalion for reconnaissance (19 T–37 tankettes and 24 BA–20 armoured cars), and 1 moto-machine-gun battalion (in lorries).

4. *Tank Brigade:* consisted of a team of 4 tank battalions (32 tanks in each), equipped with T–28 medium tanks. A corps had 1 regiment; a division, 1 tank battalion, 1 medium tank company and 2 light tank companies. The medium tank company was allotted to the infantry support role.

The cavalry division would often incorporate a mechanized regiment along with the horse regiments. Cavalry was intended to assist mechanized brigades in enveloping operations and meeting engagements. The prewar mechanized brigades were badly organized and over-complicated in structure. The various arms were not united under a central control for assignment to combat teams, according to given situations, but distributed in advance so that corps and army commanders could have independent units to combine as required. Lower units were often provided with cumbersome, intricate arrangements![59]

Experience in Spain. Clarke wrote:

In 1937 a number of Russian officers had been attached to the Republican forces in Spain, and here they saw these principles given practical endorsement. Except under conditions of street fighting the defensive was everywhere overcome by the relentless pressure of a balanced force of tanks, infantry and artillery. The Iron Ring of Bilbao, the Ebro Line—a system of permanent emplacements—seemed capable of imposing only a delay, never a stalemate. General Pavlov, the tank expert who had gone to Spain . . . had reported to Stalin and Voroshilov: 'The tank can play no independent role on the battlefield . . .', and he recommended that the tank battalions be distributed in an infantry support role...![160]

In 1937 Tukhachevsky, whilst expressing his personal view on the cavalry aspects of PU-36, questioned the existence within the Soviet Army of any ability to manoeuvre![61] He stated that assumptions on the manoeuvrability of the Soviet Army had been based solely on the experience gained during the Spanish Civil War, and not as they should have been, upon the tactics and equipment of foreign armies. The Soviet trend in armament development supported his statement. Tukhachevsky said that the availability of a large quantity of tanks and aircraft had brought into being the new 'Manoeuvre Theory', wherein the tank could not be used in co-operation with infantry without losing the effect of its speed and surprise. The Manoeuvre Theory considered that the high speed of the tank limited its productive use in combined operation with the infantry. This resulted in the complete removal of the independence of tank formations, their separation from the main combined-arms mass, a complete disregard for anti-tank fire, and not appreciating that tanks, like infantry, could not be

42. *An early BA–32 armoured car in Spain;* **43.** *The effect of mines and anti-tank guns during the Spanish Civil War is clearly discernable from this photo. A T–26B tank has been completely gutted.*

successfully employed in combined-arms combat without the support of heavy artillery. Tukhachevsky said:

> In all cases, the tank attack must be insured by artillery support, and is *not* to be permitted without such support. . .[162]

Major Hooper wrote:

> It was in this war that the flexibility of Red Army tactics was shown in some degree. For the first time in history the Soviet aeroplanes took the place of cavalry by destroying the two Italian divisions at the battle of Guadalajava. At the battle of Jarama, the Soviet tanks appeared in a completely new role. Up to then tanks had been used entirely for the offensive, but in this battle when the Spanish infantry were defeated, the lines were held by large Soviet tanks which kept the smaller Italian tanks at bay by superior fire, and yet avoided the artillery fire by great mobility and speed, presenting an elusive target. This was the first time tanks had ever been used as a means of defence![163]

Stalin purges the Red Army—the dark ages return. After Stalin's purges on practically every field of the Soviet National Defence, most of the talented and able commanders and tacticians were liquidated— including Tukhachevsky. Wheldon wrote:

> As the terror and hysteria built up through this barbarous period, Russian officers who subscribed for purely professional reasons to the Liddell Hart-Kalinovski theories of mobile war found themselves criticized and denounced not on technical grounds which could be contested objectively, but on moral and political ones. Mobile war as advocated by Fuller and Liddell Hart was denounced as reactionary, bourgeois, and unworthy of a Marxist society, inasmuch as it put faith in a suspect technocracy instead of the armed proletariat. Fuller and Liddell Hart were denounced as the effete spokesmen of a decadent capitalism which dared not place its trust in the masses, and so hid behind mechanical contrivances. . . . Such was the mood of the times that this nonsense passed for reason, and its corroborative evidence, of Communist experiences of tank warfare in China and Spain, was not objectively examined. Many supporters of mobile warfare, including Tukhachevsky and Kalinovski, were put to death. Others, less deeply committed, were able to recant and save their lives at the price of their professional judgement. . .[164]

On 28 October 1937 final approval was given to a plan for the development and reconstruction of the Red Army to be carried out over the period 1938–42 (i.e., the period of the Third Five-Year Plan). The plan did not envisage any further quantitative increases, but instead concerned itself with 'vital' changes in organization and quality. Unfortunately, the removal of the elite from the Army greatly weakened its effectiveness and proved a few years later to be catastrophic. Clark wrote:

> Tukhachevsky (Chief of the Red Army Staff 1926–8) had evolved tactical and strategic doctrines which, although not so revolutionary as those of some British tank experts, were none the less far in advance of current thinking in other European armies. However, in the late 1930s domestic politics and the shifting orientation of the Soviet Union in the European power complex led to corresponding (and dangerous) changes in its military attitude![165]

As a result of incorrect conclusions being drawn from the Spanish Civil War, insufficient importance was attached to the capabilities of large armoured formations in solving independent operational tasks. Over the period 1937–8 the organization of the Military Armoured Council and the official principles of using tanks were basically changed. From the limited experience in Spain the Command Council drew the wrong tactical conclusions—greatly to the detriment of the further development of Soviet armoured forces. They rejected the concept of the 'elastic' operational use of the tank, and envisaged it exclusively for supporting infantry. Wheldon wrote:

> In 1937 the new leaders of the Red Army, under the nominal leadership of Field Marshal Klimenti Voroshilov, announced that as minefields and anti-tank defences were now stepped in depth (as if they had not been since 1918), independent armoured operations were out of the question, and only set-piece offensives on narrow fronts, by infantry with tanks and artillery in support, could be successful. . .[166]

The view that it was impossible for tank formations to have an independent operational role was expressed by General Pavlov (who replaced Tukhachevsky as the leading Soviet tank warfare specialist), in Spain. During July 1938 a special commission had been appointed under the direction of G. I. Kulik (a representative of the People's Commissariat for Defence), who presented the War Office with his conclusions of the operations in the Far East and the Spanish Civil War. The commission was composed of, among others, Budenny, Shaposhnikov, Shadenko, commanders of military districts, and representatives of various administrations and staffs. After discussing the question of the presently extant armoured policies the Chief Administrator of Armoured and Mechanized Troops, D. G. Pavlov, on the basis of the experience gained in Spain, put forward his proposals for reforming the armoured corps. His conclusion: that the efficient command of large armoured units (the contemporary corps establishment included about 560 tanks and 12,710 men) was impossible. Pavlov convinced Stalin and Voroshilov of his opinions, and this lead ultimately to the disbandment of the independent mechanized units—in spite of protests by Shaposhnikov and Zhukov.[167] Hence, on 21 October 1939, the mechanized corps were broken up and in their place were to be formed 15 motorized divisions (8 in 1940 and a further 7 in the first half of 1941). These were to be used by brigades for infantry support (NPP). Each motorized division had 275 tanks (258 BTs, 17 T-38s or T-40s, plus reserves), 49 armoured cars, 98 anti-tank guns and mortars, and 11,650 men. The seriousness of this mistake was only appreciated during 1940 with the tremendous progress made by the German armoured forces in Europe. Clark wrote:

> Following on Pavlov's recommendation in 1939 the armoured divisions had been broken up and their strength distributed as 'brigades' throughout the infantry armies. Although the divisional organization was retained in a number of cases, the breakdown of the brigades into 'heavy', 'medium', and 'reconnaissance' spelt the end of the tank force as an independent arm. . . .[168]

The basis of the new Soviet military offensive strategy was clearly outlined in the Draft Field Service Regulations for 1939, in which it was stated that every attack by the enemy against the USSR would be met by a crushing blow from the entire might of the armed forces:

> If the enemy forces us into war, the Red Army will be the most aggressive of all the armies in history; it shall conduct an offensive war, carrying it into the enemy territory. The combined actions of the Red Army will be aimed at the destruction, the total annihilation of the enemy. . . . It is assumed that victory in war can be achieved only by the concentrated effort of all the branches of the armed forces. . . .[169]

Estimates of Red Army strength given in the foreign press during 1938 were: 100 infantry divisions, 34 cavalry divisions, 20-25 tank brigades (not including the tank units attached in infantry formations), about 100 regiments of light artillery and between 60-80 regiments of heavy artillery. About one-third of the infantry divisions are believed to have been motorized.[170]

In spite of the purges within the Army, little interference took place in the existing group of Soviet tank designers (the GUVP), and the improvements in tank design projected during 1938-9 were to lead to some excellent machines.[171] There were more and more indications that the Soviet tank designers were competent to turn out some very sound, powerful and effective military vehicles. Hence, whereas the tactical ideas for the operational use of tanks was seemingly fallacious, the correct deductions were made regarding the design of further tank models with greater armour and more powerful armament.

In the prewar Soviet tanks, simplicity and ruggedness had become the prime considerations. This was achieved at the expense of the ballistic efficiency of the armour; during the Finnish War, T-26 and BT tanks were shown to have brittle plates which shattered and flaked like the German Krupp plates. Minor turret improvements were often made which added to production complexities: spring-loaded hatches for tank commanders, and specially sealed ones for gunners, appeared on the later T-26 and BT models, replacing the crude rectangular metal plates used on the earlier models. A new anti-aircraft machine-gun mounting was installed on the turrets of light, medium and heavy tanks, and the T-26, BT and T-28 tanks were provided with additional machine-gun mountings in the turret rear. The development of sophisticated sighting and optical devices was aided by the Soviet purchase of the old German Zeiss optical plant (set up under the Rapallo Agreement). Radios for tanks were rare, owing to the lack of a telecommunications industry, and only platoon, company and higher commanders' tanks were equipped with radios. A great deal of experimentation was carried out with wheel/track tanks; Mostovenko wrote:

> One of the characteristic features of Soviet tank design during the thirties was the production of the wheel/track tanks. The employment of wheel/track drive considerably complicated the transmission and suspension of the tank. All the models of wheel/track tanks were noted for their outstanding originality of construction![172]

Revised tank specifications. Although the T-26, BT and T-28 tanks, as well as other models introduced over the period 1931-3, possessed reasonable mobility and firepower, their armour was not so good. From the experience gained with this equipment during the Spanish Civil War (characterized by the development of deep defences and the high concentration of modern anti-tank artillery) tanks with bullet-proof armour proved to be useless, and their operational ability extremely limited. Mostovenko wrote:

> Over the past thirty years the only likely threat to the tank had been from the artillery, but 1936-7 saw the adoption of 37-47 mm anti-tank guns, the armour-piercing rounds of which could pierce armour up to 55-58 mm thick. As a result the 13-20 mm armour basis formerly used in tanks was considered inadequate. . . . The experience gained during the Spanish Civil War, and the trend in anti-tank artillery development during 1936-7, revealed the necessity for considerable alteration of the fundamental combat characteristics of tanks; increases in both armour protection and firepower. With the organization of anti-tank defences, the protection of troops from small-calibre anti-tank artillery (20-37 mm) by employing normal bullet-proof armour was no longer possible. Where the effect of the machine-gun was overcome by the introduction of bullet-proof armour, so the threat to the tank became the quick-firing anti-tank gun. It, therefore, became necessary to introduce shell-proof armour and a substantial increase in firepower. The first Soviet tank with shell-proof armour, the T-46-5 (T-111) was built during the spring of 1937. . . .[173]

About the same time Reynaud wrote:

> Opinion is general that the Italian light tanks of the Fiat-Ansaldo type—weighing about 3 tons and having 10 mm armour—are very considerably inferior to the Russian tanks of the T-26 model weighing 9 tons and having 13 mm armour, and vastly inferior to the Russian tanks of the T-28 model weighing 20 tons, and having 20 mm armour plate and carrying 76 and 37 mm guns. The Germans, who also put forward one or two light tank models (PzKpfw- I and II), have also been compelled to come to the same conclusion. . . .[174]

As early as 1938, Stalin, who took a personal interest in

44. *One of the last parades in the Red Square prior to the Great Patriotic War. BA–32 armoured cars on review.*

Soviet tank development, held a meeting with the two leading Soviet tank designers, Kotin and Morozov. Here, he emphasized the requirement for increased armour, decreased turret size and new tracks. Stalin demanded superiority over Western tank designs in firepower, armour protection and mobility, and insisted upon an increased capacity for long-range employment. Through necessity, tank guns turned to using large-calibre armour-piercing projectiles, and armour was developed to provide immunity to modern anti-tank guns. The tremendous advances made in the design of the new tank models developed under the 1940–41 Tank Programme, came about from these revised specifications.

The state of mechanization prior to the Great Patriotic War.
By the beginning of 1939 the Soviet Union had caught up with Germany, France and Britain in the volume and rate of industrial production. Over the period 1935–8 the Red Army doubled the number of modern weapons of offence at its disposal, and by 1935 had between 15,000 and 20,000 tanks. The enormous increases in tank production at this time can be summed up by a statement in *Pravda* during 1939, which stated that in the previous five years the greatest

increases in armament had been first in tanks, then in anti-tank artillery. It published (as an understatement) that Russia had between 6,000 and 10,000 tanks, and that Soviet truck production by 1940 had reached 400,000 vehicles per year. Bibergan wrote:

> At the present moment we have not only caught up the lead of other countries, but have reached the peak of tank development, whereby certain foreign countries are reforming their tank parks along our lines. . . . Much has ·the wheel of history turned, that countries should learn from us![75]

In actual fact, the American designed plants of the early 1920s were producing a total of 201,700 vehicles per year, some 80–90 per cent of which were lorries. A further factory in Moscow started production during 1939 (the production of military trucks in 1937 having reached 181,700 Model A trucks and 42,000 cars at the GAZ factory alone).

About this time, special fast, tracked prime-movers began to appear for the artillery. Firstly came the small armoured Konsomolets (often used as a prime-mover for 45 mm anti-tank guns and 76 mm infantry howitzers of mechanized units), which performed very badly later

45

the Stalingrad Tractor Plant and at Chelyabinsk. Werner wrote:

> As far as quantities are concerned, the productive possibilities of the Soviet Union in this respect are practically unlimited, because it is a comparatively simple matter to switch over from the production of tractors to the production of tanks. The tank is no more than a specially constructed and armoured tractor equipped with weapons, and in 1937 the Soviet Union turned out no less than 176,000 tractors, and the big tractor works have already changed over from the ordinary wheeled tractor to the caterpillar tread variety. . . . The whole enormous apparatus of army motorization has been created to master the territorial peculiarities of Eastern Europe. This territory has always proved an invincible

46

45. *Artillery mechanization during the Russo-Finnish War. A Stalinets tractor moving heavy guns into position;* **46.** *A T–28 tank knocked-out during the Russo-Finnish War being inspected by a Finnish soldier.*

during the Finnish War, after which it was abandoned. For medium artillery the Chelyabinsk factory produced a 6 ton fast prime-mover with metal cab and rear open-topped wooden compartment for the gun crew. For heavy artillery there was a similar 18 ton Voroshilovets tractor powered by a 500 hp tank diesel engine. Werner wrote:

> With regard to motorization, the artillery of the Red Army undoubtedly takes first place. The heavy artillery, the anti-tank and anti-aircraft batteries are already fully motorized, and the medium and light artillery are partly motorized. The widespread motorization of the artillery is thus in accordance with the general high level of motorization in the Red Army, and keeps pace with the mechanized units and the motorized infantry in this respect![176]

By 1939 the Soviet Army was about 12 per cent mechanized—nearly four times the level of 1930. This mechanization brought with it modern weapons, comparable in fighting efficiency with those of any other nation. The intensive tank production of the 1930s had been carried out in 5 major tank plants; the work was done in special plants at Moscow and Sverdlovsk, and in the tank plants at Kirov and Leningrad. Tank production was also carried out at

obstacle for the enemy, but the Red Army is confident that the endurance and mobility of its troops and the durability of its technical equipment will master it completely![177]

Haudann wrote:

> The building and improvement of Soviet roads, and Soviet ways and communications plans in general, are carried out primarily from the standpoint of military-strategic considerations. Therefore, the military important districts have a relatively dense network of good roads. . . . The Soviet Union is primarily concentrating road-building activities in such districts in order to create conditions for the use of motorized units. This is true above all of the Western Frontier districts which are the centre of Soviet strategic road planning![178]

Manchuria. During August 1939 the long awaited confrontation with the Japanese in Manchuria took place. This was the first experience of the Soviet Army against a modern equipped force. On 23 and 24 August 1939 the Soviet 6th Tank Brigade, supported by several companies of flame-throwing tanks (OT–130s) were moved into the Khalkin-Gol area. As well as their own support tanks, the infantry were accompanied by independent armoured units, organized into brigades, having a total of 285 tanks. In addition, some 346 armoured cars and 400 aircraft were employed against the Japanese. The major part of the Soviet tank forces were composed of T–26 light tanks, BT–7 and BT–7Ms, and T–38 amphibious tanks.[179] Hooper wrote:

> In the battle of Chang ku feng, not more than two or three Japanese divisions can have been employed, but the most important effect was the surprise they got at the flexibility of the Russian tactics. Here was seen the biggest barrage of artillery ever put down since the last war on the Western Front. Tanks were used, not in mass, but as single units, and in some cases would move up, under cover of their armour, as close to the Japanese as possible, making use of local ground for concealment (such as folds or dips), take out their machine-guns and bring enfilade fire to bear from a forward position ahead of the infantry. This helped the Red infantry to arrive within assaulting distance. Here, too, the dive-bomber to supplement the artillery barrage, made its appearance in modern war.[180]

Due to the relatively short period of combat, little experience was gained by the Russians of the effect of tanks in modern war. They were to learn far more from the Finnish War.

Finland. With the outbreak of the war with Finland on 30 November 1939, the initial operations were carried out by units equipped with T–37, T–26, BT and T–28 tanks, as well as a few of the newer T–100, SMK and KV tanks. Both medium and heavy tanks were used directly to support infantry by attacking fortifications and fieldworks in the depth of the enemy's defences, as well as composing the storm groups of the attacks. At the beginning of February 1940 the main Soviet attack on the Mannerheim Line started in earnest; discussing the Russo-Finnish War Hooper wrote:

> On February 2nd 1940, after a heavy bombardment of artillery, supplemented from the air, the full weight of the infantry attack was launched on the Finnish right-centre sector of the Mannerheim Line, the Summa Front, on a width of some 10 miles. Tanks and troops advanced under a heavy smoke screen. Infantry used armoured sledges, 9 feet long and 6 feet wide with machine-guns, and these were pushed forward over the snow by tanks.

The Red Army has been criticized for using heavily mechanized forces in such a climate and on such unsuitable terrain. There would appear to be some justice in this, in view of the comparatively heavy losses of tanks in these Northern thrusts. But it may well be the fault lay not so much in the use of this form of warfare as the failure of the fuel in such climatic conditions. The Red authorities had had vast experience in all their great projects in the Arctic and at the pole, of the need of 'doctoring' oil and petrol for aeroplanes and land machines (tanks). If they had taken the average temperature of these parts for the last 50 years, they would have 'doctored' their fuel supply to a temperature of 25 degrees below zero. But when in this late December it dropped a further 25 degrees this special fuel would fail. The fuel 'doctored' to this new condition would be neither at their base or railroad and could never be brought up from Murmansk or Leningrad in time. This would account for the sudden immobilizing of their tank columns, thus leaving them an easy prey to the guerilla tactics of their Finnish infantry opponents. This failure to be prepared for the exceptional weather may be the reason, if not the excuse, for the losses. But it does not prove that the use

of mechanized forces here was wrong. It was the vital part of the Red Army plan to give the impression of real weight in these thrusts, and mechanized units, not just infantry, were an imperative part of the plan.[181]

> The mechanized forces of Russia have shown their great superiority. Tanks were used over the most difficult ground and in sub-arctic climate. The methods of bringing infantry up to attacking distance with a minimum of loss were ingenious. . . . Triple turreted tanks of 70 tons (SMK and T–100) were tried out as an experiment in the final stages of the offensive.[182]

In this war, a heavy tank brigade consisted of three battalions, each having 35 heavy tanks and 15 light tanks. The combats demonstrated that the T–100 and SMK heavy tanks still had insufficient armour, and that their firepower had little effect. As confirmation of the views expressed during the Spanish Civil War, the older tanks were shown to be completely obsolete. In spite of the small calibre of anti-tank guns (20–37 mm) the armour of these Soviet tanks was easily penetrated by anti-tank fire. The war in Finland confirmed the view that bullet-proof armour could no longer provide sufficient immunity for fighting vehicles.

During the Finnish War, Soviet divisions appeared to have gathered a total of only 500 motor vehicles each. Experience from this war brought home the poor state of motor transport. The Soviet infantry division, which included an MT company of 30 tanks, still relied to some extent upon horse-drawn carts. The Russians employed horse-drawn carts and coaches for logistic roles—indeed, even for radio and command vehicles. Similar circumstances were apparent during the invasion of Poland in September 1939; Antonov wrote:

> It was soon found that the administration and supply of our troops were badly organized. The rear units dragged behind. There were no fuel dumps, and many tanks, tractors, and other vehicles could not move on account of lack of fuel, and had to stop on roads and in fields. Two echelons were spread over hundreds of kilometres. . . .[183]

Even though the Soviet motor industry had made great progress it was still not sufficient to cope with both the increasing civilian and military demand. The two basic logistic vehicles at this time were the ZIS 5-tonner, (an extremely robust 4×2 version of the Ford) and the GAZ-AA $1\frac{1}{2}$-ton truck. Both of these vehicles had only one driven axle. Whilst these two vehicles alone were identified in the fighting during the Finnish War, the Soviet motor industry was, at this time, producing the GAZ–4 and the GAZ-MM in the light vehicle field, and the Ya G–4, Ya G–6, Ya G–10 and the Ya G–12 in the heavier vehicle class. All these vehicles were marked by their simplicity of design and ruggedness of construction. It was, however, in the design of artillery tractors that the Soviet Army was best served in respect of the degree of mobility available. The models available included the Komsomolets, the Komintern and the Voroshilov. There were, however, not enough of these; the absence of a reasonable quantity of powerful high-speed tracked tractors necessitated the use by the artillery arm and tank units of normal medium-speed (agricultural) tractors. The Kharkov Factory converted to tracked prime-mover production during 1940 and produced the KhTZ–3 tractor while the tractor plant at Putilov (renamed Kirov in 1934) also produced tracked prime-movers.

Rotmistrov and reorganization. In 1939 Pavel Rotmistrov

became the Marshal of the Armoured Forces, and has since been recognized as the Red Army's outstanding expert on armoured warfare. Drawing the correct conclusions from the Finnish War the tactical theories derived from the Spanish Civil War were found to be defective—that is disbanding the mechanized corps and redistributing tanks amongst infantry formations as infantry-support tanks. Rotmistrov attended a meeting during 1939, where he stated that:

> ... tanks must be employed in masses. The best situation for a tank commander is to be in command of large groups—a brigade, a corps, an army. These are splendid instruments in an offensive. A concentration of a thousand tanks—this is the dream of every tank commander![184]

Rotmistrov also stated that it was totally unnecessary for the infantry to have their own support tanks. Like Tukhachevsky, he was strongly opposed to commanders employing tanks in driblets or on secondary tasks.

During 1940 the Army was completely reorganized, the decision made earlier to disband the mechanized corps was reversed, and orders were issued during November for the establishment of 21 mechanized corps. A great effort was now being made to reintroduce the large tank formations which had been dissolved earlier for distribution amongst rifle divisions. Whereas in 1936 a mechanized corps consisted of 3 brigades, amounting to some 400 tanks, in 1940 it comprised 3 divisions (2 tank, and 1 motorized rifle division), and on establishment was intended to have more than 1,000 tanks making it far too unwieldy. Each division had 2 tank regiments with up to 400 tanks, 1 motorized infantry regiment, and 1 artillery regiment. Very few of these mechanized corps were formed by March–June 1941. This was due to the lack of equipment available for building up these corps. All the available equipment of the Army had been collected together by breaking up many of the existing units, not excluding the tank battalions in infantry divisions. Tanks were only retained by cavalry divisions (in regiments of 64 BT tanks), and air-landing corps (in battalions of 50 T–38 and T–40 tanks).

In 1940, Timoshenko, who succeeded Voroshilov as Commissar of Defence, decided on a series of small scale manoeuvres. Every unit of the Red Army took part in intensive manoeuvres with all the other arms—guns, tanks and aircraft—in order to develop the lessons of the recent two years of combat in Europe, to raise the standard of the junior commanders and the rank and file to the highest possible pitch of perfection and to develop individual initiative. But there was insufficient time to gather officers, NCOs and privates from other units, or to train commanders at all levels, and crews for tanks. (This was seriously hampered by the lack of experienced officers, liquidated during the 1936 purges.) So urgently were these large mechanized corps formed, that not only did they use RGK (Reserv Glavnogo Komandovaniia—Reserve of the High Command) tank brigades, but also the tank battalions from the rifle divisions. The removal of NPP tanks from the rifle units seriously weakened the effectiveness of the infantry.

The great concentrations on the production and the material expansion of the tank forces greatly affected the new tank designs; inevitably, it delayed the introduction of the new models, whilst production of the older models was continued longer than was strictly justified. Comparing 1939 with 1934, Voroshilov could state that the firepower of the Red tank troops was increased about fourfold over

this period. The supply of equipment was greatly delayed due to the order from the Defence Commissariat to complete all of these new mechanized corps simultaneously, so that not one was completed in time. Only about one-third of the tanks being produced were of the new 1940–41 pattern. Further, to achieve the highest efficiency from tanks it became apparent that a requirement existed for specialized AFVs, self-propelled artillery, armoured transporters, powerful tractors and lorries. Mostovenko wrote:

> Apart from the amphibious tank T–40, the only specialized tank in service with the Soviet Army up to 1941 was the flame-throwing version of the T–26 light tank. It was not considered justifiable to include this vehicle in Soviet tank battalions because of its slow speed—which in turn would greatly hamper the progress of the entire regimental column; in addition it would increase the complications of supply and maintenance. In spite of considerable experimental experience, self-propelled artillery mountings on tracked chassis were not very advanced at this time, although the situation was eventually improved. . . .[185]

In general, the mobility of the prewar Soviet Army may be summed up as a mobile armoured arm, a semi-mobile artillery arm, an infantry arm whose tactical mobility was virtually confined to its ability to march on foot, and a supply service which was totally unfitted to support wide-ranging mobile operations—either by virtue of the models of motor transport available or by their number.

The new 1940 tank programme strived to rectify the position regarding the provision of new vehicles. Mostovenko wrote:

> The correct selection of the basic combat characteristics of tanks was only achieved on the basis of a scientific analysis of the trend in future war, and the role played by tank troops therein. Such problems were considered only by Soviet experts. In 1937 the Communist Party and the Soviet Government rendered great assistance to Soviet tank designers, leading and directing research on problems in tank design. These successes in Soviet tank design were not possible without the necessary preparation of a new generation of engineer-designers and technicians. The increase in armoured tank troops also required providing the Army with the necessary quantity of commanders and engineer tank troops.[186]

The assortment of tank types with which Russia was equipped before the 'Great Patriotic War', were to be removed from service when the three standard tank models light, medium and heavy, were introduced in 1940–41. These new tanks embodied the best features of the earlier designs but incorporated refinements resulting from combats and the examination of captured foreign tanks.

The 1940–41 Tank Programme. By 1939 experiments had been carried out on the improvements of armament, diesel engines designed specifically for tank use, electric-welding of thick armour plates and independent suspension systems. The Russians also tried to improve tank handling and manoeuvrability. Efforts were made to increase the operating range of tanks to 124 miles, so as to permit long-range operations (and this was one reason why the Russians favoured diesel engines). The 1940–41 specifications were as follows:

Armament: a high velocity gun was specified (76·2 mm calibre); there was a requirement for semi-automatic breech-blocks. Attempts were made in the T–26 and BT tanks to stabilize the gun with a device known as TOS (developed by Pavlov and Tumanov), and a similar appliance was fitted to the T–28 turret by Prokofiev.

Armour: the Finnish War made the Russians very conscious of the lack of armour protection on their tanks, and so thick sloping armour was specified to provide immunity to 76 mm AP projectiles at ranges above 1,200–1,300 yards, and to 37 mm AP projectiles at close ranges. Success in the use of electric-arc welding during 1939 made possible its use in the construction of medium and heavy tank hulls. General Blyukher had submitted a report to Tukhachevsky wherein he stated that the Red Army had not had favourable experience with riveted tanks; vulnerable to anti-tank guns, the riveted tanks had shown up badly under fire during the Spanish Civil War and the operations in Manchuria. As a result he had recommended a switch to welded tanks. (The T–26S light tank introduced during 1937 had been the first Soviet tank to be welded throughout.) In selecting the form of the hull and turret, certain experiments were carried out during this period for various models of tanks with bullet-proof armour. For increasing the immunity of armour, a conical turret was employed. A decision was made, however, for various reasons, not to apply this to tanks with shell-proof armour. The classical form of the armoured hull of the T–34 was quite novel, allowing the employment of large angular inclinations for increasing the immunity to shot on the vital parts of the hull and turret. The sloping armoured hull was to project over the tracks to protect them from aerial cannon fire, and was to be streamlined to prevent the lodgement of sticky-bombs and other missiles. In the welded turret of the T–34 interlocking plates were used for the first time in the history of tank design.

Engines: the Russians specified the use of a new high-power tank diesel engine. Following a directive of the GUVP, work on the development of this was commenced during 1932—the Russians were pioneering diesel engines for tank use before the Germans (the acknowledged diesel experts) were even experimenting with the idea. A special diesel development plant was established at the Kharkov Locomotive Works during 1934 and at the beginning of 1935 work was commenced on a new high-power tank diesel engine. By the end of the year the group, under the direction of Trashutin had completed development work on BD–2—a 12-cylinder 4-stroke diesel developing 400 hp at 2,000 rpm. This engine was successfully tested in a BT–5 tank and over the period 1936 to 1938 it was further perfected under the joint direction of Tshupachin and Poddubni. When completed it was subjected to a 100 hour bench test and designated the V–2. After tests and improvements, in 1938 the V–2 diesel was mounted in production models of the BT–7M tank, experience with which revealed the superiority of this engine over the gasoline type. An improved version was developed, the 60° V–12 (Model V–2) liquid-cooled tank engine. A well-designed lightweight model of 3·8 litres capacity, it developed 500 hp at 1,800 rpm when fitted in the T–34 tank; when fitted in the heavier KV it developed 600 hp at 2,000 rpm by increasing the size of the fuel pumps and injectors. (This same engine was later retained in the IS series, but governed back to give only 520 hp.)

The use of the diesel engine led to a significant increase in cruising range, simplified the maintenance of the tank, and reduced the fire hazard. The fact that after minor alteration the V–2 tank diesel could be fitted in both the T–34 and KV greatly simplified the organization of production and repair. The V–2 diesel family consisted of three basic engines; 400 hp for light tanks, 500 hp for mediums, and 600 hp for heavy tanks.

Transmissions: Not having had the benefit of German experience in their early prototype tanks, the Russians were unable to gain any knowledge of the Maybach transmission systems, and played safe by using the conventional clutch and brake system. (Even this proved unreliable until a late stage in the Second World War.)

Suspensions: after 1938 exceptional use was made of independent suspension in Soviet tank construction, since this possessed the most suitable high-speed characteristics of greater strength, and a longer service life than other types of suspension. (Larger diameter bogie wheels became one of the external characteristics of high-mobility tanks.) The change-over to independent suspension was carried out on the basis of experience with the BT tanks, and the investigation of numerous 'coupled' suspensions, which had been employed on tanks during the thirties. After testing various types of suspension in the KV tank, torsion-bar suspension was introduced. The design and production of this suspension for heavy tanks was carried out for the first time in the Soviet Union. In the course of making this suspension new engineering problems of a complicated nature were overcome by selecting the correct materials, and the organization of technological manufacturing processes for torsion bars. The successful solution of all design and technological problems connected with the production of torsion bars allowed the application of this principle to Soviet tanks. Prior to 1938 the protection of tank suspensions (particularly on the T–28 and T–35 tanks) by using specially armoured hull sides complicated the manufacture of armour components and created maintenance problems,

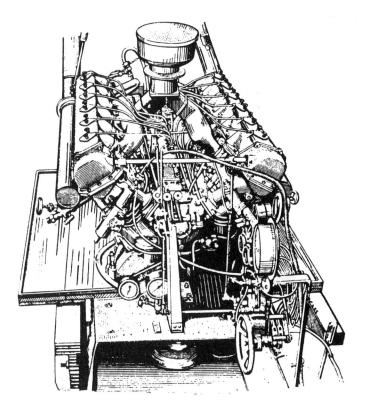

47. *The BD–2 tank diesel engine, prototype of the famous V–2.*

also leading to decreased cross-country performance. In addition, the use of these protective devices on tanks with greatly slanted shell-proof armour would have caused a significant increase in tank weight (requiring extra armour), so that it became necessary that sufficient protection for the suspension should be provided in order to discard these devices. The directive stipulating that medium tanks should have Christie suspension, and that light and heavy tanks should have torsion-bar suspension, enabled the vulnerable components of the suspension to be concealed behind armour plate. The KV–1 was the first heavy tank with a torsion-bar suspension.

Tracks: wide tracks with small-pitched links and fully-floating pins were specified. Wide tracks providing a small specific ground pressure were used for the first time on the T–34 and KV tanks. In these tanks the ground pressure did not exceed 0·7 to 0·75 kg per sq cm. (In German, English, French and American medium and heavy tanks the ground pressure lay between 0·95 and 1·0 kg per sq cm.) Multi-knuckled track plates with full-floating pins were specified for travel in snow, together with double bogie wheels and idlers, and a track plate with a central guide-horn running between the wheels to position the tracks; by this means the snow was continually forced out of, and away from, the inner surface of the track.

The Russians were very concerned with keeping their tank heights low. In the BT series, as well as the T–34 (and later tanks), they employed a flat track in order to keep the height of the tank to a minimum. Using flat tracks, however, led to difficulties; with the modified Christie system, and some torsion-bar types, wheel movements to the order of 14 inches required the track to run very slack in order to permit the wheels to move these distances. Slack tracks involved greater power-loss besides being prone to shedding.

In the design of the T–34 and KV tanks the requirement for a large production was taken into consideration as well as the need for simple and straightforward field maintenance. All the basic components were designed to ease the work of production personnel. Several other noteworthy points were proposed in the tank programme:

a. Unit construction and design of all components to facilitate repair by replacement of complete components.

b. Standardization and simplification of all equipment.

c. A high top speed and a good slope-climbing ability.

d. The weight and overall height of the new designs must be kept to a minimum.

e. At least one tank in three (essentially commander's tanks) were to be equipped with radio equipment.

f. Rear driving sprocket, to reduce the vulnerability from frontal attack and anti-tank mines.

Results from the programme were rapid, and new tanks began to enter service in 1940; the BT and T–26 were to be replaced by the new T–50 light tank, the T–28 by the T–34, and the T–35, SMK and T–100 heavy tanks by the KV. In addition, the two light amphibious tankettes, T–37 and T–38, were to be replaced by the new T–40 model. The T–34 and KV tanks represented a new stage in the development of tank technology. Mostovenko wrote:

Both tanks had a number of novelties, which were employed in tank construction for the first time. As with medium tanks for that time, in the design of the heavy tank was determined the most efficient combination of firepower, armour protection and mobility—consistent with the conditions of its combat role during the course of the Second World War. For the first time, on these tanks was mounted a long-barrelled 76·2 mm gun with,

for that time, a high muzzle-velocity (662 m/sec). [For comparison note that the muzzle-velocity of the German Pz.Kpfw–IV 75 mm AP projectile was 380 m/sec.] Both tanks employed the specially designed, powerful V–2 tank diesel engine. . . .[187]

6 The Great Patriotic War

Phase I: June 1941 to November 1942. When the Germans crossed the Russian border on 22 June 1941, production of replacement vehicles had not been under way long enough to provide sufficient numbers of the new medium and heavy tanks for the Red Army. In 1941 the Germans estimated Soviet tank strength at between 15,000 and 20,000 tanks, of which 6,000 were light reconnaissance and 300 heavy tanks, the remainder mediums. They did not however, account for the new T–34 and KV tanks which were manufactured and issued to units in great secrecy. According to Soviet statements, the number of Soviet tanks available at this time was 20,000 (lowest figure 15,000; highest figure 24,000). This was more than four times as many as the Germans had at this time—indeed, more than all the other tank forces of the world put together. The 75 per cent increase in the defence budget for 1940–41 must have been reflected to a substantial degree in the further enlargement of the tank corps. By 1941 the Russians had accumulated no fewer than 39 armoured divisions (compared with the Germans' strength of 32). The Russians had over 7,000 tanks in the forward area during June 1941. The general opinion in Russia, however, was that Germany had superiority over the Russians in tank strength and production. Kerr wrote:

> In Russia it was believed that the German Army had several times as many tanks as the Red Army at the outbreak of the war. The number of German machines was fixed at anywhere from 15,000 to 18,000. Furthermore, German tank production was greater than Russian tank production. . . . It took a very long time, then, for the Russians to catch-up with the Germans in tank production and in the first two years I do not believe that they did catch up. . . . When the Russians believed they had tank superiority they would send their own machines into battle with the German machines. More often, however, they used their tanks against enemy infantry and artillery. . . .[188]

The Germans, however, were under no illusions as to the strength of the Soviet tank forces; Liddell Hart wrote:

> When Hitler's plan was unfolded to his generals in February 1941, they were disturbed to hear that the Red Army had 155 divisions available in Western Russia, whereas the invading forces could muster only 121. Actually, the German intelligence estimate was a little under the mark. . . . The Germans had not even equality, let alone superiority, in the number of tanks—although Hitler was counting mainly on these for his chance of victory. General von Thoma, then head of the tank side of the General Staff, told me that the invasion was launched with only 2,434 tanks—excluding the very light ones, which he called 'sardine tins'—whereas Russian reports credited the Germans with 12,000. . . . On the Southern Front, where Field Marshal von Rundstedt attacked . . . Field Marshal von Kliest, who led Rundstedt's Panzer drive here, told me that he had only 600 tanks. In Marshal Budenny's opposing Army Group there were 2,400. . . .[189]

Stangely enough, at the beginning of the war, the light tank formed the standard combat vehicle of the Soviet tank forces (assuming, as the Russians did, that the BT tanks were classified as light tanks). Of the 2,794 tanks built during 1940, only 115 were T–34s and 243 KVs. The new T–34, KV and T–60 tanks entered the five military districts during April/May 1941, output being restricted to the armoured divisions. By June 1941 there were still only 1,110 T–34s and 508 KVs in service with the Army, forming

they had to pay heavily. In 1941, at least half of the total strength was in infantry-support units (NPP). In late July 1941 Stalin stated that he placed more faith in infantry-support tanks than in the cavalry divisions. The command staff lacked any real training in the tactical handling of tanks and mechanized units; in particular, the lower and intermediate commanders showed very little understanding or aptitude for armoured warfare. They lacked the experience and ability to make rapid decisions. In addition, drivers and mechanics received, in some cases, only 1½–2

48. *The crew of a T–28C tank planning a counter-attack during the early stages of the Great Patriotic War;*
49. *BA–32 armoured cars of a cavalry squadron on patrol;*
50. *T–34 tanks on a scouting mission.*

48

49

around 8 per cent of the total Soviet tank strength. Even taking into account the other tanks produced under the 1940-41 Tank Programme, the Soviet tank park of 1941 mainly consisted of tanks built between 1932 and 1939. BTs and T–26s comprised 75 per cent of the Soviet tank strength, and this basic mass of tanks was becoming obsolete and in a poor state of repair. The day before the war broke out, 29 per cent of these older machines required major overhauls and 44 per cent normal service overhauls.

In organizing the mass-production of weapons and equipment it was essential to get the KV, T–34, T–60 and T–40 tanks to the fronts in quantity as soon as possible. Consequently, a great effort was made to advance the Soviet tank industry. Large new tank plants were set up and those already existing were greatly expanded. Among the facilities available were Plant 183 at Kharkov, the Mariupol Plant, the Kirov 185 Plant at Leningrad, the Stalingrad Plant, the Leningrad Tank Plant, Voroshilov 174 at Voroshilovgrad, the Ural Railroad Car Plant 183 at Nizhni-Tagil, Chelyabinsk in the Urals, Chita and Novo-Sibirsk in Siberia, Saratov north of Stalingrad, and Plant 120 at Gorki, east of Moscow.

Apart from the obsolescence of their tank parks, the Soviet armoured formations lacked experience, for which

hours experience of tank driving before entering combat. There is no doubt that, had the command and training of the Soviet formations been of higher standard, the Russians would have easily repelled the German attack.

The lightning victories of the Germans allowed very little time for completing the new armoured formations. During July–August 1941 the mechanized corps, and later the tank divisions, were disbanded, and in their place the Soviet High Command began forming independent tank battalions and tank brigades of the Supreme Command VGK (Verchovnogo Glavnogo Komandovaniya). These were intended to be employed in close co-operation with infantry, strengthening their attack. The Russians stopped using tanks for fighting German armour and tried to avoid large tank battles, using their artillery against German tanks. Their own were directed against German infantry.

It was about this time that the Soviet High Command began forming new large tank formations additional to NPP battalions. The reorganization of the Soviet armoured forces at this time required, above all, a material increase in the striking power and anti-tank capability of rifle and other units that came under heavy direct defensive fire. The reorganization of armoured troops was catered for by the new *Instructions for the Combat Employment of Tank*

Troops in the Red Army (*Nastavleniem*), which were released during September to October 1941. *Nastavleniem* recommended that in the offensive, when breaking through the enemy defences, tank units should be used in mass along the direction of the main thrust, closely co-operating with other arms and aircraft. Tank battalions were to be used in whole and not split up into smaller units.

Facing the German Front on 1 December 1941 there were 7 army groups with 33 armies, 200 rifle divisions, 35 cavalry divisions, and 40 tank brigades. The first armoured brigades were used during the Battle of Moscow in 1941. New independent tank brigades from the Ural and Far-Eastern Reserves, equipped with the new T–34/76 tanks, played an important role in stabilizing the Soviet front in this battle, although these brigades were smaller than before the war. A brigade consisted of 1 tank regiment, a motorized

50

infantry and machine-gun battalion, a reconnaissance group, a motorized mortar company, and anti-tank and anti-aircraft groups.

Experience during the first Soviet offensive operations of December 1941 and January 1942 revealed serious deficiencies in the employment of NPP tanks. Reserve-Colonel Begishev wrote:

Tank brigades and separate tank battalions sent into operations requiring NPP tank support were often employed in small groups and distributed uniformally amongst rifle divisions and regiments. As, for example, all of the 50 tanks, which supported the 33rd Army on the Western Front during the offensive on Moscow (December 1941), were uniformly distributed amongst divisions, with 10 tanks in each. In this case, commanders of rifle divisions distributed tanks to first-echelon rifle regiments. As a result, the closest density was only 3 tanks per kilometre. . . . For organizing the breakthrough of the enemy defences along the River Lame in January 1942, troops of the 20th Army employed three tank brigades distributed amongst rifle divisions and brigades. As a result, the closest density along the frontal approach of the spearhead army group was only 5–6 tanks per kilometre. The same use of tanks was made by the 1st

Udarnoy (Spearhead), 16th and 43rd Armies on the Western Front. . . .[190]

The serious deficiencies in using NPP tanks seriously hampered their co-operation with infantry, artillery and engineers. The infantry and artillery often lagged far behind the tanks and were unable to provide timely support during the seizure and holding of objectives. Consequently, the tank units suffered unjustifiable losses and were unable to carry out their tasks. Often, to the dismay of the engineers, their supporting NPP tanks, when delayed by an enemy minefield, made a rapid detour of the obstacle. Tank units were given extremely little time for organizing and preparing a battle, owing to the fact that they usually arrived in the middle of an offensive, without adequate briefing of the enemy or terrain. This greatly hampered their effectiveness.

Russian tank tactics were clumsy, and armour was dissipated in small units scattered over wide fronts. The T–34s, like the T–26s and BTs before them, were supposed to attack at maximum speed consistent with terrain—and meanwhile take targets under fire, without halting.

During the great armoured battles at Minsk, Smolensk and Kiev, the Russians suffered defeat after defeat, and large amounts of equipment were destroyed or captured by the Germans. The initial operations of the Soviet tank armies were a complete failure: in dense groups they blindly toured the German battlefield without premeditation or awareness of the situation. These early campaigns cost the Red Army 17,500 tanks (out of 24,000), and even more important, the loss of the western industrial regions with their raw materials and skilled labour. Begishev wrote:

With the sudden attack by Nazi Germany on the Soviet Union we find our armoured troops in the initial stages of reorganization. New war material (the T–34 and KV tanks) was only beginning to enter units, and lower commanders had not yet been properly trained. Our tank divisions and mechanized corps were forced into combat with tremendous shortages of personnel, commanders and combat material, as well as having deficiences in the organization of military-technical supply. These factors, together with the rapidity of attack and the tremendous losses of tanks—which could not be compensated for owing to the evacuation to the east of a major proportion of the munitions factories and heavy industries—necessitated the execution of a wide-scale reorganization of our armoured tank troops. . . . There were also tactical blunders: we badly used manoeuvre on the battlefield, tending to employ frontal attacks, and were clumsy in using striking force and the firepower of combat vehicles. Tank brigade commanders, operating with tanks in the NPP (direct support) role, were so far away that they could not see the battlefield. Battalion and company commanders, as a rule, were too far ahead of their units and therefore often lost control of them.[191]

Kovalev has since stated:

Until the instruction of Comrade Stalin in 1942, infantry commanders often assigned tanks to tasks hurriedly, and hence not concertedly, and combined operations of tanks with infantry and artillery were not organized in a competent manner. These commanders threw tanks into battle in small groups and without account for their technical condition. Thus impermissible losses of tanks and tank personnel and mechanized troops, and also infantry, followed.[192]

The German accounts of early encounters with Soviet tank units verify these statements: Major-General von Mellenthin wrote:

51

52

55

53

54

56

They [the Soviet tanks] got in each other's way, they blundered against our anti-tank guns, or after penetrating our front they did nothing to exploit their advantage and stood inactive and idle. Those were the days when isolated anti-tank guns had their heyday, and sometimes one gun would shoot up or knock out more than 30 tanks an hour. We thought the Russians had created a tool they would never be able to handle expertly. . . .[193]

General Halder added:

The Russian policy of tank attack in 1941 was—a little everywhere. . . .[194]

It was not long before steps were taken to rectify the tactical situation; Begishev wrote:

The deficiencies by commanders in using NPP tanks were referred to in a command directive released by the General Headquarters of the Supreme Commander-in-Chief during the winter of 1941–2, which demanded fundamental alterations in the procedures of command, organization, and the use of the various troop arms. The erroneous use of tank units even continued during operations in the summer campaigns of 1942, as for example during the Kharkov offensive operations on the South-Western Front during May 1942. . . . Instead of concentrating massed tank units along the direction of the main thrust, more than 60 per cent were distributed amongst combined-arms armies in all sectors along the offensive front. Out of 13 tank brigades, intended for combined use with the infantry, 10 brigades were attached to rifle divisions, and the remaining three were issued to reserve armies. Attached to first-line divisions, tank brigades (1 tank brigade to each division) were distributed uniformly to all approach regions. The density of NPP tanks (not including the army reserves) was from 3 to 8 vehicles per kilometre of front. Negligible tank densities restricted rapid breakthrough rates and delayed the breakthrough by the 21st and 23rd Tank Corps.[195]

Furthermore, the majority of Soviet tanks were equipped with HE ammunition for 'close support', and altering the allotment in favour of AP shot was just beginning. The fatal mistakes of Marshall Pavlov demanded the highest price—he was shot for incompetence in late 1941, and Rotmistrov took his place.

The first German campaigns took over tank and tank component plants at Kharkov, Mariupol and Kirov. The Leningrad plants were taken under fire. The campaigns of 1942 cost the Soviets the large plants at Stalingrad and Voroshilovgrad as well. The plant at Stalingrad continued to produce tanks during the German operations in the area, and it was no exaggeration to say that tanks were rolling off production lines to fight the Germans in the streets—almost immediately after completion! Tanks from remotely situated factories (principally T–34s) were produced so rapidly that in many cases they were ferried to the front without even being painted. Fortunately, the far-sightedness of the Five-Year Plans had brought about the establishment of industries widely distributed throughout the USSR and, although the Germans knew from captured

51. *T–26S light tanks being used as NPP tanks;* 52. *Tank-borne infantry going into action;* 53. *T–34s being produced by the Chelyabinsk Tractor Factory;* 54. *Voroshilovgrad Tank Factory producing KVs; the proximity to the front is evident from the state of the factory;* 55. *T–34/76Ds being produced at 'Uralmashzavod';* 56. *KV–1 tanks being produced at 'Tankograd'.*

vehicles of the existence of other tank plants at Nizhni-Tagil and Chelyabinsk in the Urals, and even at Chita and Novo Sibirsk in Siberia, they obviously could not get to them even by air. Plants even at Saratov, north of Stalingrad, and at Gorki, east of Moscow, were safe except from German bombers. However, production concentrated in the Urals was a distinct handicap to the Red Army since completed tanks had to be transported great distances before delivery to theatres of war. (Between 1941 and 1943 T–34s and KVs were in production at 42 factories in Central Russia, the Urals, Leningrad, Kharkov and Stalingrad.) As the result, a considerable proportion of repairs were carried out in the field, since vehicles could not be returned to the factories, and so a special ordnance division, the Tank Engineering Service, was set up to control tank design and manufacture, as well as maintenance of armoured vehicles in the field.

With the rapid advancement of the German armies, it became necessary to evacuate the majority of the Western tank plants as far as the Urals and Siberia. To undertake this move the People's Commissariat for Tank Industry was formed by order of Molotov, and placed under the direction of Tsaltsman (later under Mavishev). In August 1941 the Kirov 185 Plant was transferred from Leningrad to Chelyabinsk, where it was joined by the Kharkov Plant (under the management of Ordyoniky). Both of these were amalgamated with the original Chelyabinsk Tractor Factory to form the 'Tankograd' combine. This came under the direction of Muzurukov, with Kotin as Chief Designer. Within 55 days of evacuation, Tankograd commenced production of KV tanks, and by the end of the war had provided the Red Army with about 18,000 heavy tanks and self-propelled guns based on this chassis, as well as some 48,500 tank engines. Evacuation to the Urals of the Kharkov Factory (Komintern), together with equipment from Zhdanov Smelting Plant (Illich), Leningrad Kirov Plant 185, Leningrad Armament Plant Bolshevik 232, Leningrad Tank Plant Voroshilov 174, and Plant No. 120 Moscow, combined with the original Ural Railroad Car Plant No. 185 at Nizhni-Tagil (north-east of Moscow), to form the Ural Tank Building Establishment 'Uralmashzavod'. This combine was directed by Maksarov with Morozov as the Chief Designer, and was responsible solely for the production of T–34 tanks and T–34 based self-propelled guns. It received the first blue-prints of the T–34 in July 1942 and the first production model T–34 from this plant was called 'Comrade Stalin'. Evacuation of the Kuybishev Factory, together with divisions of the Petrovsk and Lenin Dniepropetrovsk Locomotive Factory, Voroshilov Tank Plant No. 174 from Leningrad, and a division of Kirov Plant No. 85 from Leningrad, to the AMO Factory in Moscow formed another tank plant. Added to this also were remnants of the Polish Motor Industry. This large combine was solely responsible for the production of light tanks and vehicles based on their components.

The Volgograd Tractor Plant was completely destroyed during 1941 and was not rebuilt until 1944. The plant at Stalingrad, however, under the direction of Dzerinski, continued to produce tanks even when the city was under fire; at the peak of production during 1942, this plant was turning out 15 tanks per day. The Stalingrad plant was eventually evacuated during August 1942.

Despite the various setbacks, the new Soviet tanks were a considerable improvement over the original models in respect of the attention paid to armour and armament, and the development of the V–2 diesel engine. Major-General von Mellenthin wrote:

Russian tank designers understood their job thoroughly; they cut out refinements and concentrated on essentials—firepower, armour and cross-country performance. During the war their system of suspension was well in advance of Germany and the West.[196]

Lieutenant-General Schneider stated:

In 1941 the Russian T–34 tanks appeared . . . and severely hampered our advancing tanks; they proved to be superior in armament, armour and manoeuvrability. . . . The T–34 was sensational. . . [197]

Neue Zuercher Zeitung (July 1941) was also impressed by the Soviet tanks:

One of the greatest surprises is the extent of the Russian tank weapon, of which even the few remnants left by the Russian rearguard make a deep impression. . . . Viewing the Soviet war material, one is impressed by the big industrial organizational performance it represents. . . . The guns, caterpillars and tanks appear to be completely new. Immaculately painted, well looked after, cleanly finished and well designed, these steel machines stand there produced by a state which 20 years ago hardly possessed its own machine and armament factories. . . [198]

Due to the enormous losses during the early campaigns, Stalin urged the new tank combines to produce as many tanks as possible. In order to achieve this, it became necessary to adopt mass-production techniques to ensure the highest production output. As a result, the corrective of the war economy plan for the fourth quarter of 1941 and for 1942 compensated for the gross underestimation of the requirements as set out in the National Economic Modernization Plan for this period. Even with the loss of a large number of their tank plants, the Russians still managed to produce considerable numbers of tanks during 1941; the numbers built over the prewar level increased by a factor of 3·7, 66 per cent of production being directed to the T–34.

In 1942, labour productivity at all plants under the People's Commissariat for Tank Industry rose by 38 per cent in comparison with 1941. This resulted in a considerable reduction in the cost of tanks and made possible the construction of 9,548 additional tanks in 1942. The massive concentration on tank production demanded tremendous qualitative compromises; the reduction in armour quality itself (of plates and castings) was necessary for employing the 'Duplex' process, instead of using open-hearth furnaces. (The Russians boasted that this step saved them some 350,000 tons of steel.)[199]

From the summer of 1942 onwards, the Soviet armoured formations began to receive large quantities of tanks, the evacuation of the industry to the Urals resulting in an influx of new vehicles on a large scale. During 1942 production exceeded 24,500 tanks, of which 13,500 were T–34s. Further provision of tanks resulted from the Lend-Lease Agreement. The British supplied 7,000 tanks (of which 4,260 arrived), at the rate of 500 a month; these included Matildas, Churchills and Tetrarchs. (The Russians did not like the British tanks in the climate and conditions that they were using them, and often criticized them for being both

57. Valentine tanks in service with the Russians (note the anti-aircraft machine-gun mounting on the turret);
58. U.S. White scout cars and, 59. U.S. armoured half-tracks in Russian employ; 60. The foreground of this photo shows a captured German Pz.Kpfw-III tank; behind it is a 7·5 cm Stu.G.III assault gun.

under-gunned and under-armoured; they referred to them as 'Common Graves'.) Two-hundred Universal Carriers and several armoured cars were also supplied by Britain. The Americans provided 7,056 tanks (of which 5,258 arrived), consisting of Grants, Lees, Shermans and Sherman Crabs, and a few M–5 Stuarts, and 1,200 armoured semi-tracks. The Canadians supplied 1,380 Valentines Mks VI and VII (1,188 arrived), and Valentine bridgelayers. This flow of tanks continued until the Russians had increased their own production of T–34, KV and T–70 tanks. The Lend-Lease Programme also helped to overcome the lack of logistical transport; the USA provided Russia with over 400,000 motor vehicles, and some 6,300 armoured cars and half-tracks. This flow of material continued up until August 1945. Most of the losses, due to the Luftwaffe and U-Boats, occurred towards the end of 1941, when only 501 tanks arrived in Northern Russia. The total of vehicles that arrived by the end of 1942 was 4,084 tanks and 30,031 other vehicles. (In typical Russian fashion, they claim that the vehicles obtained under the Lend-Lease agreement did little to influence the outcome of the later campaigns. Between July 1942 and May 1943 the Scientific Auto-Tractor Institute (NATI), in conjunction with the Army, employed a special military transport company, reinforced by engineers and technicians, to conduct extensive tests on US and British vehicles obtained under the Lend-Lease Programme. The outcome of this did much to influence the development of later Soviet military vehicles in general.)

Larger quantities of new equipment allowed the formation of larger, more powerful armoured units. Clark wrote:

> The severe shortage of armour and the evident clumsiness in handling large masses which the first generation of Soviet commanders had shown combined to influence the form of the new armoured units which were built up during the spring of 1942.[200]

By the summer of 1942, the Soviet High Command entered a new phase and began to form entire tank armies. For the third time in the history of the Soviet armoured forces, corps began to be formed—firstly armoured (March–April 1942) and later mechanized (September 1942). These corps were formed in groups of three (2 armoured and 1 mechanized), together with supporting units, to form complete armoured armies. An armoured corps consisted of three armoured brigades, 1 motorized brigade, 1 motor-cycle battalion and 1 reconnaissance battalion (180 cruiser tanks in three brigades). A mechanized corps consisted of 3 lorry-borne brigades (each with a small tank regiment), 1 tank brigade, 1 motor-cycle battalion, 1 reconnaissance battalion, 1 engineer battalion, 1 anti-tank regiment, 1 anti-aircraft regiment and 1 signal battalion (about 200 tanks total). Although stated to be corps, these were in actual fact equivalent to British divisions. Throughout 1942, tanks were decentralized, and allotted to rifle divisions for NPP support. Begishev wrote:

> In spite of the use of tank units from mechanized corps in the role of NPP tanks, intermingled with tanks of the rifle divisions, operations in the direction of the main army thrusts were too weak. The low density of NPP tanks seriously handicapped the breakthrough by tank and mechanized corps. Whereas mobile units were intended to penetrate the frontal zone to a depth of 6–8 kilometres, the slow approach rate of the rifle divisions retarded the thrust by tank and mechanized corps along the main echelon to a depth of 2–3 kilometres. This greatly weakened the offensive.[201]

In late 1942, therefore, this was changed to the concept of employing tanks in mass, concentrated directly on the front in immediate infantry support. The task of the armoured corps (laid down in PU-42) was to assist infantry divisions in making a breakthrough into the enemy zone. The role of the mechanized corps was to exploit the breakthrough and to thrust far behind the front. To achieve this, they were provided with the same number of tanks as the armoured corps (approximately), but mainly composed of light and medium types. In addition, their establishment included large numbers of motorized infantry, artillery and engineers. Begishev wrote:

> During the second half of 1942 certain fundamental changes were articulated in the organization of tank and other units. Instead of mixed tank brigades, equipped with KV, T–34 and T–60 tanks, brigades were formed, equipped with only T–34 medium tanks and, in place of T–60s, T–70 light tanks (each brigade had 53 tanks, 32 T–34s and 21 T–70s). Instead of individual tank battalions, equipped with all types of tanks, separate tank regiments were created (each regiment having 39 tanks: 23 T–34s and 16 T–70s). For supporting rifle and other units during the breakthrough of strongly fortified enemy defences, and for fighting tanks, special Guards breakthrough tank regiments were formed during October 1942, each equipped with 21 KV tanks. . . . By the end of 1943, 18 of these regiments had been formed. . . .[202]

A special form of combined action developed as a result of the requirement for infantry to accompany attacking tanks—tank-borne infantry or Tank Descent (Tankovyi Desant). Colonel-General (then Major-General) Katukov wrote:

> We call infantry mounted on tanks, and using them as a means of advancing for closing with the enemy a 'Tank Descent', usually there would be about 10 men with each medium tank.[203]

Phase II: November 1942 to December 1943. From the Soviet point of view, the war entered its second phase (19 November 1942 to December 1943) when the Red Army launched its counter-offensive on Stalingrad. This period ended with the crossing of the Dnieper, the establishment and enlargement of strategic bridgeheads on its right bank, and the capture of Kiev and Smolensk. The period embraced two campaigns: the Winter campaign (November 1942–March 1943) and the Summer and Autumn campaigns (July–December 1943). The turning point was made possible mainly by the achievements of Soviet war economy, which by the end of 1942 was functioning smoothly and soundly. Armaments, military equipment and new army formations were being moved to the front in an uninterrupted stream.

Combat experience gained during the second half of 1942 demonstrated the necessity for providing NPP tanks with continuous, powerful artillery fire-support. Due to its poor mobility, the conventional field and anti-tank artillery was not suitable for carrying out this task. It was, therefore, necessary to provide troops with greater firepower, and the solution came in the form of the self-propelled artillery mounting, or SAU (Samochodno-Artilleriyskie-Ustanovki). The Defence Commissariat ordered the construction of prototype tracked self-propelled guns, and urged that this type of weapon be placed in mass-production as soon as possible. Garrett Underhill wrote:

> The SU was the product of a long Soviet-German contest to get a range advantage in both the tank-versus-tank and tank-versus-anti-tank weapons contests. Even

in World War II the SUs were trained to use direct-laid fire up to 3,000 metres. A prime reason for the introduction of the SU's large calibre gun was to obtain an HE burst easily spotted (and hence more easily adjusted) at maximum direct-fire ranges. It would appear that the rapid development of the SU—which coincided with the development of Soviet offensive action in World War II —came about from the attempt of the Soviet armoured arm (The Tank and Mechanized Troops) to find its own solution to the shortcomings of Soviet field artillery. . . . The Soviets have stated that for anti-tank and assault-gun infantry-support work they preferred the SU's lower silhouette and larger gun. The silhouette afforded greater security through concealment, enabling surprise action. It also afforded less target to anti-tank guns. The gun affords greater hitting-power at maximum ranges, as well as more devastating HE effect against infantry weapons.[204]

The first self-propelled artillery regiments were formed during December 1942; 30 independent storm-artillery regiments were placed under the Supreme Command Reserve. As initially formed, these were of mixed composition: 17 SU–76s and 8 SU–122s. It was not until early 1943, however, that SUs took part in any operations.

In the future development of the methods for the tactical employment of tanks, a very important part was played by NKO No. 325 released on 16 October 1942, which summarized the lessons learned from previous operations and defined the basic principles for the tactical and operational employment of Soviet tank troops. The fundamental doctrine contained in this directive, relating to the employment of NPP tanks, was as follows:

In offensive operations, tank brigades and regiments will be used centrally, along the direction of the main thrust and in close co-operation with other troops arms. For the support of these NPP tank operations, artillery and infantry will be allotted the tasks of destroying enemy tanks, the reconnaissance and clearing of mine-fields, the aiding of tanks in overcoming various forms of natural and artificial anti-tank obstacles, forming 'tank descents', and rapidly consolidating the captured objective or position. The main task of the artillery is to provide continuous fire-support to NPP tanks— particularly in destroying enemy tanks and anti-tank artillery in their wake. The primary task of aviation is to destroy enemy tanks and artillery and to cover the tactical approach of its own tanks from strikes by enemy aircraft.

During the Stalingrad Operation (November 1942) NPP tanks were used according to the stipulations laid down in Directive No. 325. Attached to rifle divisions, tank regiments and brigades were used to compliment their composition as integral NPP tank groups, subordinate to the divisional commander. In this operation, considerable improvement was made to the combat application of NPP tanks. The task of controlling these units during combat was given to the local commanders. For supporting tank operations in the depth of the enemy defences, each tank battalion was allotted an artillery battery. Well-timed covering fire and good artillery NP (direct support) were requested via tanks fitted with radio. In order to provide tanks with better engineer support, field engineers were attached to tank units, approximately one engineer platoon to each tank battalion. Begishev wrote:

Immediately before the war, our theory stipulated the possibility of making NPP tanks available to regiments of the mechanized corps during the breakthrough of enemy defences, which afterwards would be returned to

their own corps. On this basis, during the Stalingrad offensive operation, such a technique was employed where units of tank regiments, comprising tank and mechanized corps, were attached to rifle divisions during the period of breaking through the enemy defences. In accordance with this theory, the 26th Tank Corps turned over the 216th Tank Brigade to the commander of the 124th Rifle Division; the 13th Mechanized Corps allotted the 176th Tank Regiment for supporting the 422nd Rifle Division, and the 4th Mechanized Corps turned over to the 51st Army two tank regiments (the 55th and the 158th) for use in the NPP role. These tank units transferred to rifle divisions were, after the breakthrough of the main defensive zone, intended to be returned to their respective corps. Experiences showed, however, that re-tasking of tank units during battle was difficult to carry out in practice. Tank brigades and regiments were either completely unable to rejoin their corps, or did so during the second/third day of operations, thereby greatly weakening their effectiveness.[205]

By 1943 the Soviet Army had attained an evident superiority over Germany in war production, which had increased by a factor of 4·3 with its prewar status as against Germany's 2·4 times. Increased war production made it possible to retain the corps-based system in infantry and to form the tank armies and other leading arms. By January 1943 the tank park on all fronts reached 8,500 tanks (monthly production 2,000); 283 T–34/85s were produced in 1943 and by 1944 there were 11,778 of these in service. In addition, the Supreme Command Reserve possessed 400 tanks, and the Central and Rear Districts totalled 4,300 tanks. German intelligence sources estimated Russian armoured strength at 138 armoured brigades (a brigade at that time had three battalions, each with ten tank companies).

At the end of January 1943 the first two self-propelled gun regiments were used on the Vovchov Front, and in March two further regiments were used on the Western Front.

In comparison with the first period of the war, the density of NPP tanks during the second period noticeably increased. In the summer of 1943 Soviet forces were faced with a stable, deliberate defence organized in depth, whose penetration required a deep operational organization of the advancing armies and fronts. Prior to the decisive battle at Kursk in July 1943 Red armoured units had become a powerful attacking force. Begishev wrote:

One further factor restraining the breakthrough of the enemy defences was that in a number of operations we were compelled, for breaking through tactical defensive zones, to introduce mobile army groups and fronts. As, for example, in the Belgorod-Kharkov offensive (August 1943) where the density of NPP tanks even along the main thrust did not exceed 12 armoured vehicles (all types of tank and SAU) per kilometre. . . . The 5th and 6th Guards Armies were provided for the rifle corps in order to break through the enemy defences to a depth of 12–15 kilometres during the first few days and enable mobile units to break through. However, combined-arms units were not able to execute all their tasks, so that tank corps and armies, in order to leave the operations groups quickly, had to be reinforced by tanks of the rifle divisions. As shown by experience, the success of operations was dependent to a considerable degree upon the efficient distribution of tanks to the combat zone and the effective building up of offensive troops. Insufficient

61. *T–34/76D (NPP) tanks advancing with infantry;*
62. *T–60 tanks of an NPP Group*

distribution of tanks in first-line divisions compelled us, in order to break through as early as possible, to introduce tank and mechanized corps into battle, which left the operations group in a seriously weak position for carrying out its own tasks. . . . Throughout the entire offensive operations of the second period of the Great Patriotic War, great skill was shown in the application of NPP tanks. Lessons, learnt from the experiences gained during the operations of 1941–2, allowed us to undertake the counter-offensive on Stalingrad, and in particular the Battle for Kursk, where noticeable improvements were made to the methods of organizing and directing the combat operations of NPP tanks. A characteristic feature in the use of NPP tanks during this period appeared to be the use of regiments and brigades in the zone of the rifle divisions, not permitting them to be used piecemeal. The centralized and mass use of tanks along the direction of the main thrust became the principle reflected in the Regulations for 1942–3.[206]

During the summer and autumn of 1943 the combined-arms armies operating in the direction of the main thrust had 2 or even 3 echelons (corps following corps). Within the fronts there were powerful mobile groups (tank armies) which were sent into action. Whole combined arms armies were set aside as reserves. This was the form during the Winter offensive at Kursk (the Orel Belgorod-Kharkov operations). The change in the character of the German defences necessitated sharply increased artillery and tank densities in offensive operations. During the spring and

summer of 1943, when there already existed large quantities of self-propelled artillery, 3 new types of artillery regiment were formed: light (equipped with 21 SU–76s), medium (with 16 SU–122s and later with 21 SU–85s), and heavy (with 12 SU–152s). By July the Active Army had about 500 SPs and by the end of the year this number had increased to 1,400 (300 of which were deployed in the Supreme Command Reserve). Later, independent units (with 13 SU–76s) were formed, and were included in infantry divisions. The SU–85 was usually organized in artillery regiments of which the mobile troops—the Tank Corps and the Moto-Mechanized Corps—had one each. Each regiment consisted of 21 vehicles (two companies per regiment) plus a T–34 command tank. They supported the tanks and fought armour according to the same tactics, supported by

SU–152s. The SUs were assigned to engage targets hindering tanks and infantry. Those which the tanks could not engage were designated by tracer fire. The SU commander was provided with a periscope and the gunner also had a periscope just behind the driver.

At the start of the counter-offensive on Kursk, combined-arms units with tank brigades and regiments formed integral self-propelled artillery regiments. In first-line divisions, attacking along the direction of the main thrust, corps (armies) with integral tank and self-propelled artillery units, formed TSGs (Tanko Samochodnie Gruppi—Tank-SP Groups) composed of tank brigades (regiments) and self-propelled-artillery regiments. TSGs were deployed centrally and made available to commanders of rifle divisions. When deployed in NPP groups, tank and SAU units formed into battle order as follows: in the first line of 200–400 metres of front, the infantry advanced, with the tanks crushing all that remained of the enemy after the artillery preparation, and providing mobility for the rifle units. In the second line of 100–200 metres tanks assumed direct battle order with the infantry of the first attacking wave, and the SAUs provided all the fire-support to the offensive of the forward tanks. The role of the tank units was clearly outlined by Martell:

> They had their heavy KV tanks for the heavy fighting with infantry and the T–34 tank as a cruiser tank for the mobile role. The Russians referred to the first of these two roles as the 'breakthrough' task. They used both the KV tanks and the Churchill tanks which we had given them for this purpose. They only possessed, however, a limited number of these heavy tanks, and they often had to augment them for this role with tank regiments equipped with other types of tanks, such as the T–34. As far as possible, they kept the heaviest tanks for use against the strongest defences, and employed the regiments with lighter tanks on the flanks, or where the resistance was likely to be less strong. All these units were, however, definitely classed as 'breakthrough' regiments or brigades.[207]

Phase III: December 1943 to May 1945. During the third phase of the war there were noticeable increases in the quantity of tank units available for operating in the NPP role, and further improvements took place in equipment and organization. During the last three years of the war the annual rate of production reached 30,000 tanks, gun motor carriages and armoured cars. By 1944, the Soviets were producing 29,000 tanks and self-propelled guns and 122,500 guns of other types, annually. By June 1944 the Army had a reserve of 9,500 tanks. At this time, there were up to 25 tank and mechanized corps (not including the infantry-support NPP tanks) grouped in 6 tank armies with other supporting arms. These took part in all the large-scale operations. A third tank battalion was introduced into the composition of the tank brigade, bringing the brigade strength to 65 tanks, all of the T–34/85 type. Heavy tank regiments were equipped with the new IS tank which, in combat effectiveness, was a considerable improvement over the older KV tank. Clark wrote:

> The Russians were far advanced in their development of the Stalin, which, although it weighed only 47 tons, was intended to carry the new 122 mm gun. The Stalin was based on the old KV chassis, but with an improved hull front and larger turret. Although it was not quite a match for the later models of Tigers, its mobility and relatively low weight allowed it to keep up with the mass of advancing armour, a feat which the heavy German

machines often found impossible and which forced them to operate independently.[208]

Experience gained from the earlier tactical operations revealed the necessity for increasing the density of tanks and SAUs during the breakthrough of enemy defences along the main thrust, and also providing mobile groups with greater capability for operations deep in the enemy zone. In accordance with this, during mid 1944, the Russians began to form new SU brigades: light (SAU–76 mm), medium (SAU–100mm) and heavy (ISU–152 mm), each consisting of three regiments. Towards the end of 1944 heavy tank brigades, each consisting of three regiments, were also formed.

The offensive operations of 1943–4 clearly demonstrated the value of tanks and SAUs in the support of infantry attacks, and plans were drawn up for introducing these weapons into the rifle regiments. This decision, however, was not to be immediately fulfilled; Begishev wrote:

> For various reasons the assignment of NPP tank units to rifle units at this stage in the war was found to be impracticable. By not doing this, tank regiments and brigades composing the RVGK were able to employ tanks more effectively along the main thrust. . . . Furthermore, combat experience showed this tactic to have various drawbacks. One unfavourable result was that, by re-assigning tank and self-propelled gun units from one army to another, we experienced tremendous difficulty in achieving co-ordination between tanks and infantry, and a great deal of valuable time was expended in uniting the combat groups together. Apart from this, it was often found that, when combining tank and self-propelled artillery units, army and unit commanders did not accept responsibility for maintaining their fighting efficiency and correct tactical deployment. In order to reduce these factors to a minimum, tank and self-propelled gun units were attached to armies for a much longer time.[209]

During the offensive operations of this third period of the war, NPP tanks were employed according to the basic principles laid down in the new *Combat Regulations for Armoured Tank and Mechanized Troops in the Red Army*, which were first introduced into operations during late 1944. As a result, tank and self-propelled artillery regiments and brigades attached to rifle divisions were made subordinate to the divisional commander, but, even so, insufficient tank densities were still very apparent. Begishev wrote:

> When NPP tanks became employed by us in larger numbers, and commanders of rifle regiments and even battalions began employing them in combat, then we began the offensive operations of the second half of 1944 with two basic forms of NPP tank arrangement. Other roles specified for tanks included determining the nature of enemy defences and the conditions of the terrain where a battle was intended to take place, formulating operations and plans involving the use of NPP tanks, and also briefing and co-ordinating commanders of rifle units.[210]

Tank units were usually attached to rifle regiments during the forced breakthrough of enemy fortified defences. Regimental commanders would apply NPP tanks to various tactical problems and organize their co-operation with other troop arms. They became solely responsible for con-controlling operational groups of NPP tanks during battle. During the East-Prussian Operation, for example, NPP tanks were deployed in the first line division of the 2nd

63

64

*63. An NPP tank group in the attack. The tanks are
T–34/76Bs; 64. The 'Tank Descent'—NPP tanks moving
into action with their supporting infantry aboard, during
operations on the 1st Ukranian Front.*

Udarnoy (Spearhead) Army. Under orders from the commander of the 90th Rifle Division, tank units were assigned
the following commands: the 46th and 93rd Tank Regiments were attached to the 173rd Rifle Regiment, and the
95th Tank Regiment to the 286th Rifle Regiment, all
deployed in second echelon divisions. Tank regiments were
positioned centrally and made available to the commanders
of the rifle regiments. The tank density in the 173rd Rifle
Regiment reached 62 tanks to one kilometre of the
breakthrough front. Begishev wrote:

It must be noted, that this mass use of NPP tanks in
the deep thrust did not always appear justifiable. Experiences showed that using NPP tanks in offensive
thrusts greatly reduced the effect of the first opening
thrust and allowed the enemy to destroy tanks consistently. Take the case of the 19th Rifle Regiment, attacking on the first echelon with 90th Rifle Division,
which was completely devoid of tanks since, at that time,
the 95th Tank Regiment had been annihilated and during
the first few days of the approach could not effectively
take part in the battle. Units of the 19th Rifle Regiment,
so deprived of tank support, were not able to carry out
their mission, and this unfavourably reflected on every
individual attacking division. Similar cases involving the
misuse of NPP tanks often occurred during the course of
a battle. The mass-use of tanks along the main direction
was only effective then, when rifle and other units on the
auxiliary direction were also provided with a basic NPP
tank component.[211]

During offensives against weak points in enemy fortifications, and other cases where the battle plan necessitated
joining NPP tank groups to divisions or corps, tank and
self-propelled artillery units came under the control of
the divisional commander in the support of rifle regiments.
During the Vislo-Oder Operation units of the 5th Udarnoy
Army employed tanks in this manner. Four 'Tank-SP

Groups' were created from tank and self-propelled artillery
regiments and brigades attached to the 26th Guards Rifle
Corps for supporting the offensive by first line rifle regiments. During the initial period of breaking through the
main enemy defensive zone, tank-SP groups were made
available to divisional commanders. After breaking
through the second position of the main defensive zone, the
commander of the first line division co-ordinated his tank-
SP groups with forward divisional units for taking the
second enemy defensive zone. Following this, the corps
commander removed his tanks from divisional command
and created corps forward units composed of the 220th
Tank Brigade, the 396th Self-Propelled Artillery Regiment
and the 92nd Tank-Engineer Regiment.

During the offensive operations by the Russians for the
third period of the war, there was an evident attempt to
intensify the tank strength of the rifle units. The availability of larger quantities of tanks and the experience gained
by commanders of infantry units in the methods of employing NPP tanks eventually resulted in an increased
effectiveness.

During the later operations of 1944, and in particular
1945, tanks and self-propelled artillery regiments and
brigades were split up and attached to rifle regiments

attacking in the first echelon along the direction of the main thrust. Each rifle battalion was usually allotted a tank troop or SAU battery. In general, in order to improve tactical co-operation, tank platoons were often integrated with rifle companies which would indicate to the tank the most suitable route for its advance. Tanks were used in this manner during the Vislo-Oder and Berlin Operations.

Experience gained during these later offensive operations seemed to justify the combined use of tank and self-propelled artillery regiments and brigades. By attaching NPP tanks to rifle battalions, attacking along the first echelon, and subordinating them to the battalion commander, better co-operation and better combat effect was achieved than when using tanks in regimental or divisional groups. This was mainly verified by the increase in break-through rates and depths of penetration achieved by Soviet troops during the initial stages of the battles. Begishev wrote:

Combat experience showed that, for manoeuvring NPP tanks during battle and for the effective firing of tank weapons, it was necessary that intervals between tanks attacking in one line should not be less than 25–50 metres, and the distance between the first line and the next of self-propelled artillery—not greater than 100–200

nized forces and infantry. They kept strong reserves and committed tanks only when the advantage lay clearly on their side. Armoured troops formed the main striking force of the Soviet ground forces, and the appearance of large tank formations decisively changed the nature of the operations. They made it possible to break up rapidly the enemy defences throughout their entire depth, to encircle and liquidate large enemy groups, and to pursue swiftly the enemy to a great depth. The German commanders in the East considered the Soviet Tank Arm to be the most formidable offensive weapon of the Second World War.

By the end of the war a basic alteration had taken place in the composition and organization of NPP tank groups. Whereas, during the offensive operations of 1942–3, light tanks of the T–60 and T–70 type comprised more than 20 per cent of the armoured force and heavy tanks did not exceed 15 per cent, during the operations of 1945 light tank units in NPP groups were practically non-existent, and the relative strength of heavy tanks increased to 40–50 per cent. In the East Prussian and Berlin operations the heavy tank densities reached 60–70 per cent. As a result, by the end of the war, the basic NPP tank groups were composed purely of medium and heavy tanks. There was also a considerable increase in the quantity of self-propelled artillery mountings

65

metres. Smaller intervals between tanks hampered their manoeuvrability during battle, and caused greater losses to enemy fire, and in addition, at greater depths, echelons found great difficulty in providing supporting fire from tanks and SAUs and in co-operating with infantry. Studies determined the maximum practical NPP tank density of the first echelon during an attack with infantry to be 30–40 armoured vehicles per kilometre of front. This density of NPP tanks was employed with rifle divisions, advancing in the direction of the main thrust. In one case the tank density increased to 50–70 armoured vehicles per kilometre (8th Guard and 5th Guard Armies in the Berlin Operations). Here great depths were achieved with echelon tanks[212]

During the final stages of the war, the Soviets would only commit their armour when an overwhelming force could be rallied against a numerically inferior or badly shattered enemy. Then waves of tanks, escorted by infantry would advance. The heavy tanks of the first echelon would engage the enemy's front lines; these were followed by succeeding waves of infantry-escorted medium tanks, self-propelled guns, and finally light tanks and supporting vehicles. The Russians always carefully rehearsed their armour attacks, and achieved remarkable co-ordination between mecha-

deployed in NPP tank groups. During the 1943 operations these latter only amounted to some 15–25 per cent, but by 1945 had increased to 40–45 per cent and more.

Apart from being used to directly support tanks, self-propelled artillery regiments and brigades were also attached to combined-arms units for supporting infantry. This was particularly noticeable during the offensive operations of 1944–5 when large units of self-propelled artillery were often used for accompanying infantry. This not only fulfilled the requirement for infantry support, but on occasions made the first echelon stronger in self-propelled artillery than tank units. In the 8th Guard Army during the Vislo-Oder Operation, SAUs exceeded tanks by a factor of three or more. In numerous operations where there was a shortage of tanks, self-propelled artillery units were used in their place in front of the infantry combat order. This role for SAUs was only successful in a number of cases; in others, it led to excessive losses in vehicles and personnel of the self-propelled artillery arm. Begishev wrote:

During the course of the War the most suitable organization and preparation of NPP tanks for offensive operations was determined. This preparation usually began from the moment units arrived in the combat area. Tank and self-propelled artillery regiments and brigades met here with the representative staff of those armies to which they were assigned. From here they proceeded to the concentration area some 20–30 kilometres from the frontal zone. In this region the units deployed, prepared their equipment and also organized the various reserves. . . . Having obtained preliminary instructions, tank and self-propelled artillery units deployed in the appropriate area, some 8–15 km from the feba of the enemy defensive position, i.e., outside the range of enemy artillery fire. In this frontal region preparations were made for the offensive: combat tasks were allotted to tank and self-propelled artillery units, reconnaissance made of the terrain and enemy positions, tanks detailed to their respective NPP groups, their co-operation with infantry units organized, and finally infantry units were co-ordinated with the artillery and engineers. A major

NPP tanks and infantry to the second, and particularly the third, main positions, the enemy resistance sharply increased. Tanks and infantry had to withstand powerful enemy fire and repel counter-attacking enemy tanks. In this case, the best results were obtained when our tank units fired on the spot against counter-attacking enemy tanks whilst other units would thrust in the flanks and rear. . . . With a noticeable superiority of the enemy in tanks we employed our tanks effectively in firing from the spot or from ambush. As, for example, when breaking through the defences with the 35th Rifle Corps (East-Prussian Operation), the 260th Heavy Tank Regiment successfully repelled the counter-attack by 45 heavy enemy tanks. By employing ambushes and co-ordinated fire from the spot, the regiment destroyed 29 enemy tanks and secured its objective.[213]

65. *A 'Tank-SP' group in action on the Western Front;* **66.** *An IS–II tank covering infantry during a battle on the outskirts of Berlin, 1945.*

part of this period was devoted to combined tactical training, on which depended the question of co-operation. . . . For the advance march, NPP tanks were appointed their initial positions some 1–3 kilometres from the enemy. During the course of the artillery preparation NPP tanks would move out of their waiting area and swarm on to the leading edge of the enemy defences. Tanks and infantry attacked to a depth of 1·5–2·5 kilometres, and there then followed concentrated fire, mass-bombardment and dive-bombing. Operations by NPP tanks during the breakthrough of enemy defences were, as a rule, characterized by a methodical advance from zone to zone. But with this technique operations by NPP tanks did not employ their full capabilities, such as having commensurable rates of advance with those of supporting arms or infantry. Finally, as shown by experience, it was only possible to advance during battle, in combat order, with rates between 1·5–2 kilometres per hour. With such rates of advance it was only possible to break through the first line of enemy defences. . . . During the approach by

To assist the breakthrough of the second and third main regional positions of the enemy defences, commanders of rifle regiments and divisions often introduced all the second echelon into battle in order to accumulate thrusting force. Even at the end of the war echelon regiments, divisions and corps on the main offensive fronts were sent into battle without tank support. The diversion of 'spearhead' tanks from the first echelon rifle units in order to support the battles of the second and third echelons was considered unjustifiable. Using tanks in this way would have destroyed their co-ordination with the infantry and artillery, and would have ultimately led to a retardation of the overall offensive.

During the latter campaigns of 1945 armoured spearheads were often supported by the Red Air Force which was placed under the command of the armoured forces.

Most of the offensive operations of the Soviet Army in World War II involved river crossing. Soviet success in river crossing operations during this war can be largely credited to training, discipline and the ability to use local resources. At Stalingrad the Russians surprised the

Germans by building an underwater bridge, by which they moved infantry and tanks across the Volga at night. As the bridge could not be detected from the air, the Germans were puzzled for a long time by the way that day after day the defenders of the West bank seemed to remain as numerous as ever. During the later Russian advances they made continued use of such underwater bridges as a means of surprise.

The most important lesson the Russians learned from the war was the necessity of securing optimum efficiency in all military equipment (particularly tanks), under all tactical conditions. This fact was borne in mind for all future armour development. Combat showed that for the successful co-operation of tanks with other troop-arms, tank commanders should be thoroughly acquainted with the rudiments of combined arms combat, while commanders of rifle, artillery, engineer and other units should know about the combat capabilities of tanks and self-propelled artillery mountings and the basic principles of their tactical employment.

Towards the end of the war, Soviet armoured formations were the most numerous of any power, and undoubtedly contributed greatly to the defeat of Germany. The Germans estimated Soviet tank strength to be 258 armoured brigades by 1945. It has been stated that in April 1945 the Russians had 302 armoured and mechanized brigades, 527 rifle divisions and 34 cavalry divisions, having a total of 13,400 tanks. In all, there were 25 tank corps and 13 mechanized corps, 57–60 separate tank brigades, 180 separate tank regiments and 150 assault-gun regiments (65 tanks to a brigade and 41 to a regiment). The armoured forces formed around 6 per cent of the Army's mobilized total of assault troops (i.e., infantry, cavalry and armour). During the Berlin Operation alone, some 4,000 to 6,000 tanks were massed.

By the time of the German surrender the T–34 and the KV/IS tank series had become basically sound designs, and were used as the starting point for the Soviet postwar tank-programme. The T–34 had received the more-powerful 85 mm gun, and a redesign of the KV had brought into being the IS (Iosef Stalin) heavy tank with its 122 mm gun. German commanders in the East were unanimous in their praise for Soviet tanks; Rundstedt said:

The Russian heavy tanks were a surprise in quality and reliability from the outset. . . . Their T–34 tank was the finest medium tank in the World[214]

Manteuffel, who also fought both in the east and the west, considered the Stalin Tank to have been the best tank he saw anywhere during the war[215]

During the decisive tank battles of the war—at Stalingrad, Kursk, Belo-Russia, Livov-Sandomirsk, Yasso-Kishinevsky, Vislo-Oder, Berlin, and many others, the effectiveness of the Soviet tanks (T–34 and IS) was demonstrated to a great degree. During these operations, Soviet mechanized troops proved to be one of the most decisive means of breaking through the enemy defensive positions, for the achievement of high-speed approaches, and for the success of large-scale strategic operations. The effectiveness of the new tank models demonstrated the scientific and technical maturity of Soviet tank designers, and engineers in the tank industry, and the new Soviet tanks formed the models for tank designs in other countries. Throughout the war, the Russians strived to achieve superiority in fire-power over the Germans by increasing the calibre of their tank guns, at the same time increasing the muzzle-velocity of armour-piercing projectiles (arrowhead). The possibility of increasing the tank gun calibre facilitated, within a short period of time, the creation of a tank having a fire superiority over enemy tanks. An increase in gun calibre, however, was accompanied by a decrease in the rate of fire and the reduction of ammunition stowage within the tank. Mostovenko wrote:

In comparison with the rate of improvement of fire-power, the development of armour came considerably slower. The relative immunity of the tank suffered a noticeable deterioration towards the end of the war, and to completely destroy a tank it became necessary only to score a single hit. It therefore became the main consideration of the Soviet Tank Development Board to increase the immunity of tanks. . . . The increase in armour and firepower was followed by a considerable increase in tank weight, and it once more became necessary to create a new tank able to employ an engine for which production was available. The design and development of a new tank engine would require 5–6 years, whereas to produce a tank having more powerful armament and improved armour would take considerably less time. Hence, during the war (and to date) we retained our original tank engine, but an improvement in tank performance was achieved by the application of a new gear-

67. *T–34/76D (foreground), T–34/85–I (background), entering Berlin.*

box, steering and cooling systems. Other improvements in the basic combat characteristics of Soviet tanks were achieved by techniques of improving the design and construction processes of all components and mechanisms. The major technical achievements were the introduction of a medium-calibre, long-barrelled gun firing a round with high muzzle-velocity, the revolutionary application of armour employing advantageous inclinations to increase immunity, the introduction of a powerful tank diesel engine in quantity as the basic type of tank engine, adoption of independent suspension for all types of tanks, and wide tracks for medium and heavy tanks. Not of minor importance were the reliability of final drives in Soviet heavy tanks and the use of rollers with internal shock-absorbers[216]

In discussing Soviet tanks of World War II, Liddell Hart wrote:

The machines were rough inside and out—they were not even painted. Their design showed little regard for the comfort of the crew. They lacked the refinements and instruments that Western tank experts considered necessary as aids to driving, shooting and control. Until 1943 they had radio only in the commanders' tanks. . . . On the other hand, they had a good thickness and shape of armour, a powerful gun, high-speed, and reliability—the four essential elements. The comfort of the crew was of less importance, especially as Russian soldiers were tougher than others. Regard for comfort and the desire for more instrumental aids involve added weight and complications of manufacture. Such devices have repeatedly delayed the development and spoilt the performance of our tanks. So they did with the Germans, where production suffered from the search for technical perfection. . . . The principles on which the Russians worked in their mechanization programme can be clearly discerned. They picked up ideas from many different tank types abroad, and picked out features which they thought worth incorporating in their own tanks, and then developed the amalgam in a model on their own lines. They concentrated on the mass-production of only one or two types. They tried to make these as simple as possible in construction. This was a great help to rapid output in quantity. . . [217]

The tremendous concentration of the Soviet war industry upon the improvement and production of tanks, artillery,

68. *Artillery mechanization—an STZ–CT3 artillery tractor moving a 122 mm gun into position.*

small-arms and ammunition, greatly affected the Soviet motor industry as a whole, and the production of trucks, tractors and other vehicles continued only on a much reduced scale. Throughout the war, the Soviet tank industry supplied the front with over 102,500 tanks and self-propelled guns, and by the end of the war tanks had increased fifteen-fold with their prewar level. Martel wrote:

As regards their technique for war, they were considerably behind ourselves and the Germans. This was mainly due to the fact that they had always been less well equipped, and particularly in transport. Without full and up to date equipment, you cannot train properly, and without training you cannot build-up and learn the technique which you will use in war. Their main weapons, such as guns and tanks, were reasonably good and in sufficient numbers, but they were very short of such munitions as machine-gun carriers, tactical transport for the troops, wireless, etc. This was a great handicap to them in tactical development. . . [218]

So serious was the motor transport shortage in the Soviet Army during 1945 (even taking into account the large

numbers of trucks and staff-cars supplied under the Lend-Lease Programme) that such motor transport as was available was mostly kept in motor transport units directly subordinate to the army HQ. In May 1945, the Soviet divisions ended the war with virtually no tactical mobility in the form of APCs or even gun tractors on establishment, although a limited form of tactical mobility had been achieved by the 'Tank Descent'. From the experience of the war, the Russians realized the advantages of modern all-wheel drive and tracked vehicles, which had been revealed from the Lend-Lease Programme. The war also demonstrated the absolute necessity of a modern, large Soviet automotive industry capable of satisfying the military motor-transport requirement, and that the logistic, re-supply and maintenance services should be made as flexible as possible; during the war, field maintenance units grew so complex that they even had electric furnaces for repairing the armour of medium and heavy tanks. One other factor, appreciated simultaneously by all the European armies, was the necessity for providing vehicles for the transport of infantry, combining the fundamentals of mobility and protection from enemy fire.

Former Generalmajor in the German Army, H. B. Mueller-Hillebrand, wrote:

One must be cognizant of the development of the Russian Armour Command during the war. It assumed a privileged position in the Russian Army at that time, received excellent officer and enlisted personnel replacements and its tanks were well constructed. . . . In 1941, the Armoured Command was in the midst of reorganization and of armament conversion. In place of outmoded and light tank types came medium types, especially the T–34. Until then, the Armoured Command's major mission had been the support of the infantry, and now it was to be converted to operational use, more or less corresponding to the German view of tank utilization. In this condition, it was caught up in the German offensive and suffered heavy losses from which it was never again completely to recover during the whole war. The degree of training, especially in the subordinate command and in the mastery of weapons on the part of the individual crews, with some exceptions, remained quite low. The performance of the armoured command was negatively influenced by its limited radio equipment. To a certain degree, on the other hand, this lack of training was equalized by the fact that the Russian soldier, as a result of his affinity for nature, brought along with him into the Army skill in utilizing the advantages of terrain and of craftiness. The German soldier who has learned to know the manner of fighting of the Russian Armoured Command, has no doubt that the Command, since the end of the war, has earnestly set about to remove deficiences and today has achieved a high degree of training—high enough to allow it to fully utilize such possibilities as exist in its armoured equipment. [219]

7 Armour in the Nuclear Age-

Soviet strength and armoured doctrine, 1945. By the end of 1945, the Soviet Army was estimated to have had 25 tank and 13 mechanized corps. Each tank corps consisted of 2–3 small tank brigades, each with 3 battalions with 21 tanks each, composed of T–34 tanks, and a small machine-gun battalion, a motorized rifle brigade, a battalion of heavy tanks and self-propelled guns, towed artillery, engineer and other divisional units. The mechanized corps consisted of a motorized infantry formation with 3 motorized brigades (each with 3 rifle battalions and a small medium tank battalion) and 1 small tank brigade. Other units were similar to those of the tank corps. In addition, there were also numerous independent tank brigades and tank battalions, which together with units of assault guns, were used mainly to support the infantry mass of the Soviet Army (amounting to some 520 rifle divisions). The role of supporting the infantry necessitated twice as many tanks as required by the tank and mechanized corps. The majority of these were concentrated into 6 tank armies. After the war, the designations of the armoured formations were changed from tank and mechanized corps to tank and mechanized divisions respectively. In 1946 the Soviet Army and the Soviet High Command carried out further reorganization in order to form a fully mechanized army— technically equal or superior to those of other Western powers. Three types of line division were developed: Rifle, Mechanized and Tank. Galay wrote:

The regrouping of tank and mechanized divisions introduced considerable changes into their organization, especially strengthening their capacity for independent operations. These measures were preceded by lively discussions at the top levels of the Army about the part to be played by tank forces in future operations. The increased power of anti-tank guns and shells and the appearance towards the war's end of an effective individual anti-tank rocket, as well as the increased importance of low altitude air attacks in anti-tank operations, made the Soviet Military leaders wonder whether tanks in general had not outlived their usefulness, and whether they were not outmoded as a means of operational manoeuvring in particular. This last question was of great importance, since the part played by infantry support tanks was evident. The postwar evolution of the Soviet Army shows that the discussion was won by those who wanted the tank forces to retain their operational significance.
Tank forces were intended to carry out two tasks; co-operation with other branches of the forces, and independent operations.

For the second role, tank and mechanized divisions have been created which include tanks, infantry carried in Armoured Personnel Carriers, and self-propelled artillery. The difference between tank divisions and mechanized divisions lies in the different combinations of tank, infantry and artillery. In a tank division there are relatively less infantry and artillery, and more tanks. In the mechanized division there are fewer tanks.[220]

During 1945, Pavel Rotmistrov, Chief Marshal of Soviet Tank Troops, gave an account of postwar Soviet doctrine for the tank and armoured troops; he emphasized that tanks had become the main means of attack:

The tank, without any doubt, has solved the problems of the most complete penetration of the defence.
Rotmistrov gave five reasons for the superiority of tanks over other types of weapon:

a. Only the tank, during the attack, has the ability to

advance within a short distance of the enemy and then employ its powerful weapons to destroy him.

    b. Only the tank during the advance can carry out an uninterrupted attack, destroying the points of enemy resistance which have survived the artillery preparation, either by fire or by its momentum.

    c. Only the tank, with its powerful main armament and machine-guns has the ability during the attack to effectively destroy all the possible resistance to the advance of the infantry, and to fight against defending tanks and artillery.

    d. Only the tank, by virtue of its armour, can aggressively enter the attack without fear of machine-guns, automatic and rifle fire, and also the fire of light artillery —at the same time having the ability to fight these offensive weapons on its own. It can emerge as the victor in this struggle by skilful action.

    e. Only the tank, by having an engine and caterpillar tracks, can attack at great speed and destroy the enemy, before the latter can prepare to retalliate.[221]

The Soviets based their armoured forces on two types of tanks: the medium (weighing 30 tons) for the mobile battle, and the heavy (weighing 45 tons) for the initial assault and breakthrough. The primary role of these tanks was still not to fight other tanks, but to support attacks on prepared positions and in general, to support the infantry.

During the assault, SPs would be deployed so as to provide fire from concealed positions. They would cover the advance of the medium tanks which attacked at speed firing all their weapons. The targets singled out for the SUs would be enemy tanks and anti-tank guns. The heavier SUs (ISU–152s) were intended for neutralizing concrete or armoured defences whilst the medium models (SU–85s, SU–100s) were to exploit their mobility in order to protect the slow-moving KV and IS heavy tanks against the more mobile enemy tanks and SPs. Echeloning in depth, 'divisions' (groups) of medium SUs would accompany heavy tanks during their advance in tactical bounds (about 300 yards behind the leading medium tank wave). Their prime role was to destroy tanks and they were given the additional task of repelling enemy armoured counter-attacks, particularly on the advanced flanks. At a later stage the medium tanks and heavier ISUs could be removed from their infantry groups and deployed against the deeper enemy defences—principally the artillery positions. During a rapid advance, medium tanks would lead and be supported by heavy tanks and SPs of both types. On meeting strong armoured opposition the medium tanks would withdraw through the heavy tanks and SPs sited in ambush. In the defence, tank and mechanized divisions were normally to be held in the rear to counter major armoured penetrations.

In a rifle division SU–100s could sometimes be dug-in to strengthen defended company and battalion areas, but usually were intended to be held back in the reserve of the divisional commander for counter-attacking with the divisional medium tanks. The SU commanders left fire-plans, infantry support, harassing fire and all direct fire roles to the towed artillery.

The postwar design lull. In 1945 the Kharkov Plant, which had been evacuated in 1941, was re-established and became Transport Machine Plant Malyshev 75. Tank production was resumed in 1946. The Kutaisi Factory was rebuilt in 1945–6 from the dismantled Opel Factory at Brandenburg, East Germany; it started production during 1947, building tracked armoured personnel carriers and light tanks.

69. *ISU–152s moving into action during the final stages of the Great Patriotic War.*

In July 1946 the Soviet Government commemorated the important role played by tank forces in World War II, by publishing a decree instituting 'Soviet Tankmen's Day' to be celebrated on 8 September each year.

Up until the mid 1950s, there appears to have been a military stagnation on the part of the Soviet armoured force; this may have been due to one or more of the following reasons: firstly, the effect of the war necessitated the devotion of a large proportion of manpower and raw-materials to the reformation of industry and agriculture; secondly, the introduction of nuclear weapons demanded a large concentration of financial and technical resources towards development of these weapons in the USSR; and thirdly, the atomic era brought a 'new look' to warfare, requiring a complete revision of existing tactical theory and weapon design. Indeed, at first many Soviet officers (like those in other armies) saw no future for the tank in a nuclear war. It is also possible that, since the flow of new ideas and weapons of war resumed noticeably with the death of Stalin, the leader of the Soviet people had clamped down on military expansion and development, or at least, scared people in high places to the extent that they would not express new ideas or opinions on military and political topics. Nevertheless, due attention was paid to the question of increasing the tactical mobility and protection of the infantry; the 'tank descent' of World War II proved of invaluable use during fast approaches, but the necessity of tanks being allocated to the role of transporting infantry proved detrimental to the efficiency of both arms. From the tank's point of view, the ability to traverse and fire its guns was greatly hampered by any accumulation of infantry on and around the turret, and additional penalties were imposed, such as increases in weight, restriction of vision and difficulties in quickly deploying under cover. From the infantry's point of view, they were extremely vulnerable to small-arms and artillery fire and in most cases completely out of touch with the battle situation. Orders to tank-borne infantry squads had to be relayed over the tank radio network, which ultimately delayed the execution of their task, and even more important turned the tank airwaves into confused and unintelligible disorder. This latter fault was, to a certain extent, overcome by the use of flags and whistles, but even so it left much to be desired.

Adoption of the APC. The successes achieved by the German, British and American armies during World War II in employing special armoured infantry vehicles (half-tracks and universal carriers) for the transportation of infantry, did not go unnoticed. The first generation of Soviet armoured personnel carriers (APCs), which appeared during the early 1950s, were wheeled vehicles having light bullet-proof armour. Troops could use their individual weapons from within the vehicles, but were still vulnerable to enemy artillery fire. Based on wheeled chassis readily available (4- and 6-wheeled trucks), these APCs were reliable, fast and had reasonable mobility across country. Their performance was, however, greatly inferior to that of the tanks with which they were intended to keep pace.

Armour in the fifties. With the new military and political attitudes adopted by the Soviet Government during the 1950s, the development of Soviet armoured vehicles progressed considerably, as did other arms. Marshal Ivan Yakubovsky has since stated:

> The ground forces have undergone great alteration, and have been equipped with missiles and nuclear weapons. Their firepower has increased together with their capability of delivering deep fire and of conducting rapid operations. This qualitative advance has had a marked influence upon the nature and scope of contemporary combined-arms combat and on the methods by which it is undertaken. At the same time, the USSR has not been able to make the role and capabilities of nuclear weapons absolute—especially in achieving ground force missions. In a wide variety of situations these forces must be prepared to enter combat without resorting to nuclear weapons. They must be prepared to employ conventional, organic, classical arms—such as artillery, tanks and small-arms. . . .[222]

The reorganization stemmed from the Soviet policy of providing forces capable of operating successfully in both nuclear and non-nuclear warfare. There was, therefore, a great emphasis upon armoured strength and mobility. The line division remained the basic fighting formation (the corps echelon of command being abolished) and was only subordinate to the Army. Line divisions and regimental organizations were on a three-unit basis and clearly demonstrated the integration of armour and infantry with artillery and other supporting arms at the lowest practical level.

Because of their characteristics and comparative invulnerability to the effects of nuclear weapons, tank troops became predominant in the Soviet Army. They were organized to provide the manoeuvre and sustained shock action which the Soviets then regarded (and still do) as complimentary to nuclear firepower.

Under the guidance of successive five-year plans, the motor industry (unaffected by military upheaval) had moved forwards. Over the period of the Fourth Five-Year Plan (1945–50) the industry was characterized by tremendous growth and general expansion, which now came under rigid military control. All vehicles, including civilian, produced during this period were required to satisfy military specifications. (Plans for this rapid growth had been laid down as far back as 1942.)

The Fifth Five-Year Plan. Since the war, Soviet armoured divisions have undergone several large reorganizations which have mechanized virtually the entire army. By 1952 the total armoured strength was estimated as 57 tank and 39 mechanized divisions, together with some 55 rifle divisions. By 1953, estimates of Soviet military strength placed it at 63 tank and 36 mechanized divisions as well as one special Arctic tank division, together with 52 rifle divisions. About 20 of the tank, 10 of the mechanized, and 17 of the rifle divisions were said to be cadre formations.[223]

During the Fifth Five-Year Plan (1951–55) production of vehicles in the Soviet Union fluctuated radically. There was a marked decrease in production during 1951 which was probably due to the conversion of several plants to the production of military arms for the Korean War. From 1953 onwards, there has been a gradually accelerating improvement in the quantity and quality of Soviet armoured and supporting vehicles, which probably accounts for the reduction in divisions during 1953 from 200 to 175. 65 of these divisions were of the tank or mechanized type; after 1957 the figure rose to 75, indicating a further increase in the strength of the armoured forces. Between 1955 and 1963 the tank divisions had their medium tank strength increased considerably, partly at the expense of assault guns, but without undertaking any major alteration in organization. The number of medium tanks increased from 210 to about 375 per division, making a total (with the remaining assault guns) of about 455 gun vehicles per division. The organization of the mechanized divisions was based first on 2, and then from 1953 onwards, on 3 mechanized regiments supported by a medium tank regiment, a heavy-tank/assault-gun regiment, a towed 122 mm howitzer regiment, and other divisional troops. Each mechanized regiment contained 3 rifle battalions, 1 battalion of 31 medium tanks, a towed field-gun battalion and a mortar battalion. The medium tank regiment was similar to that of the tank division and had a total of 65 tanks and 21 assault guns, whilst the heavy tank regiment had 23 IS tanks and 42 assault guns. Altogether, the mechanized divisions of 1954 pattern had 208 tanks and 63 assault guns, and by 1958 the total number of tanks per division rose to 227 medium and 46 IS heavy tanks and 25 amphibious PT–76 reconnaissance tanks.

During the late fifties two new divisional armoured organizations appeared. These were the motor-rifle division and a new type of tank division. The motor-rifle division replaced the rifle and mechanized divisions from which it was formed, while the new tank divisions were created from both the mechanized and older type tank divisions. At the regimental level, tank and motor-rifle troops were integrated to ensure close co-operation. The medium tank regiment became the supporting unit in the motor-rifle division and with the heavy tank regiment, provided the tank strength of the tank division.

Armour in the sixties. In 1962, Marshal Rotmistrov gave his opinion of the role of the tank in nuclear war:

> Because of their high resistance to nuclear strikes, tank troops still remain the decisive force in defeating the enemy in modern offensive ground operations. However,

70. *T–54B tanks with their 'Tank Descents'.*

the changed nature of war, the decisive objectives of modern offensive operations and the greatly increased scale of these operations necessitate even further improvement in the methods of employing tank troops.[224]

To enable the performance of APCs to be compatible with that of tanks, new full-tracked APCs were introduced with the ability to cross water obstacles.

By 1963 a Soviet tank division contained 11,000 men and 280 battle tanks. The principal combat elements of a tank division were 1 heavy and 2 medium tank regiments, an infantry regiment, and the divisional artillery. In the heavy armoured regiment there were 50 tanks, of which just over half were T–10s. Each medium tank regiment was composed mainly of 3 battalions of about 300 men each. In each battalion there were about 50 tanks. In 1964 a Soviet motorized rifle division had 15,000 men with approximately 350 tanks and self-propelled guns. The 7,200 men of the motorized rifle regiments had an establishment of 475 APCs, and more than 2,000 tracked prime-movers, trucks and other vehicles. Latest unclassified estimates of Soviet strength (1967) are given as about 140 divisions, about half of which are at full combat strength. There are about 43 tank divisions, each with 3 tank regiments and 1 motor-rifle regiment (9,000 men and 375 medium and heavy tanks at full strength), about 90 motor-rifle divisions, each with 3 motor-rifle regiments and 1 tank regiment (11,000 men and 210 medium tanks at full strength). 10 of the tank divisions are said to be in East Germany, 1 in Poland, and 2 in Hungary. A further 4 are said to be in the Far East. The regiment is the basic unit in the Soviet Army (equivalent to a Western brigade); a tank regiment consists of 3 tank battalions with no motor-rifle battalions and 1 tank battalion (31 tanks to a battalion). Self-propelled assault guns are becoming obsolete, except in airborne divisions, of which there are 7 (7,000 men and 40 self-propelled guns). Marshal Yakubovsky wrote:

Today, a Soviet motorized rifle and tank division has several times greater firepower than a World War II mechanized corps. Striking power is provided primarily by the large number of tanks. In the current motorized rifle division there are more tanks than there were in a World War II mechanized corps. Tanks are considered to be one of the main means of rapid exploitation of deep thrusts made by Soviet missile forces, aircraft and artillery. . . . The provision of Soviet motorized units with armoured vehicles has increased the striking power of the ground forces. No longer is there any need to fear that the infantry will not keep pace with the tanks and be unable to reinforce their successes. . . . Today, when powerful strikes will precede the operations on the battlefield, Soviet ground forces will possess the capability of conducting rapid marches and displacements, and of manoeuvring on a broad scale in order to hit the enemy in the flank and rear. The offensive will be carried to greater depths with decisive aims, and at high rates of advance. Due to the availability of amphibious equipment within the units, and to the capabilities of tanks to ford rivers and lakes, attacking units will be able to carry out hasty crossings of water barriers unaided. . . .[225]

In 1963 Marshal Vasili Chuikov wrote:

Not one water-barrier will be met, either in Europe or Asia, that our ground forces will not be able to take in their stride. They possess the necessary technical means for this, and in the course of the exercises our troops are successfully mastering the various techniques for crossing the most difficult water barriers.[226]

The amphibious capacity. Although there is an inherent amphibious capability within a division, there is a tendency to overestimate the river crossing capability, and to underestimate the difficulties of negotiating river banks when entering or leaving the water. This problem exists to some extent on all streams, and the points where vehicles can cross without preparation of the banks are rare. With the use of power-tools, explosives and winches, together with the temporary conversion of APC-mounted infantry to pioneer labour, many obstacles of this kind would impose only limited delay on Soviet units.

In 1944 Soviet T–34 and T–44 tanks crossed the 10 foot deep River Bug and later the Vistula. The T–34 tanks which crossed the Vistula used floating sleeves on their exhausts, and the T–44 used two snorkel tubes (one for the crew and one for the exhaust). The Soviets were working on underwater snorkel crossings during the 1930s, and during the third phase of World War II, Soviet tank regiments crossed the Dnester River underwater by having all apertures blocked by old clothes and rags soaked in oil.

It will be appreciated that during a major tank assault over a frontage of several kilometres, where each tank is separated from the next by only some 15 metres, reliance upon bridges, barges and so on, would cause a considerable delay to the advance, and would also cause 'bunching'—presenting a worthwhile nuclear target. In order to overcome this, the Soviets turned to the experience gained by the Germans on underwater crossing; that is, under suitable conditions tanks may be deep-forded by use of snorkels after careful reconnaissance of the river bed by frogmen. Progress in this field developed along two lines: one was a conning tower, or chimney-type snorkel, the other a rigid type of snorkel. Most tanks are factory-equipped to accept snorkelling devices which provide fresh-air for the crew and for the tank engine. The combat snorkel can be hand erected by the tank crew, but the heavy training snorkel is lifted into position by a crane, and is sufficiently large to act as an emergency exit for the crew. The Soviets have limited the operational depth to 15 feet, thereby reducing some of the waterproofing problems.

Directional control is achieved by using the tank intercomm system connected to an insulated antenna, mounted either on the snorkel or separately. An observer stationed on the river bank watches the movement of the snorkel in the water, and gives directions to the driver over the air. The Soviets employ three types of river-crossing technique: firstly, the seizure of fording points or bridges; if this fails then an assault crossing will be used where the frontage will be determined by the degree of opposition, the number of suitable crossing sites and the equipment available. Amphibious tanks and armoured personnel carriers cross in the leading echelon, and snorkel-equipped medium tanks and ferried artillery follow. The third form of crossing is carried out when the water obstacle is defended in force, and a successful attack requires a detailed and carefully co-ordinated attack plan. The Soviets believe that crossings should be made simultaneously on as wide a front as possible, and under cover of darkness.

Armour in the seventies. Soviet ground forces will manoeuvre on broad fronts, advancing along the route of the main thrust at an average rate of 60 miles per day. In order to achieve this rapid rate of advance they will precede this with nuclear and chemical weapons. In the attack, the armoured firepower of a division executes several tasks; a proportion of the medium and heavy tanks (together with self-propelled guns) lead the assault, whilst the remaining gun vehicles guard the flanks of advancing columns and cover the advance of the infantry mounted in armoured personnel carriers. Special units of the armoured force will be allotted to the role of engaging enemy tanks and other hard targets. In the defence, the 122 mm gun of the T–10 heavy tanks, together with the 115 mm guns of the

71. *A T–55 tank snorkelling;* **72.** *T–62 tanks snorkelling a river during an exercise;* **73.** *A postwar May Day parade. BTR–60PK APCs in the foreground, BMP–76PBs in the background;* **74.** *The latest fighting vehicle of the Soviet infantry arm—the BMP–76PB armoured personnel carrier with a 76·2 mm gun, anti-tank guided missile and machine-guns.*

T–62 medium tanks, will engage hard targets at the more extreme ranges (2,000 metres). This firepower will be supported by guided weapons from Swatter, Snapper and Sagger batteries. Due to their very low silhouette, the T–10s and T–62s will be extremely difficult to locate. They will also carry out frequent changes of fire position and prove difficult to destroy. At ranges of up to 1,000 metres targets will be available to the 100 mm guns of the T–54 and T–55 medium tanks, as well as to numerous anti-tank infantry weapons. Further support will be provided by the lighter (87 and 57 mm) towed anti-tank guns. The provision of nuclear weapons has brought a steady decline in the importance of conventional artillery, particularly self-propelled guns.

In spite of the outstanding numbers of tanks and other armoured fighting vehicles, the APC forms the very centre of the Soviet concept of tactical mobility. Soviet units possess a high degree of tactical mobility based entirely upon the vehicles held in unit establishment. This mobility has been achieved through a simultaneous four-pronged replacement programme. Firstly, APCs have been provided for all infantrymen; originally represented by tracked armoured personnel carriers (BTR–50Ps), these have since been replaced by the new 8-wheeled armoured personnel carriers (BTR–60 PKs), resulting from a recent swing to wheeled vehicles. During the period of replacement, the older tracked types have been retrofitted with overhead cover, and the newer wheeled vehicles have this facility incorporated during manufacture. Both tracked and wheeled APCs have an inherent amphibious capability. The Soviet concept for the employment of APCs provides for all vehicles to have apertures in the side and rear plates so that troops may fire while moving. The other three prongs of the programme form auxiliary or supporting arms. As would be expected, with infantry given a high degree of tactical mobility, so has the artillery. The tracked prime-mover holds a prominent position in this role, due to extensive reliance on towed, rather than self-propelled, artillery. The reason why the Russians have abandoned self-propelled guns is because the two main roles for which they were used have since been taken over by other arms. Firstly, the anti-tank role has been completely absorbed by the tank, and secondly, the artillery support role has been taken over by the artillery. With modern technical means of mounting high muzzle-velocity guns in vehicles having fully-rotating turrets, there is no longer any need to produce the casemate mounting for this weapon. Further, increases in range of conventional artillery have made the support of armoured attacks possible from ranges far behind the front, so that the task of artillery support may be executed by semi-mobile, unarmoured artillery. The artillery has, however, been given a high degree of mobility to enable it to disperse widely and to move rapidly in order to maintain station with such advances as the APC-borne infantry and armour may effect. Immediately after the war, two special tracked prime-movers (TPMs) were produced —the Ya–12 and the Ya–13. These have since been replaced by the AT–T, AT–S, AT–L and AT–P, with speeds ranging from 25–40 mph, each with an estimated range of 2,000 kilometres.

The all-wheel-drive trucks employed by the Soviet Army range in payload from ½ to 7½ tons, and are all of postwar design. Extensive use of these trucks by Soviet ground forces usually begins in the army rear areas, where road transport usually terminates. Special high-mobility wheeled carriers have since been introduced to enable an extension of this service right up to the forward areas. Together with the high-mobility TPMs, these vehicles greatly increase the flexibility and rate of advance of tactical units. Each army has a motor transport regiment consisting of 900 trucks; line divisions usually have a motor-transport battalion, and regiments a company. A front generally has a motor-transport brigade to supply its armies when rail transport is not available. The total quantity of trucks deployed in the Soviet Army amounts to about 300,000. These are employed in a variety of tasks, ranging from normal troop transport to the role of missile transporter. The strategic rocket forces are now the main source of the armed forces firepower.

Modern Soviet tank technology. The war in Korea demonstrated the necessity of producing newer models to bring Soviet armour in line with that of the Western armies. At this point, there seems to have been a clear policy adopted towards future tank design. Having found very reliable and satisfactory designs for both the medium and heavy tank classes, in the form of the T–34 and IS tanks, respectively, whereby optimum mechanical reliability of automotive components had been assured, it seems to have been decided not to develop any radically new tank models. The Russians are in the position of being able to compel their satellite and other allied armies to employ tanks of their design, and therefore have a distinct advantage over other countries; they can contemplate the production of tanks on a vast scale and, thereby, not only reduce the cost per item, but also dispense with a major proportion of the problems of resupply and maintenance. (It is evident that they will not allow a recurrence of the 1941 situation, when a similar policy was adopted, so that their basic tank mass would be in a state of poor maintenance or lagging other countries in capability.) The Russians have always been able to modify these two basic tank designs to keep them in line with current US and European development. What Liddell Hart wrote over 15 years ago, still applies today:

> In sum, the Red Army has proved over a whole decade its capacity to keep abreast or even a step ahead of other armies. This story of the 'tank race' is worth telling in detail, as a warning, because it shows how the Russians concentrated on the development of the arm that mattered most, while also turning out well-designed and reliable weapons of other kinds. They seem particularly good at making weapons that are especially 'foolproof'. That may reflect an especial need on their part, due to a lower average level of education among the users, but it is a very desirable asset anywhere in view of hard-testing war conditions.[227]

The first attempt at modernizing the T–34/85, in the form of the T–44 failed owing to a lack of mechanical reliability, but later, in 1949–50, the T–54 medium tank appeared, followed soon afterwards by the T–10 heavy tank. Both these tanks were redesigns of the original basic T–34 and IS types, with medium changes as found necessary. The T–54 mounted a new 100 mm gun which compared favourably with the US 90 mm and the British 20 pdr, although there was some definite inferiority in ammunition. With the recent swing to more powerful weapons, attempts have been made to provide the T–54 series with a new 115 mm gun firing a form of fin-stabilized APDS round, but the efficiency of this system (utilizing smooth-bore gun barrels), in comparison with the British 105 and 120 mm guns, is doubted. The introduction of the guided anti-tank weapon has made it apparent to most countries, including the Russians, that the heavy tank is no longer an economic surety, and as the result it appears that the heavy tank may soon fade from the Soviet tank forces. With their postwar doctrine regarding tank development, the Russians seem once more to have found a requirement for the light tank, although experience in World War II had shown the inferiority of such a vehicle in combat. The light-tank PT–76 has been designed for the reconnaissance role and must really be classed as a tracked armoured car, its armour and armament being closely compatible with those of the current European armoured car designs.

As a result of this 'freeze' in tank design, however, the Soviet models, technically speaking, are inferior to European models (tank for tank). Engines, transmissions, communications, sighting and vision devices, loading techniques, ammunition and armour quality, to name but a few aspects, are nowhere near the standard of sophistication attained by their European counterparts. The Russians believe, however, that any inferiority in technology has most certainly been balanced by a vast superiority in numbers. In addition, the employment of such crude and unsophisticated material does ensure a higher degree of combat reliability, lower production costs, simplified training, simplified maintenance and a reduced supply problem, thereby enabling Soviet armoured divisions to have a guaranteed high battle-worthiness of their tanks after long marches of some hundreds of miles. The Russians have not, however, neglected development of aids to night-fighting and river crossing—indeed the majority of service tanks had these facilities whilst most other countries were still experimenting with the idea!

Today, the responsibility for tank design and development comes under the Chief Tank Directorate (GBTU). This organization is responsible for the specifications and order of tanks, training, finance, operations, maintenance, repair and supply. In 1965 Lieutenant-General Belyanchev, the Chief of the Soviet Main Tank Directorate wrote:

The power of the Soviet tank forces has kept increasing from year to year. This does not mean, however, that everything has been completed in this respect. The tank industry faces the task of further developing Soviet armour, both for the immediate and more distant future. . . [228]

And in the future Malinovsky sees tanks fulfilling a role which will remain vital to the Soviet armed forces:

Neither now, nor, obviously in the future are we able to dispense with the tank. The tank has many remarkable combat features which allow the successful execution of combat tasks in a nuclear war. Among all the other types of combat vehicle, the tank alone is able to survive a nuclear burst, especially the shock wave and dangerous radiation. This is a very important attribute in modern conditions. In addition, the tank has high mobility, firepower and striking force. . . . Many tasks still have to be executed by conventional firepower. Tanks are the best means for this. Thus, the tank-type combat vehicle must remain in service with our Army?[229]

75

76

75. *T–55 tanks with their 'Tank Descent'. The small size of this tank can be seen clearly from this photograph;*
76. *Nuclear artillery of the 60s. A SCUD nuclear missile ready to fire from its converted ISU tracked erector-launcher.*

PART II Soviet
Armoured Fighting Vehicles

1 Light Tanks

The foundation of the 1931–2 Tank Programme, gave a new impetus to light tank development in the USSR. However, very few of the design characteristics peculiar to former Soviet tanks were retained and the models which were evolved were based primarily on foreign designs.

T–27 tankette. Following an evaluation of the Carden-Loyd Mk VI machine-gun carriers (which had been purchased in England and tested at Veronezh) an almost identical vehicle was made in 1931. This became the prototype of the T–27 tankette (tanketka), and underwent service tests with the Army towards the end of the year. Concessions had been granted by Vickers-Armstrong Ltd to manufacture these carriers under licence in the USSR, and it was not very long before the T–27 went into production at AMO (Moscow Automobile Factory). There were basically three models of this tankette produced; the first, designated T–27, appeared similar to the British machine. It mounted a 7·62 mm air-cooled machine-gun in place of the Vickers water-cooled type, and had a built-up rear crew compartment. The two succeeding models, designated T–27A (1932) and T–27B (1933) respectively, differed from the original in the following respects:

a. The hull was redesigned with the crew compartment lengthened to the rear of the chassis, and an extra pair of bogie wheels fitted on each side at the rear. A splash-lip was welded approximately one-third up the glacis plate.

b. In place of the separate head-covers for the driver and commander/gunner, an armoured fairing was riveted to the hull top, extending across the entire width of the vehicle. This modification was principally to facilitate better communication between the driver and gunner. As a result, a hatch was required for entry and exit, and this was placed at the front of the superstructure.

c. In place of the water-cooled Vickers Type machine-gun in an open mounting, an air-cooled 7·62 mm aircraft-type machine-gun was ball-mounted in a sponson extending from the front left-hand superstructure plate.

d. The superstructure was widened to extend over the tracks, thereby allowing more room for stowage of ammunition and equipment.

e. The tankette utilized components of the Model A GAZ truck built at the Molotov Plant in Gorki.

The engine and gearbox were at the front of the vehicle with direct drive to the sprocket via a differential, which was protected by an armoured box. The relatively short length of the tankette hull was achieved, as in the Carden-Loyd prototype, by mounting the engine between the commander and driver/mechanic, and the low height resulted from the absence of a rotating turret. The driver was seated on the right, and the commander/gunner on the left of the tank: both were provided with curved bucket seats which helped them brace themselves against the motion of the tank. The working conditions of the crew, however, were not very good: the fighting compartment was cramped, and the temperature therein near unbearable. In addition, the location of the engine in the crew compartment without adequate ventilation, could cause suffocation, and so cramped was the fighting compartment that the crews of the T–27 tankettes were selected from tankmen of short stature. The crewmen's legs extended beneath the cowling, where on the driver's side, were located the standard foot-pedals and a lever for engaging the reduction gears. To the right of the driver was a lever controlling the epicyclic transmission, and another for steering. Moving the latter forward produced a right turn, and pulling it backwards, a left turn, the steering being carried out by controlling the

drive to each track by lever-operated brake-drums. The tankette was claimed to be able to ascend a slope of 49° in very low gear (there being two gear ranges: for duration and for high-power). Directly behind the seats were the fuel, oil and radiator tanks, while the engine, protected by armour plate, was located in the centre, between and below the seats. At the rear the radiator was protected by double doors which could be opened or closed at will, while below this the frame ended in a truss upon which there was a large hook for towing, and to the left was the exhaust silencer. The armour on all the T–27 models was riveted. The T–27B had larger lights on each side of the driver than the T–27A, and other internal differences included improvements in the cooling of the engine and fighting compartments, in crew comfort and so on. The model B was still in production during 1939–41.

A total of 4,000 T–27s of all types were produced, and served with cavalry units as a reconnaissance tank, receiving limited combat use during skirmishes with guerrillas in the early 1930s. It is interesting to note that the T–27 became the first AFV to be carried by aircraft beneath the fuselage of Soviet TB–3 bombers during peacetime manoeuvres during 1937, as well as in 1940 during the occupation of Bessarabia. Its fighting value was extremely limited, but it served a useful purpose in training and as an easy introduction to the problems of producing armoured vehicles in quantity. When classified obsolete in 1941, the T–27s were converted into artillery tractors or self-propelled mountings for artillery and rocket-launchers.

T–26 light tank. At the same time (1931) the Vickers 6 ton light tanks, Models A and B became the basis of a light (legkiy) tank series for infantry support and for equipping mechanized brigades and moto-mechanized corps (combined-arms units). The first models, collectively called T–26A, were based on the twin-turreted Vickers 6 ton Model A as infantry tanks and were produced between 1931 and 1933. Apart from the armament, there were virtually no changes made to the original Vickers design.

The design of the T–26 was characterized by the use of an air-cooled engine and a mechanical gearbox giving five forward gears and one reverse. The engine was mounted at the rear of the tank with the exhaust passing up to the rear deck plate. The drive was taken to the gearbox, situated at the front, by a shaft passing beneath the gunners' seats in the fighting compartment. From the gearbox the drive was transmitted directly to the sprockets, which were attached to the front of the hull. Air for cooling the engine was drawn in through a grill, immediately behind the fighting compartment, by a fan driven from the engine. To avoid drawing in the exhaust fumes from the engine, a semi-cylindrical cover was welded over the silencer which was attached along the rear plate of the engine compartment. The driver was situated on the right-hand side of the fighting compartment, while the two turret gunners were seated behind him, one on each side of the vehicle. The gunners seats were

78. *Early T–27 tankette suspended below TB–3 aircraft (1937). Note the resemblance to British Carden-Loyd tankette;* **79.** *T–27A tankette. Note change in suspension and new armour layout;* **80.** *T–27B tankette. Final model of the T–27 adopted by the Red Army. Note the armoured covers around the machine-gun mounting which distinguish it from the T–27A;* **81.** *T–26A–1 light tank. Original Vickers production model of twin turreted light tank with water-cooled Maxim machine-guns. (Vehicle shown is British vehicle with Vickers machine-guns.)*

82

83

84

85

pivoted to the roof of the transmission housing and were not driven with the turrets, so that to traverse, the gunners had to swing their seats in the required direction manually. To avoid the turrets fouling each other, locks were attached to the turret rings limiting the traverse of each turret to 265° from their frontal position. Ball-mountings were provided for the armament to increase the speed and accuracy of fire. Nearly all models were provided with splash plates at the turret fronts which moved with the guns; these were to deflect bullet-splash from the gun mountings. Sighting, laying and firing were manual. Ammunition was stowed in bins around the walls of the lower fighting compartment, and those tanks which were provided with radio had this equipment fitted to the left-hand turret where the commander was stationed. The armour was riveted on all models of the T–26A, and a fire-proof partition was fitted between the fighting and engine compartments. The suspension consisted of pivoted double arms on the ends of which were attached double bogies which were sprung by inverted semi-elliptic springs, one for each double bogie unit. There were two bogie assemblies per side, and both base arms and bogie arms were sprung.

Initially each turret was armed with a machine-gun, but these varied between models as follows:

T–26A–1: two water-cooled Vickers 7·62 mm machine-guns (one in each turret); 6 such vehicles existed, as purchased from Vickers-Armstrong.

T–26A–2: two air-cooled 7·62 mm machine-guns (one in each turret).

T–26A–3: one 12·7 mm machine-gun in the right-hand turret; one 7·62 mm air-cooled machine-gun in the left-hand turret.

In conjunction with the infantry-support machine-gun models, the T–26A was also developed as an artillery tank for infantry support, with the following armament variations:

T–26A–4: one 27 mm gun in the right-hand turret; one 7·62 air-cooled machine-gun in the left-hand turret.

T–26A–5: one 37 mm (long-barrelled) gun in the right-hand turret; one air-cooled machine-gun in the left-hand turret.

All the T–26A models had a raised portion at the rear of each turret, but some models of the T–26A–4 had flush turrets. A light was attached to the hull left of the driver's hatch on all the T–26As. Large units of twin-turreted tanks (mainly T–26A–2s and a few T–26A–5s) were formed during the 1930s.

A commander's model of the T–26A, designated T–26V–1, was developed having only the right-hand turret mounting a 20 mm machine-gun, and with a frame aerial around the hull, but this was not adopted in any quantity. Commanders were provided instead with the T–26A–4 or 5 tanks with a frame aerial around the hull, and in this form were designated T–26V.

A flame-throwing version of the T–26A was produced,

82. *T–26A–2 light tank. First Soviet conversion of the twin-turreted Vickers 6-ton tank fitted with twin 7·62 mm air-cooled machine-guns;* **83.** *T–26A–4 light tank. This artillery version mounted a 27 mm gun in the right-hand turret;* **84.** *T–26A–4 light tank (flush turret model). Identical to the original T–26A–4 apart from the absence of the stepped turret top. Note the splash shields fitted over the gun mounts;* **85.** *T–26A–5 light tank. The second artillery version of the T–26A adopted by the Red Army. Note the new gun and mounting.*

86

87

88

89

designated OT (Ogniemietny Tank) 26, in which the left-hand turret was removed and a flame-gun was mounted in the remaining right-hand turret in place of the original armament. Produced in 1933 this equipment was found to be unsatisfactory, since, when assembled in the small machine-gun turret, it was found difficult to operate and little fuel could be carried.

From 1933 onwards, production of twin-turreted T–26A tanks was discontinued, and the Soviets began building a single-turreted model for use by the cavalry arm. In this year, an attempt was made to remove one of the original turrets of the model A and mount a more powerful 37 mm gun in the remaining left-hand turret. This high-velocity 37 mm A/Tk mounting was found to be unsatisfactory since difficulty was found in loading the gun and the turret ring tended to fracture under the recoil loadings.

Failing to adapt the model A to mount a high-velocity anti-tank gun, it became necessary to produce a larger turret, and a further model of the T–26, based on the Vickers 6 ton Model B, was produced during 1933 for use by the cavalry. This vehicle had a new, larger turret which had originally been developed for the BT tanks. The first single-turreted T–26 models, which had riveted hulls, were designated T–26B–1. The first production model T–26B–1 was armed with a 37 mm gun and had no subsidiary armament. Apart from the fighting compartment and the turret, the arrangement of the T–26B was identical to that of the model A; the turret occupied the entire width of the hull, and the commander/gunner and loader were seated behind the driver, the commander/gunner to the left, and the loader to the right. The turret crew's seats were pivoted to the roof of the transmission housing (as in the model A) and were not driven with the turret, so that to traverse, the commander/gunner needed to swing his seat in the required direction manually. There was no turret basket. The commander/gunner aimed and fired the gun from the left, whilst the loader loaded it from the right. The breech operation was semi-automatic. Sighting was achieved by a Zeiss periscopic sight of the type in use with Swedish tanks at that time, whilst a large number had a complicated photo-electric aiming device for firing on the move. The ammunition was stowed in bins around the walls of the lower fighting compartment. On the model B, difficulty was found in traversing the turret, since the gun was not correctly counterbalanced by the turret. The gun was mounted in a pressed-steel mantlet riveted to the turret front, and the turret, which was cylindrical in shape, was welded and riveted with a short tapered overhang commencing to the rear of the centre-line. Wooden stowage-boxes were fitted on each side of the hull, along the track guards. A driving light was mounted centrally, to the left of the driver's visor and was provided with a folding, hemispherical armoured cover. The vehicle had heavy-weight (solid) bogie wheels.

The second production model T–26B–1 was identical with the original but mounted a 45 mm anti-tank gun.

A commander's model of the T–26B–1 (45 mm version)

86. *T–26A–4V light tank. This was the commander's model of the T–26A–4. Note the frame aerial around the hull;* **87.** *OT–26 light flamethrowing tank. First of the T–26 flamethrowers, based on the T–26A light tank.* **88.** *T–26B–1. First production model of the T–26 single-turreted tank with 37 mm gun;* **89.** *T–26B–1. Second production model with 45 mm gun. Note the moulded mantlet which replaced the earlier cylindrical type.*

was produced with the designation T–26B–1(V). This first commander's model had no stowage boxes on the track guards, no vision slits in the turret sides and no periscope for the gunner. A frame aerial was fitted around the turret (which was also used as a hand-rail) and the radio was fitted in the turret overhang, the installation of a radio displacing some of the 45 mm ammunition. A second, improved model T–26B–1(V) appeared during 1936, with improved turret hatches, and a periscope on the front left-hand side of the turret, for the gunner. A vision slit and pistol port were located on each side of the turret, no stowage boxes were attached to the track guards, and some models had an additional ball-mounted 7·62 mm DT machine-gun in the rear of the turret. The third and final commander's model T–26B–1(V) appeared during the Russo-Finnish War, and was provided with an anti-aircraft machine-gun mounting on the turret roof, a machine-gun in the turret rear, a coaxial machine-gun, armoured covers on the pistol ports, lightweight bogie rollers and stowage boxes along the track guards.

An artillery tank version of the T–26B1, designated AT(Artilleriyskich Tank)–26, was produced during 1934 for providing artillery support to cavalry tanks, and this mounted a 76·2 mm L/16.5 gun with a coaxial 7·62 mm DT tank machine-gun in a revolving turret. This vehicle was found to be unsuitable, however, and only a limited number were produced.

A tank glider was experimented with, in which a T–26B–1 (45 mm gun) constituted the fuselage. Two small tail booms were attached to the rear of the hull, and to its side one-bay biplane wings. Flaps were used to reduce the landing speed. This tank glider, designed by Antonov, was called the AT–1.

T–46 light tank. In the years that followed the Five-Year Plans, efforts were made to improve the basic tank types, particularly the T–26 and BT. The restricted mobility of the T–26 tank, particularly when compared to the BT tank, inspired Soviet tank designers to undertake the design of a further light tank during 1935. By the mid 1930s production of the T–26 was provisionally discontinued, and in its place it was intended to issue the new T–46 wheel/track light tank, which weighed slightly more than the BT tank. The T–46 was a high-speed (Christie) version of the T–26, the hull and turret being basically unchanged. The running-gear was very similar to that employed on the BT tank, although, when moving on wheels, drive was transmitted to four wheels. After the issue of a small quantity of these tanks no further production was undertaken, since they proved to be of more complicated construction and less reliable than other Soviet tanks at the time. Whilst the production of the BT models was continued, it was considered unnecessary to produce a similar high-speed tank with the same armour and armament.

New T–26 models. In 1937, therefore, a new T–26 model appeared, the T–26B–2. From 1937 onwards these T–26B–2 tanks were equipped with an improved turret mounting a 45 mm gun and coaxial machine-gun. The hull and turret were welded rather than riveted, the turret being modified from the second Commander's model T–26B–1(V) with a welded mantlet. Two mantlet configurations have been observed: one of square cross-section, and one of semi-

90. *T–26B–1(V). First T–26B commander's model with frame aerial;* 91. *T–26A. Experimental 37 mm gun mounting;* 92. *T–26B–1(V). Third type of T–26B commander's tank;* 93. *T–46 light wheel/track tank.*

90

91

92

93

circular cross-section. A semi-circular turret hatch was mounted on the left-hand side at the front with another circular hatch at the rear for the commander. Some vehicles had a stowage box on the right-hand side track guard, splash-lips around the rear of the turret ring, and resilient bogie wheels. The box-type mantlet incorporated a periscope for the gunner. The bulge at the rear of the turret was for the gun counterweight and also provided stowage for the radio (which fitting reduced the ammunition stowage as on earlier models). Some vehicles of this type had a machine-gun in the turret rear. A commander's model was produced, designated the T–26B–2(V). Internal arrangements were otherwise identical with the T–26B–1.

Since the OT–26 flame-throwing version of the T–26A tank had been found unsatisfactory, a further flame-throwing version based on the T–26B was developed, designated OT–130. This improved model was adopted for service and employed against the Japanese in Manchuria, the Finns in 1939–40, and finally against the Germans during 1941. The original tank turret was retained, but the armament was replaced by a single flame-gun mounting in the original mantlet. There were basically two versions: the first had the turret of the T–26B–1 on the hull of the T–26B–2 (with stowage boxes), and the other had the turret of the second commander's model T–26B–1(V), but with a whip aerial in place of the frame type. It utilized the hull of the T–26B–1, but with light-weight bogie rollers. An improved model OT–130 appeared in 1940 with a shorter flame-gun, and a coaxial MG mounted on the right of it, in a new rectangular mantlet.

Reports on actions in Spain and Manchuria resulted in the production of a version of the T–26B which was lower and lighter, with better sloped armour plate on the hull, and a new conical turret. This was introduced during 1938, designated the T–26S (sometimes referred to in the foreign press as the T–26C). It had an increased armour basis with electrically-welded plates, and the upper hull sides were extended over the tracks and inclined and bevelled to afford better protection. The new armour made the vehicle heavier than was intended, however, and strengthened suspension and transmission components had to be installed. All of the T–26S tanks were provided with radio, the frame-type aerial disappearing, and a single flexible type being fitted to the rear of the turret. Other modifications included the transfer of the side stowage boxes to the rear of the track guards (although some vehicles were not fitted with these), a new sheet-steel inverted-V radiator cover, welded strengtheners on each side of the turret at the rear and just behind the mantlet, a long faired, welded mantlet, square loader's hatch on the left-hand side and a circular commander's hatch at the rear of the turret. The gunner's periscope was retained on the left-hand side at the turret front as well as the coaxial machine-gun, and the turret had inclined armour with a pronounced overhang. Some T–26B–2s were retrofitted with this turret, but without the rear machine-gun, and also fitted with the old hand-rail

94. *T–26B–2 light tank. This is a later, modernised version of the T–26B. Note this model has the solid bogie wheels;* **95.** *OT–130(T–26B–1 turret on T–26B–2 hull). First of the single-turreted flame-throwing light tanks based on the T–26;* **96.** *OT–130 (T–26B–1(V) turret on T–26B–1 hull). The second production model of the T–26B light flame-throwing tank;* **97.** *OT–130 (improved model). Note the new rectangular mantlet and short flamegun. The rear machine-gun has been removed.*

98. *T–26S light tank. Note the new sloping sided turret and the faired-out hull sides;* **99** *The AT–1 76·2 mm artillery version of the T–26 light tank;* **100.** *T–26B–2 retrofitted with turret of T–26S;* **101.** *OT–133 light flame-throwing tank based on the T–26S. Note similarity to the OT–130 improved model.*

type aerial. The majority of vehicles had the machine-gun in the rear of the turret, and all models had provision for an anti-aircraft machine-gun. The fuel capacity was increased (see data tables). The internal layout and general construction of this tank was otherwise identical to that of the T–26B. Some were later fitted with elevation stabilizers for the 45 mm guns, and in this form designated T–26E.

A final flame-throwing version of the T–26, based on the T–26S and designated the OT–133, appeared during the Russo-Finnish War. This vehicle was identical with the gun tank, but had a short flame-thrower nozzle on the left of the mantlet with a coaxial 7·62 mm DT tank machine-gun to the right. The mantlet was cut short and slightly modified. The rear-mounted machine-gun was retained. The flame-throwers in all three versions functioned by compressed-air, and were completely self-contained within the tank. Both the OT–130 and OT–133 carried 400 litres of fuel in the turret on the left-hand side, whilst four air-propellant tanks were mounted on the right-hand side. (The range of the OT flame-gun under fair conditions, however, was only 40 yards.)

Quantity production of the T–26 series was undertaken at the Komintern factory from 1932 onwards, and continued through until 1939. All production models after the B were equipped with radio. Many tanks of the B and S types had a pair of powerful searchlights mounted over the mantlet for firing at night. The method of steering and changing gear in all models was identical with that used for the T–27 tankette.

Owing to its wide employment by the Soviet Army, the T–26 light tank was used as the basis for several special-purpose vehicles, including self-propelled artillery mountings (see Chapter V), artillery tractors, mechanized flame-throwers, bridgelayers and smoke tanks. Artillery tractors were converted T–26 tanks with their turrets removed—sometimes provided with a box-like unarmoured personnel compartment which occupied the position usually taken up by the turret. The standard bridgelaying version of the T–26, designated the IT–26, had the turret removed and two light-weight, lattice-construction bridge arms attached rigidly along the length of the tank. For bridging gaps, the vehicle was driven into the trench and following tanks drove over it. Smoke tanks (designated DT—Dmovaya Tank—26) were usually based on the twin-turreted T–26A tanks, which, while retaining their turrets, rarely carried any armament. Chemical containers and generators were fitted either in the right-hand turret or at the rear of the tank.

Some of the B and C models were sold to China, others were employed by Republican troops during the Spanish Civil War; the Russians themselves used them extensively during the Manchurian and Finnish Wars and the early campaigns against the Germans. In all, about 4,500 are believed to have been produced. After 1941–42 those tanks which had survived were used either as gun tractors or converted into radio-controlled tank mines. In the latter form the turrets were removed and the hulls filled with high-explosive.

102

106

103

107

104

102. *IT–26. Early bridge-laying version of the T–26 light tank;* **103.** *Unfinished first prototype of the T–33 (A–33) light amphibious tank. This vehicle has the original Vickers-Carden-Loyd suspension system;* **104.** *Second prototype of the T–33 with new, modified Horstmann suspension system and redesigned hull;* **105.** *3–2T. Early production T–37;* **106, 107.** *T–37 light amphibious tank. Later production model. Note the improved turret and redesigned air-cooling device rear of the turret.*

With the increase in weight over the period 1937–9, the performance of the T–26 tank had gradually deteriorated and production was discontinued in 1939.

T–37 amphibious tankette. In 1931, the 8 Vickers-Carden-Loyd light amphibious tanks which had been purchased in England during the 1931 negotiations were used as the basis for a new light amphibious reconnaissance tank. The parent British vehicle was the A4E11. A prototype of the new tank was completed in 1932 at AMO and designated the 'Morskoi 33'. The first prototype of the T–33 weighed 3 tons and had a crew of 2 men. The armament consisted of a 7·62 mm DT machine-gun in a fully-rotating turret and the armour varied from 7 to 9 mm. Powered by a 63 hp petrol engine, the vehicle could achieve a maximum land speed of 28 mph. The second prototype of the T–33 had an improved suspension and armour arrangement. The Vickers-Carden-Loyd suspension system was found unsuitable for Russian terrain, and it was decided to adopt a modified Horstmann scissors type, the new vehicle being completed during the following year, to become known as the T–37 plavaiushchiya (amphibious) tank. It retained practically the same hull configurations as the parent A–4E11, but with a new turret mounted on the

105

108

111

109

112

110

113

108. *T–37(V). Commander's model of T–37 light amphibious tank;* 109. *Prototype of the T–38 light tank with 20 mm ShVAK aircraft cannon;* 110. *T–37A light amphibious tank. Note the rounded welded armour;* 111. *Prototype of the T–41 light amphibious tank;* 112. *T–38 light amphibious tank;* 113. *T–38M2 light amphibious tank. Note the modified driver's visor and armour around the engine compartment.* 114. *Front view of the T–30 (A–30) light amphibious tank;* 115. *T–38M–2 with 20 mm gun;* 116. *T–50 ('Little Klim') light tank.*

left-hand side of the vehicle, and modifications were also made to the tracks and propeller drive systems. The tank exterior was strengthened against wave buffeting. The early production models, believed to have been designated 3–2T, had small welded turrets with flush tops, similar to those used on the T–26A tanks, but during the Finnish War these were replaced by a larger, roomier type with a raised hatch cupola. The suspension was of a scissors type with horizontal coil springs. The vehicle had a single propeller and rudder at the rear of the hull, with a power takeoff from

the engine for the propeller. Balsa-wood floats, encased in sheet metal, were fitted in the form of trackguards to provide additional buoyancy to the watertight hull. The engine was cooled by air from a large fan housed in a riveted, watertight box built on to the rear deck of the tank. The driver was seated to the left of the turret in the centre of the vehicle, with the engine at the right in the rear of the hull. The final drives and sprockets were at the front, drive being transmitted from the engine, at the rear, via Carden shafts passing under the crew compartment to the gearbox

114

115

116

infantry, cavalry and mechanized formations during the 1939–41 campaigns against the Finns and the Germans. Some final production models of the T–38M–2 were fitted with 20 mm ShVAK aircraft cannon to provide more effective firepower.

T–41 amphibious tankette. Designed during 1932, about the same time as the T–37, the T–41 light tank was tested as a possible successor, but its water performance left much to be desired. The vehicle did not progress beyond the prototype stage. Weighing 3·2 tons and with a crew of 2 men, this tank was armed with a 7·62 mm DT/machine-gun. The armour ranged from 4 to 9 mm. The 40 hp engine gave the vehicle a maximum speed on land of 23 mph.

T–38 amphibious tankette. Although the T–37 remained in service right up to 1941, an improved light amphibious tank, the T–38, entered production during 1936 at the AMO factory. This tank closely resembled the original T–37 but with the following differences: the most significant improvements were in the hull arrangement and transmission. The improved hull form allowed a decrease in overall height, a decrease in weight, and an increase in the manoeuvrability of the tank. The turret was offset to the left (as opposed to the right on the T–37), with the driver to the right. The turret was the same as that fitted to the later T–37 models. The T–38 had new final drives in place of the automobile differential, and a more reliable steering system than used on the T–27 and T–37 light tanks. A new, improved suspension system with wider tracks increased the performance across marsby ground, and the Russians later stated that they found this vehicle much easier to manoeuvre than the earlier T–37 models. The prototype vehicle had another lower, fixed turret for the driver situated to the right of the main one; mounted in this was a long-barrelled 20 mm machine-gun operated by the driver. Production vehicles did not incorporate the 20 mm gun, since it impaired the driver's ability to control the vehicle. Together with the T–27 tankette, the T–38 was one of the first tanks to be carried by air, mounted beneath the fuselage of Soviet ANT–6 four-engined bombers during peacetime manoeuvres in 1936. In 1938 an improved model of the T–38 appeared, designated the T–38M–2, which was fitted with a new, more powerful engine which greatly improved its performance, both engine and gearbox being taken from the M–1 automobile.

T–30 light tank. During early 1940 the Russians developed an amphibious light tank called the T–30. This vehicle in fact was the predecessor of the later T–40 amphibious light tank, having an identical hull and automotive layout. The turret, however, was different and mounted the same weapon and mantlet as the T–60 light tank—a 20 mm ShVAK aircraft cannon with coaxial 7·62 mm DT. Owing to the appearance of the T–40 no production of this vehicle was undertaken.

T–50 light tank. With the start of the new 1940–41 tank programme a replacement for the T–26 light tank was developed, designated the T–50 light tank. This tank entered production during 1940 and was in service by the summer of 1941. It was intended to be employed for the direct support of infantry, and to replace the BT in its light tank role. As with the T–26S, the T–50 was armed with a 45 mm gun and 2 machine-guns, but the muzzle-velocity of the gun was doubled and the rate of fire increased threefold. Armour 37 mm thick was introduced on the front and sides of the hull, which were steeply inclined. It is of interest to note that in this tank the front, side and rear plates were of the same thickness, with the result that, although a light-

at the front of the tank. Direct drive was taken from the gearbox, through a differential to the final drives. The method of steering and gear-changing was identical to that employed on the T–27 tankette. No provision was made on normal tanks for radio communication, but commander's models, designated T–37(V), were specially adapted with a large frame aerial around the hull. The Russians found it very difficult to form a watertight seal on this tank due to its riveted construction, and production was halted after only 70 vehicles. A modified version, designated T–37A, was produced in 1935 with thicker die-formed armour plates welded and riveted, the tank being consequently slightly heavier. The T–37A did away with the balsa floats on the trackguard. When production ceased in 1936, a total of 250 T–37 and T–37A tanks had been produced at AMO. Both models were widely used in reconnaissance units of weight tank, it had fairly effective armour protection. The T–50 was the first Russian light tank with a cast turret, and this was fitted with a heavy mantlet. The design of both the hull and the turret resembled that of the T–34 medium tank, but the internal arrangement was similar to the T–26 on which it was based. The most significant alterations were the change to independent torsion-bar suspension which was necessitated by the increase in weight, and the use of a diesel engine developing 300 hp. These characteristics enabled the tank to attain a speed of 60 kph. In addition, an all-round vision cupola was provided for the commander, and the crew was increased to 4 men. No contemporary light-tank could be considered superior to the T–50 in terms of combat characteristics. The T–50 was, however, a rather complicated and expensive vehicle, the production facilities required for its manufacture being comparable to those of a medium tank; the T–50 was terminated after only 65 had been built. The T–50 was referred to by Soviet tank troops as 'Maly Klim' (Little Klim), since it resembled a miniature KV tank.

T–40 light amphibious tank. During 1940 steps were taken to produce a light tank of less complex construction than the T–50 utilizing automobile components wherever possible. Arising from this, there appeared an amphibious (plavaiushchiya) tank T–40, having only machine-gun armament and light bullet-proof armour. This vehicle had a normal automobile transmission and engine. The engine was considerably more powerful than that used in the T–38 amphibian to compensate for the increase in weight. As with the original T–38, the engine was mounted on the right-hand side where there was a characteristic air-intake lip on the armoured hull. The bullet-proof armour was 14 mm thick and the vehicle was welded throughout. The hull was very original, slightly resembling a boat, with a large squat front, and the turret mounted slightly to the rear on the left-hand side. Flotation tanks were built into the hull to assist buoyancy, and in the water the T–40 was driven by a single four-bladed propeller at the rear and steered by two rudders. The fundamental alteration was in the running gear; as with the T–50, independent torsion-bar suspension was used. With its superior suspension the whole vehicle was a great improvement on the earlier models, and was consequently placed in production towards the end of 1940, coming into service by 1941. The turret closely resembled the contemporary Swedish Landsverk design, with the familiar box-type mantlet mounting either a 12·7 mm DShK or 20 mm ShVAK machine-gun and coaxial 7·62 mm DT tank machine-gun. As with the earlier models, the drive was taken to the gearbox at the front and thence to the final drives. The T–40 was first employed against the Finns where its performance was not found to be very satisfactory, the armour proving too thin and the armament inadequate. Early T–40s had twin lifting eyes on the lower hull nosefplate; later models (and the T–40A) had a single lifting eye. The driver was provided with a hinged visor and a large hatch overhead for entry and exit. The T–40A, introduced during late 1941, differed from the original tank in having the bow top faired away at the sides where originally flat on the T–40. The T–40A also had a trim-vane which unfolded from the bow. During 1942 the T–40S was placed in limited production as a successor to the T–40 and T–40A. Since the thin armour on the previous models became a considerable handicap during operations, this new model had the armour increased on certain parts of the hull and turret. With the increase in weight, however, the tank lost its amphibious capability

with the result that the water propulsion and steering devices were removed during production.

T–60 light tank. When both the T–40 and the T–50 light tanks were found to be operationally or technically unsatisfactory, and the obsolescence of the older T–37, T–38 and T–26 tanks became more and more apparent, a complete redesign of the light tank was undertaken. Using the basis of the T–40 chassis, a new non-amphibious light tank was developed. By mounting a 20 mm aircraft cannon and providing increased frontal armour thickness, the T–40 was transformed into the new non-amphibious light tank model T–60 during late 1941. Development and production of this tank was undertaken by the Soviet Automotive Industry as opposed to the tank industry. The hull front and turret had improved protection against large-calibre machine-gun rounds, and although cast armour had been

117. *T-40 light amphibious tank, early model. Note the twin lifting eyes on the lower nose plate;* 118. *T–40 light amphibious tank, later model. Note the single lifting eye;* 119. *T–40A light tank. Note the trim vane.*
120. *T–40S light amphibious tank. Note the new gun support;* 121. *T–60 light tank. Note the spoked bogie wheels. (Compare with T–60A);* 122. *Side view of the T–60A light tank.* 123. *T–60A light tank. This model has solid bogie wheels (compare with T–60);* 124. *T–60 light tanks being employed as tractors for 57 mm anti-tank guns;* 125. *T–60 light tank fitted with Katyusha rocket launcher.*

adopted for the medium and heavy tank classes and for the turret of the T–50, both hull and turret of the T–60 were welded throughout. It entered production during November 1941: over 6,000 were produced during the War and it was issued to reconnaissance units on a large scale. The turret was offset to the left with the engine mounted alongside it on the right and the driver placed centrally in the front. Like the earlier T–40, the T–60 had a turret of characteristic Swedish design with the same turret and mantlet as used on the majority of contemporary Landsverk tanks. A high-velocity 20 mm SchVAK aircraft machine-gun was mounted in a long boxed bracing attached to a long flat mantlet. A coaxial 7·62 mm DT tank machine-gun was mounted on the left. Although not amphibious, the T–60 tank was internally identical to the T–40, on which its design was based. Both the T–40 and T–60 tanks were specially designed for operating in snow—in the case of the former this had proved invaluable during the fighting at

Petsamo during the Russo-Finnish War.

An improved model of the T–60 light tank was produced in late 1941/early 1942, designated T–60A, and carrying increased armour. The main external difference between the two models lay in the wheels: the T–60 had spoked road-wheels and idlers, whilst those on the T–60A were pressed solid. When eventually replaced by the more powerful T–70 light tanks, the T–60 chassis were employed as mountings for M–8 and M–13 (Katyusha) rocket-launchers, and also as artillery tractors for 57 mm anti-tank guns.

T–70 light tank. By the beginning of 1942 it became apparent that the T–60/60A light tanks were too lightly armoured and did not possess sufficient firepower to cope with the new German tank models. At this time a new model, the T–70 light tank, appeared and was subsequently produced in quantity at the Gorki Automobile Works. The T–70 replaced the T–60 in light tank units during late January 1942. It had the same chassis (with a front drive, instead of rear), slightly reinforced to take the extra weight, but mounted a 45 mm gun and coaxial 7·62 mm DT machine-gun in a redesigned welded turret. This turret had a semi-circular hatch in the roof, and a curved external mantlet with conical sleeve for the gun. The hull armour was also modified to give a cleaner outline and better protection, and the driver was provided with an armoured visor. The engine power was doubled by providing two engines of the type used in the T–60, Soviet versions of the Hudson 110 hp straight-eight car engines. Twin exhaust pipes were attached on each side at the rear of the hull. The tracks had twin guide-horns on each track plate, and the T–70 could attain a speed of 32 mph. A lipped air-intake was welded on the right-hand side of the hull below the turret, and an engine-servicing hatch was fitted on the right-hand side of the glacis plate. During mid 1943 the T–70A was produced with increased armour and slightly more powerful engines. The turret (which was more heavily armoured) had a squared-off rear, as distinct from the rounded type of the T–70, and had welded strengtheners along the joints. Production of the T–70/70A light tanks was discontinued in the autumn of 1943 as the result of its poor combat performance. Probably its main shortcoming was that the commander acted also as gunner and loader, which slowed down its speed of engagement. Nevertheless during the War, 8,226 T–70 tanks were produced, until 1944 when the existing chassis were converted to self-propelled mountings for 45 mm anti-tank guns, captured 47 mm Czech anti-tank guns, and later for the newer 57 mm and 76·2 mm anti-tank guns. The T–70 tanks were distinguished for their low production costs resulting from the utilization of existing automobile components and facilities and mass-production techniques. A total of 8,226 T–70 and T–70A tanks were built.

T–80 light tank. Towards the end of 1943, a further light tank was produced which appeared to be identical with the

126. T–70 light tank; 127. T–70A light tank. (Note the squared-off turret rear); 128. T–80 light tank. Last Soviet produced light tank of World War II; 129. T–34 light tank. 130. PT–76 light tank. In the foreground can be seen the earliest model with the multi-baffle muzzle brake. In the background the most recent model with double-baffle muzzle brake and bore-evacuator; 131. PT–76 final model with bore evacuator and double-baffle muzzle brake; 132. Final variant of the PT–76 during an amphibious operation.

126

127

128

129

T–70A, but carrying a heavier turret and thicker armour; this was designated T–80. The addition of a cupola for the commander and the employment of an internal mantlet improved its fighting efficiency, but the T–80 was not used on any large scale.

Soviet light tank policy at the close of the war. In spite of the fact, that at the beginning of the war, the light tank formed the standard combat vehicle of the Soviet armoured forces, during the course of the war the combat effectiveness and numerical strength of the light tanks continually decreased. 1941–2 showed a marked increase in the output of light tanks over previous production so that the Army's requirement for tank equipment could rapidly be satisfied; during the second half of 1941, 1,923 light tanks were produced, and during the first half of 1942, 5,100; but during the second half of 1943, only some 1,265 were produced and

130

131

132

later, production of this type of vehicle ceased altogether. The defects of the light tank were its poor armour protection and insufficient armament. A final wartime study of the light tank was carried out during 1944 by Lipgarta, who designed a light tank with armour and armament equivalent to that of a medium tank; this project was not continued, however. As with the Allied and German armies, the Russians never found a satisfactory light tank during the war, and no further development of this type of vehicle took place before 1945.

T–34 light airborne tank. Between 1945 and 1950, however, a further attempt was made at producing a light tank for use by airborne forces, which resulted in the T–34 light tank. The T–34 utilized components of the T–34 medium tank which it closely resembled (hence its designation). Other components (principally automotive) were based on the T–70/SU–76 series. The vehicle had only three roadwheels per side which gave it an extremely poor cross-country performance, and only limited production was undertaken, no tanks being actually delivered to units.

PT–76 light amphibious tank. No new light tank appeared until 1952, when the PT–76 was introduced. The PT–76 amphibious tank was designed as a reconnaissance vehicle to fulfil a role similar to that of the armoured car, but added the ability to cross water obstacles in the first wave of an attack, and to provide artillery fire-support during the establishment of a bridgehead. The tank was seen in unit service for the first time during 1955 and has since been produced in quantity for both the USSR and satellite armies by the Volgograd Tractor Plant; at the time of writing 3 to 5 are deployed per reconnaissance company. Apart from its role as a reconnaissance tank, the basic hull and chassis have been used for a wide range of supporting vehicles including tactical missile launchers, APCs and self-propelled guns.

The PT–76 is of welded construction throughout; it is lightly armoured to provide protection against small-arms fire and shell fragments. It has great manoeuvrability in water, and the gun can be fired whilst the vehicle is afloat. The armament consists of a 76·2 mm gun with various modifications in muzzle-brakes and fume extractors. The engine is situated in the left side of the rear deck, just below the turret. It consists of one bank of the V–12 engine used in the T–54 medium tank. For use in water, a deflector plate is mounted on the bow. Propulsion in deep water is accomplished by a hydro-jet system based on water-pressure developed by a set of pumps driven by the tank engine. Water is taken in via two openings in the bottom of the chassis and expelled under pressure through two primary ports in the upper rear plate. When not in use, these ports are covered by two clam-shaped covers, which are also used to vary the thrust of each jet during steering operations. The chassis of this tank was originally designed for the Penguin Arctic Tractor in 1948, and utilizes a torsion-bar suspension with the track running atop of the six road wheels on each side. The general interior arrangement of the tank has not yet been made available. Later PT–76 models have a short snorkel attached to the rear of the turret which may be for training purposes.

Future light tank development. No information has been made available to the general public on a possible successor to the PT–76 Soviet light tank series but it may be that further development of this type of vehicle will continue. On the other hand, the Soviet acceptance of highly-mobile wheeled vehicles may lead them to introduce an armoured wheeled vehicle to fulfil the light tank role.

2 Medium Tanks

The BT series. During 1931 the two Christie M–1931 (T–3) tanks purchased from the USA were tested extensively by the Russians at Voronezh to determine their suitability for use by the Soviet Army. The results of these tests were favourable, and during the same year a new Soviet tank was designed based on the Christie model and subsequently produced at the Komintern Factory in Kharkov. This design took full advantage of the Christie feature of running on wheels or tracks as required, but was not accepted for general production owing to its complexity. A simplified version of the tank was designed in 1931 and became known as the BT–1 (Bystrochodya Tank), or fast tank. Although the BT eventually developed into a new series of medium tanks, it was considered at this time to be an independently operating 'fast tank'—intended for use by large and completely independent mechanized formations. The basic models adopted for service were the BT–2, BT–5, BT–7 and the BT–7M. (Although the BT series has been included in this chapter for convenience, it was classified as neither a light nor a medium tank; it possessed its own unique role as a 'fast' tank.)

As with the original Christie tank, the BT could run on either wheels or tracks, a change from one to the other taking about thirty minutes. The general construction was fairly conventional for the time, apart from the unique Christie suspension utilizing large-diameter road-wheels. The general construction closely resembled that of the original Christie vehicle, in housing the engine and transmission at the rear, the drive being transmitted to the rear sprockets when on tracks, and to the rear pair of wheels when moving on wheels alone. When running on tracks, the chain sprocket on each side of the driving wheel was replaced by four rollers which drove the tracks via the driving lugs carried on alternate track links. When running on wheels, the power was transmitted from the main driving wheels to the rear pair of road-wheels through a chain drive (the tracks being carried on shelves running along the sides of the hull). The rear pair of bogie wheels carried about one-third of the tank weight; thus, the tractive effort of the tank when moving on wheels was considerably less than when moving on tracks. Wheeled motion was only advantageous on hard-surfaced roads, since on soft ground the driving wheels would obviously dig into the soil and spin. As a result, the capability of moving on wheels was greatly limited. The main advantage of the BT was not that it was a convertible wheel/track vehicle, but that it could develop a high speed on tracks: BT tank units demonstrated conclusively the feasibility of fast-moving tanks during training and manoeuvres. In the wheeled mode, the tank was steered by the front pair of wheels, and in the tracked mode by the conventional clutch and brake method and the driver controlled the tank with a steering wheel rather than with levers. Although the BT incorporated this faculty for running on either wheels or tracks, throughout its period of use with the Soviet Army, it was rarely used in the wheeled mode. This was probably due to the long time required for the conversion operation (thirty minutes), necessitating the change-over to be made outside the combat area. There were complaints that the tracks had a tendency to shed, especially if turns were at all abrupt and the tank was not handled smoothly. In the manufacture of the original US vehicle, extensive use had been made of electrical arc-welding, but the early Soviet BT models were riveted throughout. In general the performance of the tank was excellent, owing to the high power-to-weight ratio and the unique Christie suspension

133

134

of room inside the tank. The suspension was also vulnerable, complicated and difficult to maintain in the field. The BT–1 was powered by a 400 hp Russian version of the Liberty V type engine used in the original Christie tank. The driver was seated centrally at the front of the tank, and the turret—which was identical to that used on the original Christie tank—was mounted amidships. Manufacture of this first model commenced on 23 May 1931 and it was completed by June. Two further prototype BT–2s were commenced during August 1931, and by early September these, too, were completed in time for all three vehicles to take part in the October Parade in the Red Square. The Soviet High Command now requested the installation of manufacturing facilities for the mass-production of these first BT tanks.

BT–1 fast tank. The BT–1 was armed with two machine-guns in the turret. Trials with this tank proved the turret and armament installation to be inadequate and production was halted after only a few vehicles had been built.

BT–2 fast tank. A second model, designated BT–2 (or Christie-Russkiy 1931) was constructed in late 1931; it closely resembled the BT–1, but had a turret of a new design. The prototype, like the BT–1, was armed with two machine-guns, but production models mounted a 37 mm M–1930 tank gun and one machine-gun. The 37 mm gun was aimed with the aid of a shoulder support, and the 7·62 mm DT machine-gun was located separately in a ball-mounting to the right of the gun. The BT–2 was thoroughly tested and released for production in January 1932.

BT–3, 4 fast tanks. Even though the adoption of the BT–2 marked a significant advance in Soviet tank development, the BT–2 was still not found to be up to requirements. Two

135

136

133. *BT–1 fast tank (note the twin 7·62 mm machine-gun mounting and the separately-mounted ball MG;* **134.** *BT–2 fast tank. This is an early model with original mantlet;* **135.** *BT–2 fast tank, later model with new mantlet. Compare with 56;* **136.** *BT–3 fast tank. Similar to later BT–2 but with solid bogie wheels;* **137.** *BT–4 fast tank.*

which consisted of four large wheels per side, revolving on pivoted axle arms. Each wheel had dual rubber tyres, and each axle arm was controlled by a long adjustable coil spring housed vertically inside the hull side-plates. The liberal compression amplitude gave each wheel an independent maximum vertical movement of about 14 inches, and this suspension provided a remarkably stable gun platform, although necessitating a double-wall construction (there being an inner skin of 7·5 mm) which took up a lot

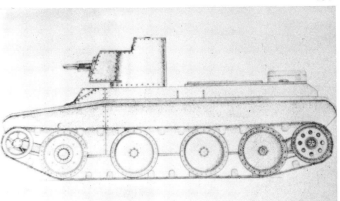

137

further models, BT–3 and BT–4 were developed to investigate various armament combinations. Whereas the BT–2 had mantlet guards and spoked wheels, the BT–3 models were provided with a slightly modified turret (with rear stowage box) no mantlet guards and solid pressed-steel wheels. In place of the 37 mm gun a 45 mm anti-tank gun was mounted, but the separate ball-mounted DT machine-gun was retained. Only limited production of this third model was undertaken. The BT–4 was an unsuccessful attempt at producing an infantry version of the BT equipped with the twin turret arrangement of the T–26A light tank series. Since no requirement for this latter vehicle materialized, only a few prototypes were produced.

These first four BT models were powered by the Liberty 400 hp aircraft engine giving a power-to-weight ratio of about 35 hp per ton, enabling the employment of a gearbox with four forward gears and one reverse.

BT–5 fast tank. Towards the end of 1932 requirements were laid down for a further BT model with the following features: the provision of more powerful armament, a coaxial mounting for the machine-gun, the provision of radio equipment, and more room in the turret and fighting compartment. Better mobility was to be achieved through the use of a newly-developed Soviet tank engine. A further model was therefore manufactured mounting a 45 mm M–1932 tank-gun with coaxial machine-gun mounting, and these were installed in an improved turret with radio equipment. The 45 mm armour-piercing round of this gun had a muzzle-velocity of 2,350 fps— which provided a firepower greater than that of all foreign light, and most medium tanks right up to the outbreak of World War II. The new tank, designated BT–5, also had a more powerful engine, the twelve-cylinder M–5 aircraft model of Soviet design. The new BT–5 turret was simultaneously adopted for the T–26B light tank, the original BT–5 turret being cylindrical, although later models had a faired-out overhang. Twin optical sights were provided (telescope and periscope), and another major improvement was the adoption of stronger suspension components. The armour, meanwhile, remained unaltered. A commander's model, provided with radio and designated BT–5(V), was produced with a frame aerial around the turret roof.

The BT–5 was placed in production towards the end of 1932, an extremely robust, successful application of the Christie chassis, and utilizing the link-plate track later used for the T–34/76A medium tank. The BT–5 became a standard model and remained in service up until 1941. Apart from the turret, the general arrangement of this tank closely followed that of the BT–1; the turret and fighting compartment were similar to those used in the T–26B light tank (see page 000). A version of the BT–5 armed with a 76·2 mm L/16.5 gun (and 1 or 2 machine-guns), designated BT–5A, was produced for use in second echelons as artilllery fire-support for assault tanks (Artilleriyskich Tank).

Experimental BT–3 variants. Two experimental special purpose tanks were developed on the BT–3 design: in 1937 a BT–3 was converted into a bridgelayer with a crude wooden bridge that was folded over the turret and manually lifted forward by the crew; secondly, a flame-throwing version was produced between 1937–40 which had the turret and armament of the OT–133 (T–26C light flame-throwing tank).

The early T–28 models. During 1932, in the Leningrad Kirov Plant, a prototype medium (sredni) tank was designed and became designated the T–28. This became the first

138

139

140

1

142

143

144

138. *BT–5 fast tank;* **139.** *BT–5(V). Commander's model of the BT–5;* **140.** *BT–3 bridge-laying tank;* **141.** *The first prototype of the T–28 tank with a 45 mm gun.*
142. *T–28 medium tank. The very first Soviet medium tank placed in production. Note that no radio equipment is fitted;* **143.** *T–28(V). Earliest commander's model of the T–28 medium tank. Note the frame aerial around the main turret;* **144.** *T–28A medium tank. Second production model of the T–28 tank (erroneously called T–28V by the Germans).*

...oviet medium tank to be adopted for service and it closely resembled the contemporary British A–6 and some of the German prototypes under development at Kazan. The T–28 was designed primarily to fill an urgent requirement from combined arms units. It was intended for breaking

through strongly fortified defensive positions. For this role it was required to possess a sufficient fire capability to enable it to engage targets on all sides during an assault. Its role was closely related to that envisaged at the time for the heavy tank, and this was reflected in its general construction. It was to be employed in tank brigades, assigned to support infantry formations, giving fire support from covered positions as a substitute for artillery; alternatively it could act ahead of infantry for breaking through enemy positions and destroying artillery. It is believed that a few of these tanks were tried out in Spain. The first prototype of this three-turreted tank, which was submitted for trials during 1932, was armed with a 45 mm gun in the main turret and two machine-guns mounted each in a subsidiary one-man turret with limited rotation at the front of the hull. It weighed 17·3 tons, had armour ranging in thickness from 20–30 mm, and a maximum speed of 37 mph. In the production version the armament consisted of a 76·2 mm gun (L/16.5) and 3–4 machine-guns located in three turrets. The 76·2 mm gun was located in the main turret together with one of the machine-guns, which was placed in a ball-mounting to the right of the main weapon. This main turret was set centrally, midway along the length of the vehicle, whilst one machine-gun was located in each turret forward of the main one, either side of the driver. The first model was designated T–28. The centre-of-gravity was well forward, facilitating the climbing of slopes and enabling it to cross a trench nine feet wide. The turret was provided with an all-round vision cupola for the commander, and the combined firepower from the three turrets could be brought to bear over a considerable frontal arc. The tank provided a stable firing platform compared with previous types, being noted for its smooth ride and good obstacle ability. The engine and transmission were placed in a compartment at the rear of the hull, separated from the fighting compartment by a fire-proof bulkhead—an arrangement which ensured a cooler atmosphere in the fighting compartment and increased the accessibility of the engine and transmission. Petrol was carried in two armoured compartments mounted one on each side above the tracks, minimizing the the fire risk. In adapting the M–17 engine for use in this tank the Russians encountered some difficulty for it required large radiators. The first model of the T–28 had the Vickers standard type of vertical-plunger suspension with 12 bogie rollers per side, and 5 upper track-support rollers covered by an armour skirting. The tank was gas-proof and commander's models were provided with radio equipment and smoke generators, the turrets on these tanks bearing the standard frame-type aerials. Some tanks of this type had a 45 mm gun in place of the machine-gun in the right-hand subsidiary turret. These subsidiary turrets were identical to those fitted to the T–37 light amphibious tank (with flush tops). The driver was provided with large, pyramidal head covers.

A second model of the T–28 appeared during 1933, designated T–28A (also referred to by the Germans as the T–28V). The suspension system employed on the original model had been found inadequate and so the Model A had 12 bogie rollers with 4 exposed track-support rollers per side, the method of springing being the same as before. The frontal armour on this model was slightly increased.

The BT–7. In the meantime, further development of the BT tank resulted from the introduction of a powerful modern engine with decreased fuel consumption, and led to the construction in 1935 of the BT–7 (the BT–6 never having passed the paper stage). It eventually became the most

numerous Soviet tank model, and was greatly favoured by the Soviet tank troops. The success of operations involving tank units (DD) equipped with BT–7s, during the battles with the Japanese in the Khalkhin-Gol area, and also during the entry of Soviet troops into Poland in 1939, was made possible mainly by the high mobility and reliability of these tanks. The BT–7 was powered by the new M-17T engine (originally designed for aircraft use and also employed in the T–28), developing 450 hp at 1,750 rpm. It was also provided with a new steering system, transmission and suspension. A new clutch and considerably stronger gear-box was designed in which the number of forward gears was reduced to three. The fuel capacity was increased to provide a greater operational range and a small-pitch track was fitted. The early production models (designated BT–7–1) had the old cylindrical turret of the BT–5 while at the same time commander's tanks (designated BT–7–IV) had the turret of the BT–5V with frame aerial and radio. Shortly after production was started, however, a new conical turret (similar to that used on the T–26S) was introduced giving improved immunity with armour increased to 15 mm. The hull front armour was increased from 13 to 22 mm, but the side armour was unaltered. The armour components of the hull and turret, formerly riveted, were now electro-welded, and this greatly increased the strength and immunity of the hull. The ammunition stowage for the 45 mm gun was increased and a coaxial mounting was installed for the 7·62 mm machine-gun. The BT–7–2 was the first of the series to have the twin-horn periscopes. Some vehicles were also fitted with an additional machine-gun in the rear of the turret (as with the T–26S) and a machine-gun for anti-aircraft defence.

A supporting artillery version of the BT–7 was produced mounting a 76·2 mm gun and taken into service as the BT–7A. This vehicle fired an AP projectile having a muzzle-velocity of 1,190 fps. A machine-gun was located in a ball mounting to the right of the gun.

Owing to the great increase in weight of the BT–7, wheeled travel and also the steering wheel were no longer employed.

The T–29 fast tank. Although the T–28 tank was fairly good for its time it did not develop a very high speed, and the tracks quickly wore out, greatly limiting the range of action. This prompted the design of a future medium tank provided with facilities for moving on both wheels and tracks like the contemporary BT. During 1934, at the design bureau of the Leningrad Factory, the first wheel/track variant of the T–28 was built and designated T–29–5. Taking part in the design of this model was a young engineer named M. I. Koshkin. Although the armour and armament of the T–29–5 did not differ radically from those of its predecessor, the T–28, the tank had a new chassis. In fact it resembled a T–28 mounted on the chassis of the BT–7M tank. All four pairs of wheels were driven by a special transmission which facilitated driving on roads by wheels as well as cross-country. A year later a further variant, the T–29 tank, was built which developed the same speed on wheels as on tracks. This was achieved thanks to the use of a special synchromesh transmission. Both these

145. *BT–7–1. Early production model of BT–7 fast tank with cylindrical turret (the photo of the vehicle on wheels has had the aerial removed);* **146.** *BT–7–1(V). Commander's model of early BT–7 tank;* **147.** *BT–7–2 fast tank. Most numerous Soviet tank of the thirties. Note the improved conical turret.*

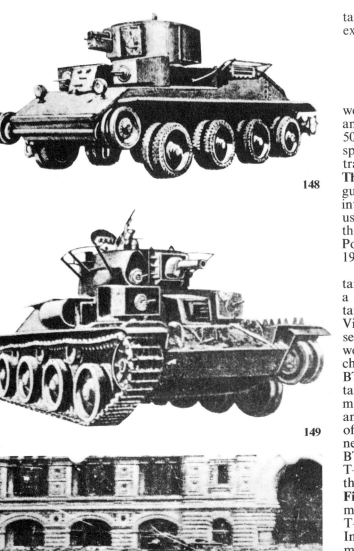

148

149

150

151

tanks, owing to their complicated design, were purely experimental Mostovenko wrote:

Taking into account the weight of the tank, the calibre of the armament and the speed on tracks, one cannot consider the production of the T–29 in 1936 as one of the major steps towards a new medium tank.[230]

The main characteristics of the T–29 were as follows: weight 28·5 tons; crew 5 to 6 men; armament 76·2 mm gun and 4 to 5 machine-guns; armour up to 40 mm; engine 500 hp petrol; power/weight ratio 17·6 hp/ton; maximum speed on roads 35 mph; range on wheels 220 miles; and on tracks 150 miles.

The BT tanks brought up to date—the BT–7M. During 1938 gun-laying in BT tanks was considerably improved with the introduction of a vertically stabilized sight, as well as the use of an electric fuze primer. The BT–7 tank was used in the Khalkin-Gol operations in Manchuria during 1938, in Poland during 1939, and finally against the Germans in 1941.

The success of tests with the V–2 tank engine in a BT–5 tank prompted the design and manufacture during 1939 of a number of production model BT–7M tanks—the first tanks with a satisfactory diesel engine, designed by Vickman and Tshupachin. These were distributed amongst service (DD) units. The BT–7M (also known as the BT–8) weighed 14·6 tons, mounted a 76·2 mm gun and had several changes in hull and turret arrangement from the preceding BT series; the glacis plate occupied the full width of the tank and was in the shape of an inverted 'V'. A hull machine-gun mounting was installed next to the driver, and ball-mounted machine-guns were located in each side of the turret, which itself mounted the 76·2 mm gun in a new rectangular mantlet—a departure from the original BT series and more closely resembling that fitted to the T–28 medium. It has been stated by the Germans that all the BT series had poor transmissions.

Final T–28 development. Between 1938 and 1939 a modernized version of the T–28 appeared, designated the T–28B (also referred to by the Germans as the T–28M). In this tank both subsidiary turrets were armed with machine-guns, and the driver was provided with a visor as opposed to head covers. The most important change was the provision of a more powerful 76·2 mm Model L/10 (L/26) gun. The gearbox in this vehicle incorporated a locking device which prevented accidental gear disengagement without prior operation by the clutch. The turret was provided with a suspended basket. The general arrangement of Model B was otherwise identical to that of the A, although some vehicles had an additional machine-gun in the rear of the main turret.

The war in Finland, however, showed the older T–28s to be unsatisfactory. After the battles in the Karelian Isthmus, during December 1939, the armour of the T–28 was modified, the thickness of the frontal armour on the hull and turret being increased from 50 to 80 mm and the sides and rear to 40 mm. This was achieved by 'screening' the tank (that is, by attaching additional armoured screens). As with the Model B, these tanks were equipped with the new 76·2 mm Model L–10 (L/26) tank gun. So modified, the new T–28C performed fairly successfully in breaking through

148. *T–29 medium wheel/track tank. Compare with the T–28;* **149.** *The T–29–5 wheel/track medium tank;* **150.** *BT–7M (BT–8) fast tank. Last production model of the BT series; powered by new diesel engine;* **151** *T–28B medium tank (referred to by the Germans as the T–28M).*

the Mannerheim Line during February 1940. They were
also used during the invasion of Poland in 1939, in the
Finnish War in 1939–40, and during the initial stages of
the war with Germany. The Germans in 1941 stated that
this tank had the same mechanical deficiencies as the
previous models—rough-running, and generally poor as
regards steering and transmission. All the later T–28 models
were equipped with radios and smoke generators.

A bridgelaying version of the T–28 was constructed and
supplied to Soviet engineer units in limited numbers,
designated IT–28. In this vehicle the main turret was
removed but the subsidiary turrets were retained; the
bridge was of a long rigid lattice type and was launched by
being pushed forward mechanically over the front of the
tank. During the motion of the tank, the bridge was held
in place by six steel struts, three on each side of the vehicle.
The Russians stated that this bridge could be laid and
retrieved from within the vehicle. The Germans reported
the existence of a flame-throwing version of the T–28,
designated OT–28, but this has not been confirmed. T–28
production ceased in 1940.

The 1940–41 Tank Programme—the BT–IS. In accordance
with the new specifications being compiled for the 1939–40
Tank Programme (see Chapter 1), a modified version of the
BT–7M model was produced during 1936, in an attempt to
meet some of the requirements. The new tank was designated the BT–IS and was built in prototype form only,
under the direction of engineer Tsigankov, and became the
first Russian tank to incorporate the familiar sloping
armour arrangement later employed on the T–34. This
tank was called 'Ispitatelniy' (Investigator). Mostovenko
wrote:

> In this vehicle the method was tested of making the
> armoured hull, in which all the armour components on
> the front, sides and rear were greatly inclined to increase
> the immunity. The turret was constructed on the same
> principle. . . .[231]

During wheeled operation with this tank, three pairs of
bogie wheels were driven.

T–111 (T–46–5). With the incorporation of several improved features of the BT–IS model, a further mock-up to
the new specification was made in March 1937 by Alexsandr
Morozov, in the form of the T–111 (T–46–5) tank. The
T–111 had a greatly increased armour basis (60 mm at the
front), designed to provide immunity to 37 mm AP projectiles at close ranges, and 76 mm armour-piercing projectiles
at ranges above 1,200–1,300 yards). This tank weighed
28 tons, was powered by a 300 hp diesel engine, and could
achieve a speed of 18 mph on tracks. The engine was
coupled to the driving portion of the suspension system at
several points for wheeled travel, whilst for tracked travel
the driving sprocket was at the front instead of aft as on the
BT series. The armament consisted of a 45 mm anti-tank
gun and two machine-guns (one coaxial with the main
armament and one in the rear of the turret), and the tank
was manned by a crew of 4. The T–111 was, in essence, an
attempt to adapt the Christie suspension to small-diameter
bogie wheels, the complicated suspension being arranged
inside the hull. Its suspension and its light armament let it
down, however, and it was rejected. Mostovenko wrote:

152

153

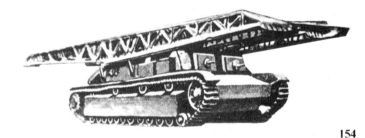

154

155

152. *T–28C medium tank. This is an early model without
armoured screens;* **153.** *T–28C later production model
with armoured screens. Note the variation in minor turret
mantlets;* **154.** *IT–28. Bridgelayer version of T–28 medium
tank;* **155.** *BT–IS fast tank.*

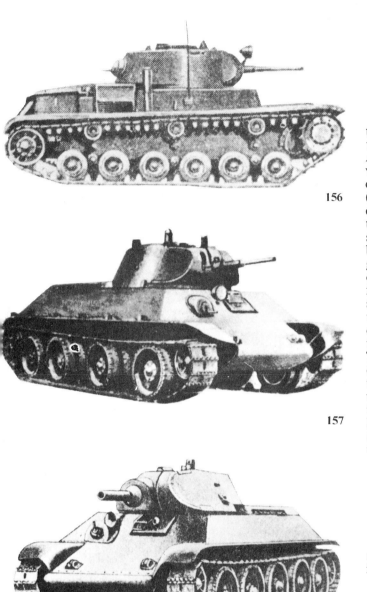

156

157

158

In comparison with previous tank models, the only basic change was in the armour. The significance of this tank in the history of Soviet tank design lay in that, during its manufacture, vital experience was gained in building tanks with shell-proof armour. In addition to good armour protection, however, it was necessary to increase the fire-power and improve the mobility. . . [232]

The new V–2 diesel engine, which had been mounted in the BT–7M tank, was selected to power future medium tanks.

A–20 and A–30. Towards the end of 1937 an improved version of the BT–IS built to a 20-ton specification was designed by a team under the direction of Mikhail Koshkin (including Morozov and Tarshinov, who designed the hull configuration). This new 18-ton tank retained the wheel/track characteristic and the Christie suspension of the BT series. The A–20, as it became known, was distinguished by its new turret of rolled armour plate, mounting a 45 mm gun, thicker, sloping hull armour, and also a new design of drive for moving on wheels. The armour (60 mm on the front and 25 mm on the turret and hull sides) was to the same specification as on the T–111, while the chassis basis was that of the BT–7M with the new 500-hp V–2 tank diesel engine. To cater for moving on wheels (at 50 mph) the rear three axles were driven in place of the normal BT system. The front axle was used to steer when on wheels and the clutch and brake method was used when on tracks (as in the earlier BT models). The A–20 was steered by a steering wheel. An attempt was made to up-armour, and up-gun this tank to 76·2 mm (L/30.5)—but this failed owing to a lack of turret space and the inability of the turret ring to absorb the recoil of this more powerful gun. This improved version was designated A–30. Mostovenko wrote:

In selecting, at this time, the conditions for alternative types of motion, the most suitable conditions for the tactical employment of tanks together with the unnecessary complications of combat vehicle design, were special points influencing the design of the new medium tanks. . . [233]

Koshkin (head of the Tank Design Bureau) and Morozov submitted a report to the Soviet High Command in which it was stated:

In view of the tactical reluctance to employ the BT tanks in the wheeled mode, added to the difficulties in technology associated with producing a tank which is able to travel on both wheels and tracks as required, it is suggested that future efforts should be directed towards the development of a less complex vehicle, running on tracks alone and employing the coil-spring (Christie) suspension of the BT series.

T–32. Following this, the High Command issued a specification for a new cruiser tank running on tracks alone early in 1939. No decision was made, however, to adopt this type of tank in preference to the original wheel/track type, at this stage. On their own initiative, therefore, Koshkin and Morozov undertook the design of a heavier purely tracked medium tank based on the A–30. Drawings of this new 19-ton tank, which became known as the T–32, were submitted at a conference on new medium tank designs during August 1938. The Defence Department (and Stalin, of course, who took an active interest in Soviet tank development) approved the proposed model, and requested

156. *T–46–5 (T–111) medium tank;* 157. *A–20 wheel/track tank;* 158. *T–32 medium tank. First stage of the T–34 series;* 159. *Rear view of the T–32 tank.*

159

the production and evaluation of a prototype as soon as possible. The T–32 was a fundamental development of the BT series with an entirely new hull shape, increased armour (ranging from 30 to 60 mm), and a new steering and transmission system. The new steering system was controlled by levers as opposed to a steering wheel. (The Russians had found earlier on the BT series that the steering wheel was by no means the best method of steering a tracked vehicle, but it was virtually impossible to steer a wheeled vehicle with steering levers.) The tank carried a 76·2 mm gun.

Both the A–30 and the T–32 were demonstrated to members of the tank design bureau during the summer of 1939. Both models were found to be mechanically reliable and proved themselves to be superior to any of the other models available. With the new requirements for armour protection arising from the analysis of the war in Spain, however, it was requested that the armour should be increased still further.

T–34/76A. During August 1939, after considering the various medium tanks with wheel/track drive, the Main Military Council accepted the design group's proposal to produce the medium tank as a pure tracked vehicle. This decision allowed the production of a less-complex medium tank, work being directed towards providing an improved tracked suspension specially for tank use. The T–32 was therefore returned to the drawing-board. Morozov and Koshkin synthesized the tank design experience of the thirties in the development of the new tank. Morozov headed the transmission group and Nikolai Kucherenko (a veteran of the old GUVP) designed the hull. Other members of the group included Baran and Spekher. It was realized that the new tank should have not only increased armour protection, but also more firepower and a more reliable transmission system. The new design was completed during December 1939 and became known as the T–34. (Its rival wheel/track design, the T–33, was rejected at the drawing-board stage.) On 19 December 1939 the drawings and models of the new T–34 were submitted to the High Command who accepted them for production, even before the prototype had been completed. Such a decision at this early stage probably resulted from the urgency of the situation developing in Europe at this time. With the apparent success of the first prototype, two further models were produced for military and engineering tests, and in February and March 1940 these tanks were driven on a long march from Kharkov to Moscow, then on to Smolensk and back to Kharkov.

Following the rectification of a few minor faults (mainly in the transmission) the tanks were fitted with the new 76·2 mm L/30.5 Model 1938 (L–11) tank guns and sent for firing trials at Minsk. These first two prototype T–34s were dispatched to Soviet forces in Finland during March 1940 for use against the Mannerheim Line, but by the time they arrived the Russo-Finnish War had terminated. Although the prototypes had been manufactured at the Kharkov Locomotive Works, mass-production of the T–34/76A tank was at first undertaken mainly at the new Kirov Tank Plant during May 1940, and the first T–34/76A left the production line in June. Up to December of that year 115 T–34s were produced, and by the following June, a further 1,110. Due to the rapidity with which the first T–34s were turned out and issued to units, it was not possible for some of the component plants to keep in line; a shortage of the new V–2 diesel engines necessitated the equipment of some early T–34s with the older M–17 gasoline engine of the BT–7 and T–28 tanks. A hasty demand for a large number

of transmission assemblies also produced serious repercussions—the earlier units were so unreliable that tanks went into battle with spare transmission units secured to the engine compartment deck by steel cables.

After their experiences with the older tanks in the 1939–40 war with Finland, the Soviet Army made great efforts to speed the production of the new T–34s. Together with the new KV heavy tank, its existence was kept an absolute secret from German Intelligence (even though it was exhibited to US photographers at the Stalin Tank School, near Moscow, during May 1941), and the German handbook and tank recognition material on the Red Army, published during 1941, contained nothing on these vehicles. When the heavy KV and the original T–34/76A tanks were encountered during the early battles in Easter Poland and Russia, the Germans were completely unprepared for them. The German High Command had to produce a quick supplement to their Soviet tank recognition manual, which even then confused the heavy KV with the more mobile T–34. The existence of these two tanks did much to influence Hitler's demand for the Tiger and Panther. (The 88 mm-gunned Tiger tanks first appeared on the Leningrad Front during November 1942.) The Soviets claim that during the winter of 1941 the German High Command 'raised the question of manufacturing the T–34 in Germany, but discarded the idea'. The T–34 first saw action in July 1941 and became the pride of the Soviet tank industry. (Since the Russians introduced no standard nomenclature for distinguishing the various models of T–34 tanks, the author utilizes the designation given to these models by British military intelligence during the Second World War.)

The first production model, the T–34/76A, was produced in late 1939/early 1940, and had a rolled-plate turret and short 76·2 mm L/30.3 Model 1938 tank gun, mounted in a distinctive, cast, contoured cradle welded to a flush external

160

mantlet. The first 115 produced had a ball-mounted DT machine-gun in the turret rear, but succeeding models dispensed with this weapon. Besides relying on its high speed and mobility to give it a measure of protection, the early T–34 had 45 mm armour on the nose and glacis plate, and 40 mm armour at the sides. Most of the turret armour was 45 mm thick. Though the slope of the armour surfaces helped considerably in giving additional protection, experience with German anti-tank guns soon caused the Russians to weld on small plates in waffle-like patterns. With their firepower, armour, speed and mobility, the T–34s made a great impression on the Germans; on encountering the US Sherman later in the war, they called it 'the T–34 of the West'.

Following the Soviet standardization practice, the T–34 and its companion vehicle, the early KV tank, had a great number of interchangeable parts, such as the engine, armament, transmission, periscopes and so on. In its design the Russians had aimed at mechanical simplicity, a large general purpose gun, good armour protection and above all, a design facilitating quantity production with limited resources in specialized machine-tools and skilled labour. As a result, certain features received less attention than they might have had in other European countries at that time. The tank was conventional in its design, having the engine and transmission at the rear, the driver and hull-gunner at the front, and the turret mounted centrally. All models had the same hull and suspension components, although the differences may be noted in the type of track and bogie wheels employed. Many tanks were fitted with steel-tyred bogie wheels due to the shortage of rubber early on in the war, but when rubber once more became available in 1943 a return to rubber-tyred bogie wheels was made. The turret on all models was very low, primarily to reduce the overall height of the tank—however, it is interesting to note that this feature restricted the depression of the main and auxiliary armament, especially when firing on a reverse slope or at ground troops on foot at close ranges (in spite of which the Russians have continued this design policy even in their current tanks). The hull was of welded construction throughout; all plates were well sloped to increase their immunity to armour-piercing rounds and with few exceptions, only three different thicknesses of rolled plate armour were employed. The fighting compartment had no turret basket and led directly into the driving compartment at any position of traverse. Only one bulkhead was fitted within the vehicle, separating the fighting and engine compartments. The glacis plate was free from apertures, apart

of the roller type used on the BT series, and drove a cast manganese-steel track with centre guide horns on alternative track links. An interesting feature was the method of retaining the track pins; welded to each side of the hull rear, level with the upper track, was a curved 'wiper' plate. The round-headed pins were inserted from the inner side of the track blocks, with no retention device at the outer end. As the tracks rotated, these pins were pushed in. This method facilitated quick removal and replacement of track blocks. Track guards covered the entire top of the suspension system and extended 10 inches beyond the hull at the front and 4 inches at the rear.

The engine, which was mounted at the rear, was the V-type 12 cylinder, water-cooled diesel, developed for the BT–7M, and producing 493 hp at 1,800 rpm. The main fuel tank was located in the hull, but auxiliary tanks could be carried, four cylindrical tanks on the sides and two smaller ones on the rear hull plate.

The T–34 was steered by the clutch and brake system and control gear. As mentioned previously, the power train in control gear. As mentioned perviously, the power train in general was troublesome. This first model of the T–34, the T–34/76A had a distinctive turret overhang. The turret hatch was clumsy –it occupied the entire rear part of the turret, making it heavy to lift and also blocking the view of the commander when open. Only one periscope was fitted on the turret, at the front on the left-hand side. The tank had a flat, linked-plate track. Some later models of the T–34/76A had the cast turret of the model B, but had the original A-type gun cradle and short 76·2 mm gun. These tanks were later provided with long 76·2 mm guns. Only one periscope was fitted, and none of the As had radio equipment.

With the death of Koshkin in September 1940, Morozov took over as chief designer of successive T–34 models.

161
162

160. *T–34/76A medium tank. First production model of the T–34 tank.* **161.** *T–34/76B. Second production T–34, welded turret;* **162.** *T–34/76B cast turret version.*

from the driver's and hull-gunner's hatches and the ball-mounted machine-gun, as were the side plates. The rear deck immediately behind the turret was slightly raised and accommodated a row of engine compartment grills and an engine access plate, with an exhaust pipe on either side.

The suspension was of the Christie type, having five large double road-wheels on each side, with a noticeably larger gap between the second and third wheels. The drive sprocket, located at the rear (to reduce vulnerability), was

During 1941 a small number of early T–34s were fitted with the 57 mm gun ZIS–4, a long-barrelled high-velocity weapon, which was intended for engaging light armoured vehicles (armoured cars, half-tracks and light tanks) at greater ranges than the 76·2 mm L–11 gun. It was shown by experience, however, that this weapon did not compensate for the reduced calibre and therefore further vehicles reverted to the 76·2 mm gun.

T–34/76B. The second model of the T–34 tank, designated T–34/76B, appeared in 1941 and was basically a commander's model A with a rolled plate turret mounting a more powerful Model 1940 76·2 mm L/41.5 gun. This turret had the same clumsy hatch as the A.

163. *T–34/76B (cast turret) hybrid gun cradle;* **164.** *T–34/76B (cast turret). Model A's gun mounting;* **165.** *T–34/76B (welded turret) with extra welded-on armour plates;* **166.** *T–34/76B (welded turret) with smoke-candle containers;* **167.** *T–34/76B ATO–41 flamethrower mounting;* **168.** *T–34/76C. Note the new driver's visor and ball MG mounting in the glacis plate;* **169.** *T–34/76B hybrid turret and gun cradle (compare with 163 above);* **170.** *T–34/76D. Medium tank. Note the new hexagonal turret and bulbous mantlet;* **171.** *T–34/76E. Note the new commander's cupola;* **172.** *T–34/76F. Final production model of the T–34 76 mm gun tank.*

Later models had the twin periscope arrangement on the turret front employed on the later BT models. Aerials on commander's tanks were located on the upper right-hand side of the hull at the front. Commanders' tanks were also provided with short-pitched, spudded tracks. There was no change in hull configuration, although Commanders' tanks had a stowage box on the right-hand track guard. The most significant alteration on model B was the replacement of the peculiar cast gun cradle by a new angular bolted type;

as with the original, this was asymmetrical from the front. The mantlet was no longer flush, and splash-lips were welded along each side.

During 1942 a model B appeared with a cast turret. The only noticeable difference from the original rolled type was the rounding-off of the front turret undercuts. This model was also provided with a new, wider track, and twin-horn periscopes on the turret roof at the front. Some of these tanks were provided with a flame-thrower ATO–41 and

169

170

171

had an armoured fuel container on the rear plate of the hull. A further model of the T–34/76B with cast turret has been identified, with a modified turret and gun cradle. The turret has straight undercuts at the front as opposed to the smooth, curved undercuts on standard models. Whereas the normal gun cradle has a characteristic change of angle when viewed from the side, the cradle on this model continues to a point. It is believed that hybrid productions such as this were manufactured by some of the subsidiary plants supported by donations from collective workers.

T–34/76C. An improved model B, having a new cast turret, appeared during 1942. The new turret weighed 4·32 tons and had a ring diameter of 4·6 feet; this model was designated T–34/76C. The tank incorporated several improvements: the large clumsy hatch was replaced by two separate ones—one each for commander and gunner—an improved

hull machine-gun mounting was installed, the driver was provided with twin episcopes in place of the single one on previous models, the right-hand periscope on the turret was removed, and improved, webbed and spudded tracks were provided. This model also had the glacis plate welded to the lower nose-plate—as opposed to the riveted type on earlier models; later production model Bs had this feature.

T–34M. During early 1942 a project was undertaken for a redesigned T–34, the T–34M, with a new chassis somewhat resembling that of the KV tank (i.e., smaller road wheels) and a completely redesigned hull and turret. This new tank was, however, not accepted for production. In the construction of an improved successor T–34 model only the hexagonal turret of the T–34M was retained since it was more convenient for mass-production. The new model became the T–34/76D.

T–34/76D. The Russians had a great deal of trouble with the Germans at close combat, where it was the accepted practice for German soldiers to climb on the back of T–34s, and wedge a Teller mine under the rear turret. The overhang created a shell trap, which is to say it deflected shells in this region to the turret ring. A remedy to this situation was demanded of Morozov, who introduced a new cast, hexagonal turret with no overhang for the model D, which appeared in the spring of 1942, and was primarily a commander's tank. It also incorporated improvements in other directions including the techniques of welding the armour plate components. Two of the most important features were the employment of cast bogie wheels, and the increased fuel capacity. The new turret had a modified gun cradle mounted in a flush mantlet which rode in a prominent bulge at the turret front. Only one periscope was mounted on the turret front, at the left-hand side. Otherwise the hull was identical to that of the T–34/76C.

T–34/76E. Further improvements in the design and production of the model D led to the production of the model E. In this tank, which appeared during early 1943, the commander was provided with a new cupola to improve observation. The turret and hull were otherwise very similar to the D. In the meantime, research had produced a more effective air-cleaner and lubrication system. In this model the construction of the hull was simplified further by the employment of automatic welding processes using improved welding materials which gave higher quality joins.

T–34/76F. The model F, which had a cast turret in final form, was introduced in 1943. The turret was a cast version of that on the model D, but with no commander's cupola, with contoured undercuts around all sides and the front giving it a distinctive appearance. This tank marked a sig-

172

nificant step in the development of the T–34, since it was the first model to possess highly efficient automotive components; the engineers responsible for its development—Morozov and Kucherenko—were awarded the Stalin Prize. The main clutch was improved and the 4-speed gearbox replaced by a new 5-speed type making it easier to change gear and increasing the average speed of the tank. The air-filter was further refined, and the general reliability of all mechanical components of the tank increased. A stronger track and new cast wheels made a noticeable improvement, particularly to the vehicle's speed (which had gradually been decreasing with each successive model owing to weight increases). These significant improvements in the reliability of the tank simultaneously decreased the difficulty of its manufacture. However, production of the model F was halted after only 100 vehicles.

In many tanks, pistol ports were abandoned and periscopes reduced to one, although the driver received double episcopes on the top side of his hatch in the glacis plate of model C. Some T–34s had extra armour, about 15 mm thick, welded on several places in waffle-like patterns; the same thickness of armour was also welded to the front and sides of the turret. The machine-gun ball-mounting in the glacis plate was redesigned in the model C and successive models, and armoured to prevent small-arms fire from damaging the ball.

T–43. During the winter of 1942–3 a new T–34 was produced with several modifications; primarily in the armour thickness: the turret, which was a hexagonal type remodelled from the commander's model D, was provided with an improved mantlet whilst the front and sides of the turret was increased to 90 mm; the glacis plate was increased to a thickness of 110 mm, and other parts of the hull to 75 mm. This tank, designated T–43, was also fitted with a new 5-speed gearbox. The engineers responsible for the improvements in this tank, Baranov and Shpayklerov, received a prize from the State. The principal deficiency of the T–43, however, was that, although in comparison with the earlier T–34 models it had increased armour protection, the armament remained unaltered. With the appearance of the German long-barrelled 75 mm (L/48) and 88 mm tank guns firing high-velocity projectiles it was considered insufficient to retain the 76·2 mm tank gun as the main armament for the new tank models.

T–34/85–I. A rapid means of providing the Army with a medium tank having more powerful armament was found by modernizing the T–34 to mount the new 85 mm tank gun, and this was accomplished towards the end of 1943. The new tank designed by Morozov and Krylov was designated the T–34/85–I. Essentially an up-gunned T–43, this tank utilized a turret originally designed for the KV–85 heavy tank with a ring diameter of 5·2 feet and which accommodated an extra crew member (thereby easing the work-load of the gunner and commander). Designed during the summer of 1943 the tank entered production during the winter of 1943–4, and was issued to elite Guards Armoured Divisions during the spring of 1944. The gun (85 mm M–1943), which was a tank adaptation of the prewar M–1939 85 mm AA gun, had an effective range of 1,000 metres and was claimed by the Russians to have been able to penetrate the 100 mm frontal armour of the German Tiger, as well as that of the Panther; the ballistic performance of the 85 mm Arrowhead round (AP), which the Russians introduced for this gun, may have enabled this (although it must be stated that this round was inaccurate and therefore penetrations could only have been achieved

173

174

at close ranges).

The early vehicles mounted the 85 mm gun D–5T designed by General F. F. Petrov. The later gun (also known as the ZIS–S–53) was designed by General Grabina.

The Russians claimed that the T–34/85 was superior to the Panther in mobility, reliability and speed; certainly the Russian tank had the edge in numbers—during 1944 production of T–34/85s was 2½ times that of the Panther. The increase in weight of the T–34/85 tended to impair its performance. Soviet tank historian Mostovenko, later wrote:

The basic combat characteristics of the T–34 medium tank proved themselves in battle. This factor allowed us to retain the tank in units throughout the course of the Great Patriotic War, during which the tank experienced modifications in armament and minor alterations in armour arrangement. During the War, the T–34s formed the basic mass of the Soviet tank armies. In general, the output of the Soviet tank industry over 1941–5 comprised about 68% T–34 medium tanks. The improvement in the armament of the T–34 by the introduction of the 85 mm gun removed the advantage of the German Panther tank in armament over the earlier T–34/76. In overall mobility, reliability, number of speeds, armour protection and general performance, the balance was consistently on the side of the Soviet tanks. In making our medium tanks and their improvements, the most outstanding creative contributions were introduced by the talented Soviet designers—M. I. Koshkin, A. A. Morozov, N. A. Kucherenko, A. I. Baran, M. I. Tarshinov, A. I. Shpaykhler, A. A. Maloshtanov, B. G. Matukhin and others. Chief Designer A. A. Morozov was awarded the title Hero of Soviet Science. . . .[234]

Up to the end of the War 39,698 T–34s of all types were

175

177

176

178

173. *T–43 medium tank. Heavier armour version of T–34/76E;* **174.** *Original T–34/85 medium tank, retro-fitted with KV–85 turret. Note the rounded-off turret front and bolted ring gun mount;* **175.** *T–34/85–I medium tank. Note the new mantlet and single mushroom shaped ventilator on the turret front roof;* **176.** *T–34/85–II medium tank. Note the absence of the front turret ventilator;* **177.** *T–34 elevatable bridgelayer;* **178.** *T–34 ARK type bridgelayer.*

built. An official report by the Aberdeen Proving Grounds, USA, on the T–34 tank gave the following conclusion:

In summing up, the T–34 tank appears to be a good design and proves adequate for mass-production and the employment of unskilled labour. . . . Outstanding features of the T–34 are: it is low, streamlined, powerful, of simple construction, possessing a small unit ground-pressure, and great angular inclination of the armour—providing excellent all-round protection; there is, how-ever, very limited room in the fighting compartment. . . .

Mostovenko also wrote:

During the course of the war, the medium tank became the basic armoured tracked combat vehicle. It was, there-fore, very important to choose correctly the basic combat characteristics of this type of tank, and the method of its construction, complying with the requirements of mass-production and the conditions of field maintenance. Throughout the War, the Soviet Army consistently armed with one basic type of tank—the famous T–34. The fact that this tank design remained virtually unchanged throughout the war, without losing superiority to the enemy, is significant proof of the ability and genius of Soviet tank designers and production engineers. . . [235]

Although Mostovenko's statement is undoubtedly not a little biased there is little disputing that the T–34 was the best tank in its class in the world at the start of its produc-tion, and the impression that it made was to influence greatly subsequent tank development throughout the world.

T–34/85–II. During 1947 an improved model of the T–34/85 tank was introduced, designated T–34/85–II. This was basically the same tank with improvements in trans-mission, armour arrangement, and more sophisticated fire-control and vision devices; it was used extensively during the Korean War. Some 85 mm guns in these tanks were fitted with muzzle-brakes during the Korean War. After the Korean War its value to the Russians was shown by the immense increases in numbers that followed, firstly in the Soviet Army, and later in the satellite armies. Production of the T–34/85 tank ceased in June 1964 by which time some 12,000 had been produced. (The production of all T–34 models up until 1945 totalled 40,000.)

Special purpose variants of the T–34. There have been several special purpose conversions of the T–34 tank and extensive use was made of turretless T–34 tanks for recovery pur-poses. Generally, the gap left by removing the turret was covered with a light armour plate which, in some cases, was supplemented by the addition of a commander's cupola from a T–34/85 tank. Certain chassis used in this role were equipped with a boom, permitting the use of the vehicle as a mobile crane for armoured workshops, in addition to its role as a straight towing vehicle. The weights of these vehicles varied, but generally they were in the region of 30 tons. Such ARVs were designated TT–34. In addition, ARVs were converted from SU–85, SU–100 and SU–122 gun motor carriages, which were themselves basically T–34 hull and chassis. In this case, the casemate turret was

179

180

181

182

retained and the aperture left by the mantlet was covered by armour plate. All vehicles of this type were provided with earth anchors, winches, and so on.

So far as is known, there have been three distinct versions of the T–34 in the bridgelaying role, all produced since the end of World War II. The first was an early Russian type with a rigid 'ARK' type bridge, the second a Russian model with a rigid bridge launched by pivoting about a roller at the front (designated T–34/MTU), and a more recent type, employed by the Czechs, which retained the turret (less armament) as a house for the bridge actuating motor. This latter type had a folding scissors-type bridge. The first Russian model consisted of a rigid bridge structure which was attached to the tank in such a way as to be able to adopt any required attitude. The bridge could not be removed from the tank and the idea was to drive the vehicle into the trench to be spanned, and to adjust the bridge until it coincided with the two peripheries of the trench (which were not necessarily in the same plane). The second Russian version had a bridge of about 39·5 feet in length, which could span some 37·5 feet, and carry loads of up to 40 tons; the bridge was of lattice steel construction and was launched forward by a single boom. The Czech scissors-type had a bridge some 65 feet long when fully extended, which was hydraulically operated and could carry up to 35 tons. Certain improvised wooden bridges were attached to T–34s during the war, and some T–34s were fitted with fascines and core matting to assist in crossing anti-tank ditches and trenches.

T–34s were also fitted with various mine-clearing equipments, as follows:

a. Mine rollers: there were basically two types; one had a single axle with 'A' shaped beaters attached to the rims of the discs while the other type had a split axle. T–34/85 tanks so equipped were designated T–34/PT–3s (PT standing for Protivotankoviy).

b. Snakes: the snake is a term generally applied to explosive line charges either pushed or projected across minefields and concrete obstacles. Types of both classification are known to have been fitted to the T–34/85 tank, although the Russians do not seem to favour this method in comparison with the mine roller device.

c. Tank dozers: most models of the T–34 were fitted with either a manually or hydraulically operated dozer blade for general engineer work in clearing mines, snow, earth, and so on. In such cases the turret and main armament are always retained. These tanks are designated T–34/STU.

Under the conditions of a large tank offensive against a heavily defended position established behind a minefield, it is thought that the Russians might well have driven a battalion or two of conventional gun tanks across the minefield. Although this sounds a brutal method of achieving an aim, it would most likely produce less casualties than conventional methods, and most certainly save a great deal of time—especially when one realizes that the minefield is probably the most effective deterrent to powerful armoured thrusts.

With the standardization of the T–34 and KV programme, flame-thrower installations were designed for both tanks, the T–34 being originally tried out with a type designated ATO–41. Further flame-thrower development was influenced by the policy of the US and British Armies,

179. *T–34/76F flail tank;* **180.** *T–34/85–II with mine rollers;* **181.** *T–34/76E–STU. Dozer tank;* **182.** *T–34/85–STU. Dozer tank.*

the former preferring the replacement of the main armament by the flame-gun, and the latter insisting upon the retention of the main armament at all costs; of the two, the Russians preferred the British method, although they were against the employment of towed fuel trailers. In 1943, under the Allied Aid Agreement, a unit of British flame-throwing tanks (Churchill Crocodiles) were shipped to Russia from the PWD (Petroleum Warfare Department) at Langhurst for training purposes. As the result of the experience gained from the PWD installation in the Churchill tank, the T-34 system was completely redesigned, and the flame-thrower redesignated ATO-42. Tanks so equipped became known as OT-34s (Ogniemetnyi Tank 34), and were first employed against the Germans in 1944. The OT-34 (ATO-42) carried 44 gallons of fuel (as against 22 in the ATO-41 model) and was operated by compressed-air; it could achieve a range of 82–98 yards with unthickened fuel, or up to 120 yards with thickened fuel, under ideal conditions. The flame-gun was mounted in an armoured casting to the right-hand side of the glacis plate with five degrees of traverse each side of centre. Operation was by electric pump and started by firing a 20 mm cartridge. Ignition was by sparking plug actuating a petrol jet. Six shots could be fired, each of two seconds duration, and the whole unit was self-contained within the tank. A few experimental models are believed to have been fitted with dual flame-guns mounted on the glacis plate—one on each side of the driver.

In its final stages of use by the Soviet Army, the T-34 was provided with facilities for deep wading. This equipment necessitated sealing the hull and turret components and providing a breathing tube for the engine and crew compartments.

When it was eventually phased out of service with front line units, the T-34 was supplied in large numbers to Soviet satellites and other Communist countries. Some were retained, however, and reworked into supporting vehicles (principally tracked prime-movers and recovery vehicles), and also for training purposes.

T-44. During 1944 a new medium tank was built based on the T-34/85 and designated T-44. Due to the pressure placed on its designers, this tank was not given time to mature and resulted from the initial stages as a clumsy failure, although technically it was a great step forward in respect of its low silhouette, powerful armament, strong armour and new transversely-mounted transmission system.

The T-44 was a 35-ton medium tank originally mounting an 85 mm gun. In early 1945 it saw limited action, and in 1946 production of the T-44 was undertaken in three major tank plants. Because of serious deficiencies, however, principally in the new suspension system, the T-44 was issued to service units in limited numbers only before production was halted in 1949. The T-44 has never been seen in use outside the Soviet Army; it was used by the Russians in limited numbers during the latter stages of the Second World War, and again during the Hungarian Revolution of 1956. It was believed to be still in use for training purposes as late as 1963.

The T-44 utilized the best combat-tested features of the T-34/85 tank; it was the first service tank produced by the Russians with a transversely mounted engine and torsion-

183. *T-34/76D OT-34 (ATO-42 flame-thrower);* **184.** *T-34/85-II with snorkel;* **185.** *T-44/85 medium tank;* **186.** *T-44/85 (modified). Note the slightly altered turret front.*

bar suspension. The hull differed from that of the T–34/85 in having vertical upper sides, and the 5-man crew employed in the T–34/85 were reduced to 4 in this tank by the elimination of the assistant driver/hull-gunner. The reduction of the crew to 4 men allowed more convenient stowage of ammunition, some of which was placed in the empty hull-gunner's station. Apart from the automotive components, the major improvement in the T–44 over its predecessor was the strengthening of the glacis plate by removing the driver's hatch, hull machine-gun mounting, and by up-armouring to 90 mm at 45° instead of 60° as on the T–34/85.

The turret was centrally mounted, and like that of the T–34/85, was hexagonal in shape, but larger and more heavily sloped at 10–20° from the vertical on the sides with the rear almost vertical. The turret had angular corners and was fitted with the standard T–34 85 mm gun. To the right of the commander's cupola was the loader's hatch, and there were two periscopes in the turret roof (one each for the commander and gunner). As on the T–34/85, the gun was mounted in a curved external mantlet and had a cylindrical steel sleeve.

The hull had vertical sides and was box-shaped, and its thickness was increased from 45 to 75 mm. It had a flat roof which joined at the front to a long, sloping glacis plate. The hull, which was similar to that later used on the T–54 tank, was of welded construction throughout. The only openings in the glacis plate were the driver's vision slit and a small aperture for the hull machine-gun; this box machine-gun was electrically-fired through a hole in the glacis plate like that of the T–54, and was internally mounted with the muzzle flush with the glacis plate. As distinct from the T–34/85, the driver's hatch was located in the hull roof and not the glacis plate, which strengthened the latter considerably and also reduced the work required for waterproofing the tank. Attached to the track guards were three rectangular stowage boxes, two on the right, and one on the left.

The suspension was a modified Christie (torsion bar) type, with 5 double road wheels on each side, the first being set forward of the remaining four which were equally-spaced. The rear drive sprocket was of the same type as used on the T–34.

Owing to the increased thickness, the armour was heavier than that used on the T–34/85 tank. The engine was the same V–2 12-cylinder, water-cooled diesel used in the T–34 series, developing 512 hp at 2,000 rpm. Mounting this transversely in the rear of the hull decreased the overall length of the tank and allowed the turret to be mounted further to the rear. A large exhaust pipe passed from the engine compartment to the left track guard.

Originally, the armament consisted of an 85 mm gun and two 7·62 mm machine-guns, this 85 mm gun being slightly longer than that fitted to the T–34/85. A few of the later T–44 tanks were provided with 100 mm guns. The only external difference with this gun was the absence of an external conical sleeve.

T–54/T–55. Finding the T–44 to be mechanically unreliable, the Russians developed a further cruiser tank based on the T–44 design but with an improved suspension and transmission. This new tank, designated T–54, was found to be altogether a much more reliable and effective tank. The prototype T–54 (produced in 1947) had an external mantlet and a similar angled, cast turret to the T–44. Immunity trials with early pilot models showed the external mantlet to be weak, and the undercut, sharply-angled turret created shell pockets which tended to deflect rounds to the turret

ring. As a result, a new turret was designed with the familiar carapace shape of the Iosef Stalin heavy tank, and released for use on production models of the T–54, which was placed in production during 1947–48, and appeared in Soviet units during the following year. Basically a redesign of the T–44, the general design features of the earlier tank were perfected in the T–54. It incorporated all the advances in design technique made as a result of the lessons learned from the T–34 and T–44 tanks, together with the latest technological advances of the time. The running gear was very similar to that of the T–44, but the hull and turret were designed from the experiences gained with the IS–III heavy tank. The 100 mm gun of the T–54 was mounted in a special turret and the resulting vehicle was found to be very satisfactory. Its first appearance in any sort of combat was during the Hungarian Uprising in 1956 when, together with the T–44, it entered Budapest. The T–54 dispensed with the long-pitched track and the method of driving the track through guide horns on alternate track blocks (which Christie had introduced in the twenties and which the Russians had adopted right up to the T–44).

The turret was a smooth, one-piece casting with an internal mantlet extending slightly beyond the hull sides. To the rear of the turret were the commander's cupola, loader's hatch, periscopes and ventilator, all of which were attached to two armour plates welded into the turret roof. The hull was very similar to that of the T–44 tank, being box-shaped and having a long, sloping glacis plate, and the sides were vertical with the rear plate slightly undercut. As with the T–44, the driver's hatch was attached to the left-hand side of the hull top plate at the front.

The suspension was of the torsion-bar type with 5 wheels on each side. There was a noticeably larger gap between the front and second road wheels. The rear drive sprocket had two rows of teeth which engaged track links bolted to both edges of the track blocks, and the track had a central guide-horn.

The engine was the same V–2 type as fitted in the T–44 (V–2–54), a V–12 water-cooled diesel developing 512 hp at 2,000 rpm. As with the T–44, the engine was mounted transversely in the rear of the hull.

The main armament consisted of the 100 mm D–10T modified tank gun with an internal mantlet, the gun trunnions being located further back from the mantlet than before. The telescopic sight was located to the left of the gun, and the coaxial machine-gun to the right, in front of the loader's seat. The commander was provided with a rotating cupola having three episcopes, with two additional periscopes in the roof. The aerial base and the telescope were attached just forward of this cupola. The loader's cupola, situated to the right of the commander's, mounted a 12·7 mm DShK anti-aircraft machine-gun. The driver and loader each had their own periscopes. A further 7·62 mm machine-gun was located next to the driver firing through the glacis plate (like the T–44). The hull glacis plate was bevelled at 30° whilst the sides were vertical, the hull being faired out over the tracks to accommodate the turret ring. There have been various models of the T–54 produced, all

187. *T–54 prototype. Note the sharply undercut turret rear;* 188. *T–54 medium tank (first production model);* 189. *T–54(M) medium tank. Reworked T–54 with IR equipment;* 190. *T–54A medium tank;* 191. *T–54A with training snorkel and periscope;* 192. *T–54A with snorkel attached to hull rear;* 193. *T–54A during snorkelling operations.*

187

188

189

190

191

192

193

differing in some basic modification.

The first model of the T–54 had a carapace turret with rear overhang, but this was later replaced by the conventional rounded T–54 turret with no overhang. It was provided with commander's and loader's cupolas and a 12·7 mm DshK anti-aircraft machine-gun. The turret had a ventilator dome but no fume-extractor, no stabilizer and no built-in snorkel equipment; only the driver was provided with infra-red equipment. At a later date, some of these early T–54s appear to have been fitted with infra-red equipment for the gunner and commander, and these were designated T–54(M).

The second production model of the T–54 appeared in Hungary during 1956. It basically resembled the original T–54 but was fitted with a fume-extractor on the gun and an elevation stabilizer. Some of these vehicles had snorkel

equipment and there were other internal changes including an increased fuel capacity. It is estimated that production began during 1954. The gun appears to be the 100 mm D–10S M–1944 from the SU–100 gun motor carriage redesignated D–10TG. The vehicle is also fitted with a 12·7 mm DShK anti-aircraft machine-gun. Some vehicles have been observed with a training snorkel and periscope. Some of these second production models have since been observed with commander's and gunner's infra-red equipment, designated T–54A(M).

The third production model had a bore-evacuator at the end of the gun barrel, a two-plane stabilizer, commander's and gunner's infra-red, and a raised cupola on the loader's hatch mounting a 12·7 mm DShK anti-aircraft machine-gun.

The fourth production model entered service during 1958 and was designated the T–54B: it was similar to the previous

194

197

195

198

196

199

model but was provided with full snorkel equipment which consisted of two pipes carried on the rear deck. When assembled they were mounted over the opening of the loader's periscope. Some of these vehicles were fitted with a training snorkel and periscope. Another important change was the installation of the D–10T2S gun, stabilized in both planes.

The fifth production model of the T–54 (also known as the T–55), entered service during 1958. It has a new and improved turret casting with no ventilator dome, and the loader's cupola and anti-aircraft machine-gun have been replaced by a flush hatch. This tank is fitted with an improved 100 mm D–10T2S gun with two-plane stabilizer and more stowed ammunition. It is believed that a turret basket has been added. The turret is fitted with gyroscopic controls, a built-in computer, and factory-fitted infra-red and snorkel

equipment. The tank also has a more powerful engine.

A re-worked second production model T–54 with flush hatch in place of loader's cupola appeared during 1961.

The final production model T–54 entered service during 1963. This tank has a fairing around the commander's hatch and the loader's and driver's hatches appear to be thicker. The hull machine-gun has also been removed.

Those tanks which were fitted with infra-red equipment usually had the following components: three infra-red lights, one being a 20 cm searchlight mounted on the cupola for

194. *T–54A(M) medium tank;* **195.** *T–54B medium tank;* **196.** *T–54(X) medium tank;* **197.** *T–55–I medium tank;* **198.** *T–55–II medium tank;* **199.** *PT–54 mine-clearing tank;* **200.** *T–54 BTU dozer tank;* **201, 202.** *T–54 MTU bridge-laying tank;* **203.** *T–54 experimental gun mounting.*

200

202

201

203

use by the tank commander (range 400 metres), secondly a 35 cm light mounted coaxially with the gun on the mantlet (range 800–1,000 metres), and finally, a smaller driving light was mounted on the left-hand side of the hull for driving at night.

Several special-purpose tanks are known to have been constructed on the T–54 series hull and chassis by the Russians; these are:

a. An anti-mine tank, similar to the type developed from the T–34; designated PT–54 (Prtivotankoviy–54).

b. A tankdozer, consisting of an hydraulically operated dozer blade attached to the glacis plate (sometimes fitted with a hedge-clearing device or plough); designated T–54 BTU.

c. A bridgelayer, consisting of a gutted T–54 with a

204, 205. *T–62 medium tank.*

$12 \times 3\frac{1}{2}$ metres long, rigid, lattice-type bridge which is winched forward over the front of the tank; designated T–54/MTU or MST–54 (Mostovy Tank).

d. Amphibious armoured recovery vehicles, of which two types are known.

It is likely that a flame-throwing version of the T–54/55 series has been produced, but no information has been released to date concerning the existence of such a vehicle.

T–62. Although the T–54/55 series forms the current Soviet medium tank strength (about 30,000 produced up to 1958), a further medium tank has been produced recently in the USSR designated T–62. It is believed that the T–62 is intended to support, rather than replace, the T–54/55 series. The T–62 entered production during late 1961 and was first shown publicly during 1964. This tank is basically similar to the T–54/55 series in size (the hull having been increased in length by 25 inches to cater for the larger ammunition, the turret ring moved 16 inches to the rear, the ground contact length increased to 13 feet and the hull widened by three inches) and weight, but has a new turret mounting a new high-velocity smooth-bore 115 mm anti-tank gun. The turret is almost circular and does not overlap the hull. The new gun is easily distinguished from its pre-decessor, since it is noticeably longer and has a cylindrical fume-extractor about one-third of the way down the barrel from the muzzle. The suspension is torsion-bar, but the space between the first and second bogie wheels—charac-teristic of the T–54/55 series—now appears between the third, fourth and fifth bogie wheels. The tank also appears to have improved armour arrangement, and a commander's cupola is fixed into the turret, set further to the rear than the loader's hatch. The tank has a more powerful 700 hp

diesel engine and has a single-unit hull. A biochemical protective device is provided. It is also factory equipped with snorkel and infra-red equipment.

Due to its recent appearance in the Soviet Army, little else is known about this tank—although it is most likely that the general mechanical arrangements are similar to those of the T–54/55 series. The 7·62 mm machine-guns may have been replaced by the new 14·5 mm tank machine-guns.

The future. That the medium tank has a future in the Soviet Army is indicated by an article which appeared in a 1967 edition of *Starshina Zhergeant*:

During World War II the Soviet Union held first place in tank construction . . . and does not intend to abdicate first place. . . .[236]

It could be that future developments of the Soviet medium tank class may continue for a long time based on the T–54/55 components. There might be improvements in armour type and arrangement, fire-control, armament, and vision devices, and also in the techniques of water-crossing and air-transportation. It may be also that gun-fired anti-tank missiles will be used in the place of, or at least as a supplement to, the conventional tank gun.

3 Heavy Tanks

Development before the Five-Year Plans. The development of Soviet heavy tanks began in 1929. As outlined in Part 1, the Russians originally envisaged the heavy tank in the role of a mobile fortress for independent operation, and consequently their early models were biased very strongly towards the provision of heavy armour and armament.

There was a great deal of misconception during the mid 1930s concerning the existence of certain Russian super-heavy tanks, particularly from German sources. It has been substantiated that a number of heavy tank projects were considered as design exercises, ranging in weight from 100 to 1,000 tons, but none of these vehicles was ever exploited. No doubt, such misconceptions arose from German relations with the Soviets at Kazan.

During the experimental period at Kazan a series of heavy tanks TG (Tank Grotte) were designed: the TG5/T–42 (see Chapter 1), the TG3/T–29 (a 30-ton model having a 76·2 mm gun, two 37 mm guns, numerous machine-guns and 35 mm armour), and the TG1/T–22 (a lighter 25-ton machine, having one 76·2 mm gun, two 7·62 mm machine-guns and 35 mm armour, later to be developed into the T–28 medium).

Following the TG series, further heavy tank projects were considered, including the TP, BS and S–II; no photographs or data concerning these vehicles have been made available.

T–32. The first Soviet heavy tank adopted by the Army was the T–32 (also referred to in military literature as the M–II), which appeared during 1930–31, and was based on the TG3/T–29 design mentioned earlier. The T–32 carried to the extreme the multi-turreted idea which had arisen in England and with which the Germans also experimented in

206. *T–32 heavy tank. Note the long gun and extended skirting plates, with rounded extremities. This model had 6 bogie wheels per side.*

prototype form about this time. The idea of heavily armoured tanks with multiple turrets was supposed to enable units to operate independently, and to make possible the engagement of targets in all directions simultaneously. Their great firepower and heavy armour would allow them to attack heavily defended positions, such as trenches and fortresses, accompanied by masses of infantry. The T–32 was based on the then current British A–1 'Independent' tank, and had five turrets: the main one carried the same armament as the T–28 medium tank (76·2 mm gun), two smaller ones, each mounted a 37 mm anti-tank gun, and the other two carried a machine-gun each. The 76·2 mm turret was mounted centrally, with the 37 mm turrets placed diagonally to the front and rear of it (at the front on the right-hand side, and at the rear on the left-hand side). Each machine-gun turret was placed next to a 37 mm turret, while the 37 mm turrets and the 76·2 mm turret were provided with subsidiary machine-guns.

The general interior arrangement of the tank was identical to the T–28 medium. The hull was of riveted and welded construction, and hermetically sealed against gas attack. The transmission system used was a hydraulic type and was not very satisfactory. The suspension consisted of six large wheels per side, combined in bogie units of two each; they were sprung by a scissors system using compression springs.

T–35. In 1933 a successor to the T–32 appeared which, like its predecessor, was created as a combat vehicle of 'extra-ordinary' capability for breaking through heavily-fortified lines. This tank had improvements in armour arrangement, suspension vision and transmission and weighed about 50 tons. Produced from 1933 to 1939 and designated the T–35, its main feature was the availability of numerous weapons, which were located in five turrets. The armament was of the same type and arrangement as on the T–32. The subsidiary 37 mm turrets were of the same type as used on the Soviet BT–2 tank, and the machine gun turrets were of the type used on the T–37 light tank. In addition, the tank carried five machine-guns. To employ this abundance of armament a large crew was required—consisting of ten men! The ammunition stowage was sufficient, consisting of 96 76·2 mm, 220 37 mm, and 10,000 rounds for the machine-guns. The armour was bullet-proof. The suspension was protected by additional (screened) 10 mm plates. The tank was powered by a 500 hp M–17 engine, driving through a mechanical gearbox with 4 forward and 1 reverse gears. The suspension consisted of units of two bogies each and the bogie wheels were fitted with external rubber tyres. The tank was also provided with radio equipment and had a frame aerial around the main turret. Mostovenko wrote:

> Apart from its weak armour and large dimensions, the T–35 had an unsatisfactory steering system. Between 20 and 30 of these tanks were produced. Some tanks took part during the initial stages of the Second World War. . . [237]

During 1935 a modification of the T–35 was carried out. The suspension was improved and the 37 mm guns were replaced by 45 mm guns. Experiences in exercises and combats in Finland necessitated further alterations: some tanks had the two smaller machine-gun turrets removed and others were reported having only the main, and front subsidiary turrets mounting a 45 mm gun and a machine-gun. The final production models used during the Finnish War were welded throughout.

A flame-throwing version of the T–35 was produced with the flame-gun mounted in the front machine-gun turret; this turret was similar to that fitted to the OT–26 (T–26A light flame-throwing tank). The only T–35 tanks encountered by the Germans were at Lvov in Poland where they had run out of fuel. The T–35 proved itself to be poor both technically and tactically. When deployed, T–35s were allocated to the RGK (Supreme Command Reserve).

During 1938 a group of engineers selected from the Kirov-Zavod tank plant at Leningrad, were placed under the direction of Kotin and Dukhov, and were ordered by Stalin to develop a new multi-turreted heavy tank to replace the T–35 series. Mostovenko wrote:

> The characteristic design features incorporated in Russian medium and heavy tanks (T–28 and T–35) at that time, appeared to be the use of several turrets for mounting the armament, which were manned by numerous troops. The increases in hull and turret armour for such tanks with large dimensions would be great. In

207

208

207. *T–35 heavy tank. First observed model. Note the cylindrical turret with overhang and the extended skirting armour. This model has wireless fitted;* **208.** *T–35 second observed model. Note the new turret with separately-mounted 7·62 mm machine-gun;* **209, 210.** *T–35—second*

209

210

production model; **211.** *T–35 third observed model. Note the new sloping sided turret with welded armour and modified track and suspension skirts;* **212.** *T–100 heavy tank;* **213.** *SMK (Sergius Mironovitch Kirov) heavy tank;* **214.** *KV–1 heavy tank.*

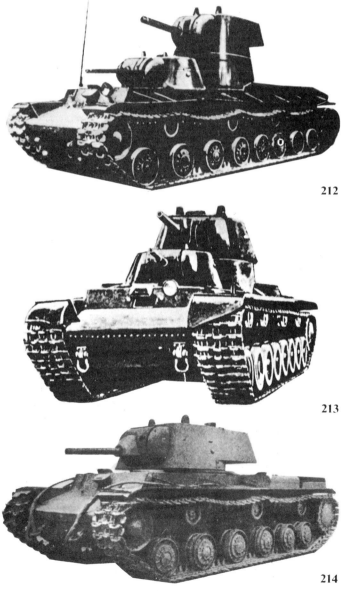

212

213

214

changing-over to shell-proof armour the retention of several turrets would excessively increase the weight of the tank.[238]

The 1940–41 Tank Programme—birth of the KV. During 1938 a new heavy tank specification was laid down, and a heavy tank project was put forward by the group under Kotin. Two models were originally suggested, each having three turrets. Kotin took drawings of these tanks to Stalin, who was intensely interested, but suggested that one of the turrets should be removed and the saving in weight be used to increase the armour basis. Mostovenko wrote:

Two heavy tanks were designed with shell-proof armour during 1938, initially intended to have three turrets; during the course of design work the number of turrets was reduced to two. The retention of several turrets was influenced by the old methods of design approach to heavy tanks, as well as to other fighting vehicles having several guns; this seemed justifiable in the case of heavy tanks with bullet-proof armour, but considerably increased the weight when employing shell-proof armour.[239]

T–100/SMK. Kotin revisited the Kremlin and showed Stalin further drawings of three new heavy tank projects; these included two twin-turreted concepts and one single-turreted concept. Stalin was most impressed by the designs, particularly the single-turreted model, and requested that prototypes of all three should be constructed as soon as possible. Kotin undertook the construction of the two twin-turreted models, at the same time continuing design of the single-turreted tank. The twin-turreted tanks so produced were designated T–100 and SMK (Sergius Mironovitch Kirov) respectively, and were almost identical in appearance. Both had an upper central turret mounting a 76·2 mm gun, with all round traverse, and a lower, front turret mounting a 45 mm gun, with 180° traverse. The chassis utilized a new torsion-bar suspension, with eight independently-sprung, small-diameter bogie wheels on each side (with resilient, rubber-bushed hubs). The upper track was supported by four track-return rollers on each side. A new, very wide, cast track was used with heavily-spudded, small-pitch links. The tanks had crews of 6–7 men and weighed 56 and 45 tons respectively. Both tanks were powered by 400 hp petrol engines. The armour, which was cast on both hulls and turrets, was designed to provide immunity to 37 mm AP shot at all ranges, and was up to 60 mm thick. Results from the combats in Finland, however, where small quantities of these tanks were used (hence the erroneous designation of T–35C adopted by the Germans), showed that the designs were not what was required in this tank class.

KV–I. The problem was to increase armour and firepower without increasing the weight which would reduce mobility. Thus, in the process of work on designing a heavy tank, the group of engineers (headed by Kotin) at Kirov came to the conclusion that a heavy tank with shell-proof armour should have only one turret and be armed with one very powerful gun. After completion of the single-turreted model, Kotin revisited the Kremlin where his heavy tank design was selected and renamed the KV (Klementy Voroshilov). Stalin approved the design except for the armoured skirting proposed for protecting the suspension; the Soviet tank designers wanted to retain this feature, but Stalin was emphatic and his will prevailed. A new form of torsion-bar suspension was developed for this vehicle. In September 1939 Kotin completed the prototype of the new KV, which Stalin accepted for production before the new suspension had been fully developed. Before large-scale production was undertaken, a limited number of these experimental heavy tanks were successfully employed along the Soviet-Finnish Front during December 1939. Production started in the same month at the Kirov tank plant, and the KV entered service proper during 1940. Mostovenko wrote:

Further design work was directed towards producing single-turreted tanks mounting only one gun. This was an important step in determining a new way of designing medium and heavy tanks, and facilitating the production of tanks with shell-proof armour—not yet undertaken abroad. A saving in weight was achieved by the reduction in the number of turrets and in the internal volume of the tank by employing a small crew. This provided the necessary conditions for increasing the armour thickness without increasing the weight of heavy and medium tanks, in comparison with the T–28 and T–35.[240]

KV–II. An artillery version of the KV, designated KV–II (also known as 'KV with big turret') was produced but was not tactically successful. Very early production models mounted a 122 mm howitzer, but later this was replaced by a 152 mm howitzer.

The KV–1 (which initially became referred to as 'KV with small turret') took over the roles of both the T–28 medium and the T–35 heavy tanks. The Russians considered it to be the best tank in its class in the world at that time. This

first model, the KV–I, was manufactured during late 1939 and early 1940 at the Kirov factory in Leningrad, and carried armour on the hull and superstructure up to 75 mm thick. The turret was also on a 75 mm basis, but used heavier armour on the mantlet and turret front. This massive armour was designed to provide immunity to artillery and anti-tank rounds up to 76 mm calibre at all ranges. The hull was welded, which greatly simplified manufacture. The armament on this first model consisted of a 76·2 mm M–1938/39 L/30.5 tank gun, the same as that used on the early T–34 medium tank. The KV inherited the steel-tyred resilient bogie wheels and wide tracks as developed for the SMK and T–100 tanks, but had improved independent torsion-bar suspension. It also used an early version of the same 500 hp model V–2, V–12 diesel engine as used in the T–34 tank, which enabled it to move extremely fast, in spite of its excessive weight.

Together with the KV–II the KV–I was successfully used during the breakthrough of the Mannerheim Line and as expected, the 75 mm armour reliably protected the tank from 37 mm anti-tank rounds. During 1940 243 KVs were built, and a further 393 during the first half of 1941. Both the KV–I and the KV–II were considered powerful breakthrough tanks. In 1941 the situation necessitated a bias towards the KV–I, and shortly after the beginning of the war production of the KV–II stopped.

The KV–I was originally employed for the assault of fortified positions, and proved quite effective against the Germans during the early campaigns—although there were insufficient numbers to cause any great effect. The original KV–I had an angular turret of rolled plate with a pronounced rear overhang; this was suited to production in

215. *KV–IA heavy tank (note the new gun mounting);*
216. *KV–IB (bolted turret) heavy tank;* **217.** *KV–IB (cast turret) heavy tank;* **218.** *KV–IC heavy tank;* **219.** *KV–Is heavy tank;* **220.** *KV–85 heavy tank.*

215

217

216

218

the older plants, and was eventually produced simultaneously with cast turrets. Mostovenko wrote:

At that time it was rather a complex task to make 7-ton turrets with a 100–120 mm thick armour retaining high immunity. But this problem was successfully solved and as a result manufacture of turrets never limited tank output during the war.[241]

In addition to the 76·2 mm gun, the KV mounted three machine-guns, one to the right of the main armament, one in the right front of the hull, and one in the turret rear. The turret had two episcopes at the rear (one on each side), one for the driver, two gunners' periscopes, and a vision slit with a pistol port on both sides and in the rear of the turret. The general interior arrangement of the hull was practically identical to the T–34 in order to reduce problems in maintenance and resupply. The creation of the KV–I determined the future development of the heavy tank by virtue of its unique combination of powerful armament and heavy armour.

KV–IA. During 1940 an improved model of the KV–I appeared, designated KV–IA (German Intelligence designation—the Russians adopted no standardization of their own), and was provided with a gun of higher velocity (76·2 mm L/41.5 Model 40), firing a longer round. The tank also had new bogie wheels. The KV–IA was initially intended as a commander's tank, but later other KV models received this more-powerful gun as it became available.

KV–IB. The significant effect of German anti-tank guns at close range during the early campaigns of 1941, forced the Russians to up-armour the KV tank. Extra 25–35 mm plates were welded to the glacis plate and the driver's plate, and plates 35 mm thick were bolted to parts of the side

219

220

superstructure armour and the sides of the turret. The frontal armour was likewise increased. This up-armoured version was designated KV–IB (bolted turret). Production of the KV–IB was undertaken just after the outbreak of the war with Germany, and resulted from a demand by Stalin to increase the armour on the KV. Stalin had asked for double the thickness without a decrease in combat efficiency. The experts opposed this suggestion, but were as usual, overruled. The manner in which the extra armour was attached, suggested that the original armour structure was weakened rather than improved. Before the Germans even attacked, the Russians had been dissatisfied with the angularity and weakness of the crude KV–IA turret, and consequently KVs with cast turrets were integrated with KV–IAs during early 1942. These tanks were designated KV–IB (cast turret). As with the T–34 model D, the turret overhang was eliminated to deter shells and explosives from wrenching off the turret.

KV–IC. With the apparent success of the cast turret on the KV–IB (cast turret) a further model of the KV was produced in early 1942 with the turret armour increased to 120 mm; this model was designated KV–IC. The KV–IC employed the same 76·2 mm L/41.5 Model 40 tank gun as the KV–IA. The armour casting of the turret not only had improved ballistic properties, but also strengthened the turret base. The frontal armour on the KV–IC was similar to that of the KV–IB, although the armour on the hull sides was increased to 90 mm with an extra thickness of 40 mm added on parts, giving a total of 130 mm. The KV–IC was, all-round, a more efficient tank than the KV–IB. Although the weight had increased to 47 tons, its new 28-inch wide tracks gave it a good ground-pressure of 10·4 lb per sq in. The V–2 engine was up-rated to 600 hp and gave the vehicle a speed of 18 mph.

KV–Is. As a result of combat experience it was considered necessary to increase the overall mobility of the heavy tank and also remove several design faults. Modernization of the KV–I heavy tank was carried out during the second half of 1942. Stalin instructed Kotin to design a revised version, which became known (by the Russians) as the KV–Is (where 's' stood for skorostnoy—fast). It was appreciated in the specification of the KV–Is that since it was impossible to provide it with full immunity, no matter what was sacrificed, it would be better to smooth out the radical difference in performance and mobility from the T–34 with which it was required to operate. In order to increase its speed, the tank's weight was reduced to 42·5 tons by employing less armour thickness (the armour on this tank was reduced from 75 to 60 mm) and by reducing the overall dimensions of the hull. It was further modified with a newly-designed gearbox and main clutch, together with improvements in the engine cooling and lubrication systems; these design innovations increased the tank's speed to 25 mph. To improve observation, a commander's cupola was introduced. Only a few models of this tank were produced during the period from August 1942 to June 1943.

KV–85. During the summer of 1943 the KV–1 was fitted with a new cast turret having improved ballistic shape and mounting a more powerful 85 mm gun. Mostovenko wrote:

Owing to improvements in armour, during the Kursk Battle we were able to employ tank units in conjunction with powerful Soviet Army self-propelled artillery mountings to destroy German armour. However, the Kursk Battle confirmed the necessity of providing the heavy tank with more powerful armament and tougher armour on the KV–Is. During the Autumn of 1943, therefore, the heavy tank KV–85 appeared on the Polish Battle Front. . . .[242]

The modified hull of the KV–Is mounted a new turret with stronger armour. Various technological improvements enabled the crew of this vehicle (and all subsequent Soviet heavy tanks) to be cut down to 4 men (commander, gunner, driver and loader). The KV–85, as it later became known, was basically a re-armed and returreted KV tank, designed to take the M–1943 tank version of the M–1939 85 mm anti-aircraft gun. The turret was provided with a commander's cupola, bringing the overall height of the tank to over nine feet. The turret had a curved mantlet with a circular hole for the gun, while the armour on the hull was slightly reduced to counterbalance the increased turret weight (60–65 mm), and the tank was mass-produced

221

during the autumn of 1943. The new turret design was later used for the T–43/85 medium tank—although in this case the rear machine-gun mounting was removed. KV–ICs were also retro-fitted with the new turret, and both models of the new KV–85 entered service in time to encounter the German Tiger I. After only limited production, the KV–85 tank was taken out of service in the winter of 1943.

KV–IIA. As previously mentioned, an artillery tank version of the KV was produced. The KV–IIA (German designation), appeared during January to February 1940 and mounted a 152 mm M–1938/40 L/20 howitzer in a high, box turret with all-round traverse, upon the KV–I hull. This vehicle was found to be operationally ineffective due to the inability to traverse the turret when on an incline, to provide anti-tank fire and to fire on the move. It was usually fired from stationary and concealed positions. Even so, development of this model continued. Garret Underhill wrote:

> The 12-ton turret caused an excessively high silhouette of 13·7 feet, as against 8·75 feet for the KV–I. It brought the weight up from 48 to over 57 tons. The projectiles were those of the corps artillery 152 mm howitzers and gun-howitzers, but the ammunition could be loaded fixed. Two men (for a total of 6) were added to the crew to handle them. The gun had low velocity compared to the M–1937 corps gun of the same calibre, but the Soviets said that the KV–2 proved quite successful against the Mannerheim Line, against which it fired concrete piercing shells. Since the KVs were produced at the large Kirov plant in Leningrad and were coming out in the latter part of 1939, the 2s were ready for use in the late February of 1940 Steamroller that terminated the winter war. If the KV–2s were a success in positional warfare

assaults, they were a notorious failure in the mobile campaigns fought against the Germans in the summer of 1941. KV–2s were in action as early as the third day of the German attack (June 29th) at Soposkinie in Poland. The KV–2s disappeared after the first summer of the German attack; they were never reported in action again. . . .[243]

KV–IIB. During 1940 Kotin produced a second model, the KV–IIB which had a new turret and wider tracks, being based on the newer KV–IB chassis. This model was taken into service, but showed little improvement (if any) over the first version. The most significant external difference was the asymmetric mantlet. A flame-throwing version of the KV–IIB was produced in limited numbers.

Experimental KV developments. During 1943 Kotin pro-

222

221. *KV–IIA heavy tank (note the assymetric gun cradle);* 222. *KV–IIB heavy tank;* 223. *KV–II–1. Experimental 85 mm gun version of KV–II;* 224. *IS–I (IS–85) heavy tank with 85 mm gun;* 225. *IS–I (IS–122) heavy tank with 122 mm gun.*

duced two experimental KV–II variations: the KV–II–1 with the 85 mm anti-tank gun of the KV–85, and the KV–II–2 with the new 122 mm anti-tank gun. Even these models of the KV–II failed to meet the requirement of tank, assault gun or self-propelled artillery; no further development of the KV–II is known to have taken place.

A flame-throwing version of the KV–IC was produced, designated the KV–8. This was almost identical to the KV–IC but had a 45 mm gun and flame-thrower in the turret in place of the normal armament.

The third generation of heavy tanks—birth of the Stalin. The development of the heavy tank had now reached the stage where its size necessitated more powerful armament than that used on the medium tank, and its speed should be improved. Further, the appearance of new enemy 75 and 88 mm self-propelled artillery mountings presented armour which the KV–Is could not penetrate, and a larger gun was required. Expecting Germany to continue the construction of heavy tanks and gun motor carriages, the gun versus armour race began, and the Commissariat for Tank Industry was ordered to undertake a new heavy tank project with increased firepower and immunity.

IS–I. Towards the end of 1943, 21 different prototypes of tanks and self-propelled gun mountings were built, six of which were passed for quantity production (the two experimental KV variants mentioned above being included in the total). Among these was the heavy tank IS (Iosef Stalin), designed by Kotin, which was a thoroughly revised KV–85. This tank had an 85 mm gun in a new cast turret and a modified suspension and engine, and became known as the IS–I (IS–85). The tank weighed 44 tons and had a similar turret to the KV–85. The transmission in the tank was improved, a two-stage planetry mechanism for turning being introduced. Manoeuvrability was greatly increased and the average speed rose by 25 per cent compared with the old KV. The KV chassis were reworked into SUs, ARVs and artillery tractors. This IS–I was issued to the Army during 1943, but its production was restricted to a small quantity during the period from the end of 1943 to the beginning of 1944. An up-gunned version appeared during late 1943, called IS–I (IS–100) mounting a new 100 mm tank gun. This tank was also rejected and in mid-

223

224

225

1944 the IS–I tank was given a new turret with a powerful 122 mm gun (adapted from the corps artillery gun), and was designated the IS–I (IS–122). Mostovenko wrote:

Even though the 85 mm tank gun was not inferior to the current German 88 mm gun, the 122 mm gun provided the IS tank with a superiority in fire power over all other types of heavy tank likely to be used by the enemy. It was true, however, that the change-over to the 122 mm gun brought about a considerable reduction in ammunition stowage and in rate of fire. Further, design improvements providing a more compact arrangement of components allowed an increase in armour thickness without exceeding the weight of the original KV–I, in spite of the significantly more powerful armament. In all, the increase in general fighting ability of the IS tank provided the possibility of defeating enemy tanks at greater ranges, of providing stronger armour protection, and an increase in general mobility and performance.[244]

Based on a modified KV chassis, engine and transmission, the IS tank represented a considerable advance from the KV. The driving sprockets, idlers and return rollers were lowered to enable the space between the top of the track and the hull roof to be used for panniers, thereby making possible the provision of a larger turret ring. The hull nose was made in a single casting, and the upper and lower tail plates were made from single plates, each sloped at approximately 45°. Previous tanks of this type had the armour at the front of the driver made of a flat, slanted plate running from side to side, but on this tank a shaped casting was used instead. This casting was faired away on each side of the driver, who was located on the centre-line. The armour casting around the driver sloped upwards as well, so that the frontal portion of the superstructure had a streamlined, rather than box-like form. In consequence, the superstructure did not attain its fullest width until a point approximately opposite the centre of the turret. Soviet designers also parted from original KV tank design by providing a rear hull plate which had acquired the upward and forward slope once peculiar to the T–34 medium tank. This plate incorporated two transmission servicing hatches. The KV suspension was used together with the standard Model V–2 12-cylinder diesel engine. The tank mounted the 122 mm A/Tk gun D–25 model 1943, together with a coaxially mounted standard 7·62 mm Degtyarev air-cooled machine-gun. The 122 mm gun was a comparatively long one with a German-type double-baffle muzzle-brake. The 122 mm of the Stalin with semi-fixed ammunition was less easy to handle and yet not as powerful as the 100 mm. A bracket was provided at the hull rear for retaining the gun during travel. Another 7·62 mm machine-gun was ball-mounted in the rear of the turret, and a third was in the bow to the extreme right of the driver. A further machine-gun could be mounted on the turret for anti-aircraft use.

The driver was provided with three episcopes; there was another to the right of the main armament, and one in the commander's cupola on the left of the turret. In place of the pair of gunner's periscopes usually fitted to the right and left of the turret on Soviet tanks, there was only one, on the left. A vision slit with pistol port below was found on each side of the turret, and also in the rear.

During 1943 102 of the IS–I (IS–122) tanks were produced at the evacuated Kirov plant. This tank was issued to units in late 1943 and appeared in action in early 1944. It was first used in the spring 1944 campaigns which cleared the Germans from the Ukraine and from part of Poland, and later in the drives from the Baltic States. Garrett

226

227

228

229

230

Underhill wrote:

The IS tank took over both the heavy-tank break-through role against fortified positions, as well as the over-watching fire and anti-tank missions of the SUs. However the Stalins were pooled in with divisions where they were needed, and the SUs remained the organic light assault artillery of the mobile divisions—the Tank Corps and the Moto-Mechanized Corps. They were faster, more mobile than the heavier Stalins. . . .[245]

The Germans felt that the Stalin tank gained 50 per cent increased immunity over the KV through its shape alone.

IS–II. In 1944, Kotin undertook a complete redesign of the hull of the Stalin tank, resulting in a vehicle with less weight and increased performance. This new model was designated IS–II (IS–122), and 2,250 of these tanks were

226. *IS–II (IS–122) heavy tank. Note the improved glacis plate and shaped cast hull;* **227, 228.** *IS–III (IS–122) heavy tank 'Pike';* **229.** *T–10 'Lenin' heavy tank;* **230.** *T–10M heavy tank.*

produced by the end of 1944. The new model had a modified glacis plate, entailing the replacement of the stepped glacis plate by a flat, sloping type, faired at the sides into the superstructure side plates. This change necessitated a redesign of the driver's vision arrangements. The driver's visor on the IS–I (IS–122) was replaced by a vision slit and glass block mounted in a bulge on the glacis plate. Otherwise the tank was identical to its predecessor. Mostovenko wrote:

Employed on the front during 1944, the IS–2 heavy

tank quickly won esteem for its high combat reputation. Experience in combat provided a basis for its modernization which was carried out at the end of 1944. The basic alteration was in the armour arrangement. The armour was designed from experience gained during the development of the T–34 medium—allowing the new tank to have large angular inclination, contoured or shaped armoured castings and a new streamlined turret—revolutionary feature of IS–3 the final Soviet heavy tank development of the war. . . [246]

IS–III. Towards the end of 1944, Kotin designed the IS–III tank mounting the 122 mm L/43 tank gun in conjunction with Shashmurin and Rybin as co-designers. The IS–III was an excellent tank, but was not supplied to Soviet tank troops until January 1945 and therefore not in time to take part in the war. The IS–III retained all the advantages of the earlier IS models but had greater armour, a new glacis plate of characteristic shape, and a new mushroom-carapace shaped turret. The glacis plate was free from openings and the driver sat with his head right under the turret, on a seat that could be raised or lowered. The driver's periscope was in the hatch cover. The new glacis plate was comprised of two plates welded together so as to form a roof with the apex traversing the centre-line of the tank; this latter feature gave exceedingly good ballistic properties. It was because of this pointed nose that Soviet tank troops called the IS–III the 'Pike'. As necessitated by Soviet military policy, handles were welded around the turret for use by tank-borne (Tank Descent) infantry.

The IS–III was provided with smoke generators which were mounted in the upper tail plate, and fired electrically. Experiments were carried out with snorkelling IS–IIIs, but no such modification was standardized. Mostovenko wrote:

The development of heavy tanks over 1941–45 was characterized by the qualitative improvement of fire power and armour protection. The 1941–45 period saw the steady growth in armour thickness increasing the immunity of the hull and turret. Even though the old KV provided immunity to 37–50 mm shot, the armour of the later tanks provided immunity to 75–88 mm shot. In combat potential, the last model Soviet heavy tank was the most successful by comparison with heavy tanks of other nations which appeared during 1943–45.

Soviet designers composing the Heavy Tank Construction Corps were under the direction of Hero of Soviet Industry, winner of the Stalin Prize, Z. A. Kotin. They designed, elaborated and improved tanks in conjunction with: winner of Stalin Prize N. L. Dukhov, A. S. Ermolaev, L. S. Troanov, L. E. Sichev, N. F. Shashmurin, A. I. Blagonravov and others.[247]

IS–IV. Following the war in Korea, the Soviet Army requested that the IS–III tank be brought to a more modern state, especially since the T–44 medium had not turned out as expected. The result was to provide armoured skirts for the suspension, a fume-extractor midway along the gun barrel, and a few interior modifications. This improved model was designated IS–IV, and weighed slightly more than the original IS–III. It was provided with a more powerful engine developing 690 hp, which allowed the addition of thicker armour on the hull sides. The heavier armour necessitated the use of stronger torsion bars and buffers in the suspension system.

When production of the IS and KV series was eventually discontinued, the hulls were employed for special purpose vehicles such as ARVs and mine-clearing tanks; some IS and KV chassis were used for the basis of self-propelled artillery mountings and ballistic missile carriers. A snake was produced for IS tanks.

T–10. In 1953 a new heavy tank entered production and became known as the T–10, or Lenin Tank. The T–10 was designed by Kotin and represented a redesign of the IS–IV. The T–10 is generally similar to the latter, but with the following alterations: essentially a lengthened IS chassis with an additional bogie on each side, the frontal armour is angled to give an equivalent of 150 mm at 60°, the 122 mm L/45 gun has a travelling stablizer, the ammunition stowage has been increased from 28 to 50 rounds and a fording plate is fitted across the glacis plate. As with the IS–IV, the turret is dome-shaped, and located forward on the hull. There are two equal-sided circular hatches fitted well to the rear on the turret roof, and raised slightly above its general level. A small round ventilator, is located centrally on the turret roof and forward of the hatches. The suspension is torsion-bar with seven double road wheels, three return rollers, and a rear sprocket drive. Provision is made for protecting the suspension with skirting armour. The engine, mounted at the rear, is the same 690 hp V-type twelve-cylinder diesel as used in the IS–IV. A departure from the IS series is the glacis plate, which has a central V with horizontally-extended arms to the track guards.

T–10M. One modification of the T–10 is known to have been produced during 1957, and was designated the T–10M. The T–10M differs from the T–10 in the following respects: the inverted 'V' glacis plate extends to the full width of the vehicle, there is a different location in the mantlet for the gun sight and IR equipment, (for commander and gunner), the stowage box on the rear of the turret, and finally 12·7 mm machine-guns have been replaced by the new 14·5 mm type. In addition the ventilator on the turret roof has been eliminated, and the gun (which is fully stabilized) has been fitted with a five-baffle muzzle-brake (as opposed to two on the T–10). The T–10M appeared in service in 1957.

Rumours have been reported concerning the existence of a T–14 heavy tank, based on the T–10 design, but mounting a 130 mm gun; however, no official confirmation has been given concerning such a vehicle, and it is unlikely that the Soviets will develop any further heavy tank replacement for the T–10.

4 Self-Propelled Weapons

Before the Revolution. Although the self-propelled weapon often approaches the configuration of a tank or armoured car, there is a distinct difference between these types of fighting vehicles. Apart from the obvious distinction of the tank and armoured car being used by the cavalry or infantry, and the self-propelled weapon by the artillery, the vehicle in the latter case is designed primarily to facilitate the mobility of a particular weapon. The tank, on the other hand constitutes a balance between the three prime factors of armour protection, firepower and mobility. This classification has been fairly universal, and the Russians are no exception to the rule.

With the appearance and rapid development of combat aviation, a general requirement arose for anti-aircraft mountings. In the year preceding World War I the Putilov Firm undertook the development of a self-propelled 76 mm anti-aircraft gun mounted on a Russo-Baltic truck chassis and during 1914 this vehicle entered production at the Putilov Plant.

On 7 January 1916, a General N. M. Filatov filed a report on his 'Gun armoured car'. In this report, General Filatov stressed the necessity of producing a semi-open gun mounting on a partially armoured car.

Also in 1916, under the direction of General Filatov, several other self-propelled guns were designed and built; among these were two 3 inch (76·2 mm) assault gun mountings, on three and four wheeled automobile chassis. The construction of these vehicles was carried out at the Officer Range School, and they were tested at Oranienbaume (now Lomonosov) on 13 October 1916. An interesting feature of their design was the use of a folding trail-spade for absorbing the powerful recoil of the gun. The adoption of these weapons was approved by the Commission conducting the trials and later Filatov also began building a similar mounting for a 42 Line (4·2 in) gun, on an armoured car chassis with four-wheel drive. Mostovenko wrote:

> The absence of a suitable tracked chassis necessitated the use of automobile chassis in modified form for these self-propelled guns. Naturally, wheeled running gear was not capable of providing the high mobility required.[248]

Soviet developments. Early Soviet development in the field of self-propelled weapons was orientated around the requirements for providing fire-support to infantry and tank units. Up until 1930 the virtual non-existence of any suitable tracked chassis necessitated the adoption of existing wheeled vehicles for this role. Although no tracked self-propelled gun was standardized before 1935, several experimental models were produced and evaluated. The most significant of these was built in 1923, when Karatieyev designed the first Soviet tracked gun motor carriage (for the 37 mm gun). This was, however, found unsuitable for use by the Army.

SPs in the thirties. The new improved industrial situation resulting from the execution of the First and Second Five Year Plans facilitated the production of more satisfactory vehicles of this type. With the foundation of the 1931-2 Tank Programme, provisions were made for five main classes of self-propelled weapons:

1. Those for the direct support of armoured units (providing mobility for the 76·2 mm gun and the 122 mm and 152 mm howitzers). These were required to be mounted on tracked chassis and partially protected by ‚armour plate.

2. Those for supporting tanks in the offensive; these were to be designated AT (Artilleryskiy tanks) and to be identical to conventional infantry and cavalry tanks, but mounting 76·2 mm guns in place of the original armament.

These were to be based primarily on the chassis and components of the T–26 and BT tanks.

3. Those for supporting infantry in the offensive. To be similar to the AT tanks, but to mount infantry howitzers and/or machine-guns.

4. Those for replacing the non-mechanized elements of the Artillery Arm.

5. Those for providing defence against aircraft attack.

The new self-propelled guns were designated SU and SAU (Samakhodnaya Artilleryskaya Ustanovka—Self-propelled mountings).

During 1931 work was immediately undertaken on vehicles for fulfilling these requirements. In this year the SU–2, a self-propelled 76 mm artillery mounting, was built on the chassis of the Kommunar tractor, and a new series of 'tank fighters', were produced on the T–27 tankette chassis, mounting 37 mm guns.

In 1932 Chlistov was appointed head of a team of Soviet engineers commissioned to adapt standard tank designs to the task of fulfilling the self-propelled gun roles. For the direct support of armoured units, the 152 mm gun/howitzer was mounted on a T–28 medium tank chassis modified for this purpose. The group also produced a 76 mm anti-aircraft mounting on a T–26 light tank and a

231. *SU–7 experimental 203 mm Self-Propelled Howitzer;*
232. *76·2 mm field howitzer mounting on GAZ-AAA truck.*

231

232

T–28 medium tank chassis.

Towards the end of 1933 an engineer named Tolotskov proposed a project for a 152 mm self-propelled coast-defence mounting, based on a special armoured tracked chassis, a modified T–28 tank weighing 20 tons. The advantage of this mounting was its ability to rotate through 360.° When deployed, the tank hull could be lowered to the ground and the tracks raised; a special plate was attached to the hull floor enabling the whole vehicle to rotate at a speed of 10° per second, the power for this operation being provided by the tank engine. When completed the vehicle had a crew of 6 men, was powered by a 400 hp engine and could reach a speed of 15 mph. The armour varied from 20 mm on the front to 8 mm on the sides.

In 1933 work was undertaken on the SU–7, weighing 106 tons and mounting a 203 mm gun/howitzer or a 305 mm howitzer in an interchangeable mounting. This vehicle could move at 18 mph and to stop it from running amuck during recoil it was provided with two telescopic supports.

For cavalry and reconnaissance units a specification was laid down for a light self-propelled mounting 'type K'. A prototype of this vehicle was built based on the T–37 light tank chassis. The gun was fitted with an experimental automatic loading device.

An artillery tank version of the T–26, designated AT–1 was also commenced during 1933, and was equipped with the 76·2 mm tank gun PS–3 firing the 76·2 mm round of the Model 1920/1930 gun. The gun was mounted on a reinforced and slightly modified T–26 light tank chassis, a design which facilitated increased observation by allowing the rear and side walls of the crew compartment to unfold. (In 1938 work on the AT–1 was suspended due to the Army decision to adopt the BT–7A as the standard 76·2 mm artillery tank.)

Truck-mounted weapons. While experiments continued with prototype tracked mountings, the Army was provided with various forms of weapons mounted on truck chassis; these were produced in fairly large quantities. Guns ranging in calibre from 37 to 152 mm were mounted on the rear of truck chassis and were provided with armoured shields to protect the crews from light fire. These improvised carriages were principally used for the support of cavalry and infantry units, as well as providing defence against low-flying aircraft. The old ZIS–6 truck became the prime-mover for most of these mountings. Two types of AA mounting were developed: on the GAZ–AA for infantry and motorized units there was a twin 25 mm machine-gun mounting, and for the other arms a single 76·2 mm AA mounting on the ZIS–6. This latter vehicle had folding sides, jacks for stabilizing the vehicle, and a crew compartment at the extreme rear of the chassis. For anti-tank support, a 76 mm gun with a large armoured shield, providing 270° field of fire, was mounted on the rear of open-body ZIS–6 trucks. For infantry support, both the 76 mm M–1927 and 152 mm infantry guns were mounted on ZIS–6 and GAZ–AA trucks. A prewar Soviet Moto-Mechanized Corps usually included a battalion of 12 of the 76s in each of their two mechanized brigades. The 76 mm gun fired a 13·6 lb shell to a maximum range of 9,350 yards.

During 1934 research was undertaken into a further self-propelled tracked mounting, which became designated the SU–5. From the start, this vehicle was designed to support tank and cavalry detachments, and was based on the T–26 light tank chassis and automotive components. On this chassis it was planned to mount three different weapons: the 76 mm divisional gun M–1902/30 (SU–5–1), the 122 mm

233

235

234

236

divisional howitzer M–1910/30 (SU–5–2), and the 152 mm divisional gun/howitzer Model 1931 (SU–5–3).

During 1935 experiments were carried out with three armoured mountings based on the T–27 tankette chassis and components. These vehicles, which mounted the 76 mm regimental gun Model 1927 were designed for direct infantry support.

In 1935, the armoured mountings SU–6 and SU–8 were built. The SU–6 was based on the T–28 medium tank with several modifications, the main and auxiliary turrets being removed, and a new armoured superstructure attached in their place. Two machine-guns were mounted in the superstructure and a revolving platform was provided for the 152 mm gun/howitzer. An armoured shield was also fitted around the driving and crew compartments. When completed, the SU–6 weighed 17·6 tons and had a crew of 6 men. The gun could traverse through 60° each side of the centre, and elevate from 0° to 72.° About 47 rounds of 152 mm ammunition were carried, and the vehicle could attain a speed of 28 mph. The 76 mm gun motor carriage SU–8, also based on the T–28 medium tank chassis, weighed 19 tons. In this vehicle (which became known as the 'Discoverer') the gun was unprotected, and was mounted on a central pedestal, allowing it to be traversed through 360.° This gun could be elevated from −5° to +86.° To facilitate firing broadside, the chassis was provided with folding supports which braced against the ground during firing (primarily to reduce the recoil and to prevent the vehicle from overturning), and with these supports extended, the vehicle increased in width to 15 ft. In travelling order the vehicle could move at 28 mph. A further 76·2 mm gun carriage for supporting armoured units, was built on the chassis of the T–26 light tank and weighed 11·3 tons. Initially, it was found that this

light tank could not take the recoil of the 76·2 mm and the chassis was therefore provided with 4 telescopic supports which could be unfolded from the vehicle.

In 1935 a new 203 mm project was commenced. This armoured mounting, designated SU–14, mounted the 203 mm M–1931 gun and was based on the chassis and components of the T–28 and T–35 heavy tanks. In order to provide a steady firing platform, the vehicle was provided with trail-spades, which were unfolded from the vehicle either by hand or by electric motor. The vehicle could travel at 20 mph and weighed 40 tons. The armour plating separating the engine and crew compartments was 20 mm thick, that on the hull and superstructure fronts 20 mm thick, and on the sides and rear 10 mm thick. A further model of the SU–14 was produced mounting a 152 mm Model 1935 Naval gun B–10, designated SU–14–1 (also referred to as the SU–BU–10). Firing trials were carried out with this equipment near Kiev during June 1936, where it was established that the rate of fire (one shot in 5–7 minutes) was too slow. The Russians failed to construct a suitable loading mechanism to overcome this fault and this, together with the difficulties in stowing sufficient shells in the vehicle, prompted the decision to terminate the project.

In 1936 chemical battalions were equipped with 6-wheeled vehicles with heavy flame-throwers; no reports of their use in action have been published, however.

Developments 1936–40. The majority of self-propelled guns built before 1936 were experimental types produced in small quantities only. Work on a more satisfactory mounting continued over the following four years, in parallel with the production of new tank models. During this period the Soviets concentrated mainly on medium and large-calibre

237

238

239

gun mountings.

In 1939 the Soviets undertook a project for a new anti-tank mounting utilizing the 85 mm anti-aircraft gun Model 1939. The long recoil travel of this gun necessitated an increase in the dimensions of the basic vehicle, and as a result the project was discontinued. In the meantime, therefore, the 85 mm gun was mounted on the old ZIS–6 truck in a similar fashion to the earlier 76·2 mm anti-aircraft mounting. In this form it was to be used in both anti-tank and anti-aircraft roles. In the same year a mounting was designed on the basis of the SU–14–1, designated SU–14–Br.2. This vehicle, when built, had a separate armoured fighting compartment holding 6 men, as well as the driver, who seated himself at the front of the vehicle. This vehicle weighed 65 tons and could move at 18 mph, the armour being up to 50 mm thick on the front. The vehicle mounted the 152 mm gun/howitzer Model 1935 (Br.2) which was distinguished for its firepower (with a muzzle-velocity of 2,900 fps), firing a 49 kg shell. It was intended for destroying bunkers and strong fortifications.

With the introduction of the new T–100/SMK heavy tanks, the Russians used their chassis as the basis of the SU–100Y gun motor carriage. This vehicle was armed with a 130 mm Br.3 gun having a muzzle-velocity of 2,900 fps, and it weighed 60 tons. It was manned by a crew of 6 and had armour up to 60 mm thick on the front. The engine was a 500 hp diesel giving the vehicle a maximum speed of 28 mph. Small quantities of the vehicle were manufactured during 1939 and supplied to the Army.

During the initial stages of the war, self-propelled guns were not very widely used by the Russians, but the successful use of SU–14–Br.2s and SU–100Ys during the 1941 campaign, encouraged the decision to continue manufac-

233. *SU–5–1 76·2 mm gun motor carriage based on T–26 light tank;* **234.** *SU–14 152 mm Self-Propelled Howitzer;* **235.** *SU–14–Br. 2 152 mm Self-Propelled Howitzer;* **236.** *SU–100Y Self-Propelled 130 mm gun;* **237.** *Quad 7·62 mm Maxim AAMG mounting on GAZ-AAA;* **238.** *SU–45 45 mm A/Tk mounting based on Komsomolets tractor;* **239.** *SU–57 57 mm A/Tk mounting based on Komsomolets tractor.*

turing hybrid conversions of tank, tractor and armoured car chassis. In 1941 an AA armoured car was produced on the basis of the 6-wheeled BA–32 which mounted a 37 mm gun and three machine-guns. The Russians also mounted quadruple 7·62 mm Maxims on ZIS–6 and GAZ–AA lorries and various tracked prime-movers.

Two conversions of the Komsomolets armoured tractor were produced in quantity by the Russians during 1940–41; a 45 mm mounting designated SU–45 (which was used against the Finns at Viipuri when they retook the Karelian Isthmus), and a 57 mm mounting designated SU–57 (which was employed against the Germans in their drive to Stalingrad and the Caucusus in mid 1942). The 45 mm version consisted of the basic Komsomolets hull and chassis with an armoured box-like superstructure built-up from the hull. The 45 mm gun was mounted in a limited traverse mantlet at the front of this superstructure. The 57 mm mounting was open, with the M–1941 gun on a central pedestal attached to the floor of the rear fighting compartment. A light gun shield was fitted to the gun which could be traversed through 360°.

Rockets. In parallel with the development of gun mountings, during the early 1930s the Gas Dynamic Laboratory at Leningrad developed models of various rocket projectiles as weapons for aircraft and rocket anti-tank guns. The development of rockets was directed by an Army engineer named Petropavlovsky, who was an expert in this field, but his death in 1935 prevented him from completing many of his projects. However, the work inspired by him was successfully continued by his associates and including a team led by Andre Kostikov which developed the famous Katyusha rocket launcher. On 15 July 1941 the first battery of Katyushas (called 'Kostikov's Gun') were employed against the Germans. No American or British observer was allowed to see it in action, even after some models had fallen into German hands. It was one of the Red Army's closest-guarded secrets; whenever these were transported about a heavy tarpaulin covered the working mechanism and the Russians stated that Katyushas were fired only by NKVD or police troops.

Owing to the concentration of Soviet industry on the production of tanks, it was found difficult during the first phase of the war to undertake the production of tracked self-propelled mountings on a large scale. The earlier lorry-mounted weapons, both guns and rocket launchers, filled the requirements of the artillery and infantry arms. Between 1941 and 1942 three basic self-propelled artillery rocket launchers were introduced: the 36-rail 8 cm rocket launcher M–8 mounted on the ZIS–6 truck; the 16-rail rocket launcher M–13 (Katyusha) also mounted on the ZIS–6 truck and the T–70 and T–60 light tanks; and finally the 12-rail 300 mm rocket launcher M–31 mounted on the GAZ–AA truck. Throughout the war, the Soviets employed solid fuel rockets on a larger scale than any other Army. Originally Soviet rocket launchers were all of the multi-round, short range type, employed in area saturation fire. The majority of these launchers were mounted on trucks, and this opened a whole new chapter in Soviet self-propelled artillery development.

War requirements. Further development of the self- propelled weapon demonstrated the necessity to adopt suitable mountings for supporting tanks in the attack. Technically, the SU-type offered (at the expense of traverse) the possibility of mounting more powerful weapons on a given chassis than in a turreted version. By late 1942 the requirements for tank chassis by the cavalry, infantry and reconnaissance units were being satisfactorily fulfilled and it became possible to undertake the production of self-propelled artillery mountings based on standard tank chassis. The Russians classified SPs into 3 categories according to weight: light (up to 20 tons), medium (up to 40 tons), and heavy (over 40 tons). It was not until 23 October 1942 that the Chief Defence Commissariat issued specifications for the design and construction of self-propelled mountings utilizing, as closely as possible, components of tanks already in production. Since the Army found the light tank to be ineffective in the combat conditions of that time, it was decided to turn the light tank facilities over to the production of self-propelled artillery.

The contemporary light tank, the T–70, was therefore used as the basis for a 76·2 mm A/Tk mounting, the SU–76. The vehicle consisted of the 76·2 mm divisional gun M–1942/43 Model ZIS–3 L/42 mounted on a lengthened and modified T–70 light tank chassis. The driver, engine and fuel tanks were all moved to the front, so that the gun crew could stand on the floor of the hull rear and this arrangement kept the silhouette down to little more than that of the T–70 tank. The overall length was increased by an extra bogie being added to the running gear. The gun was served by a crew of 2, the gunner being to the left (in normal field artillery position). Here he was provided with a field artillery style on-carriage fire control, Schneider 1917 range-quadrant and mount graduated for various projectile types as well as in in metres, and a sight for the panoramic telescope, the head of which protruded above the compartment armour. The section commander also acted as the SU commander standing at the right, where he was provided with a standard tank-type episcope for observing targets and fire, being also provided with a vision port in the frontal armour. The gunner had his own episcope.

Several modifications in the armoured superstructure have been observed, but generally it was rectangular in shape, open at the top and situated at the rear of the chassis. In an early version the rear had two folding plates of armour, which provided both access and protection. On this version the radiator was located over the track on the right centre side (instead of to the right rear, as on later models). The sides and front sloped inwards, towards the roof. The rear of the superstructure and hull were of single-piece construction and incorporated a large door for access by the crew. The recoil mechanism for the 76 mm gun extended beyond the mantlet and was protected by an oval-shaped armour cover. The hull was box-shaped, constructed of armour plate, with a sloping front plate, undercut rear plate, vertical sides and flat roof. A rectangular driver's hatch was located centrally in the front plate, just below the edge of the hull roof. Stowage boxes were mounted on the rear of the left trackguard and along the right side of the hull and an air intake and an exhaust muffler were located on the right side towards the rear. The suspension, engine, transmission and other automotive components were as for the original T–70 light tank. The armour ranged from 25 mm on the hull to 10 mm on the floor. The newer vehicles were propelled by two 6-cylinder GAZ–203, in-line, air-cooled petrol engines, developing a combined output of 138 hp at 3,400 rpm. They were tandem-mounted in the right-hand side of the chassis. The SU–76 had a front drive sprocket.

The 76 mm gun, which was provided with a double-baffle muzzle-brake, fired ammunition at the rate of 20 rounds a minute. It could fire a $13\frac{1}{2}$ lb shell to a range of 12,250 yards. In order to properly engage contemporary German armour, the SU–76 had to use the high-velocity arrowhead shot, which meant engaging at relatively short ranges (550–440 yards).

SU–76s were produced by the Uralmashzavod combine under the direction of Silnishchikov and Gorlick. Production began in December 1942. Some models had a 7·62 mm machine-gun mounted near the top of the superstructure, either at the right or left rear. The SU–76M used the GAZ–203 85 hp engine instead of the older GAZ–202 type.

Originally developed for a tank destroyer role, the SU–76 was soon relegated to an infantry support role, largely through its lack of immunity to enemy fire, and also because of the rapid increase in German armour thickness. When phased out of service the SU–76 chassis were used as ARVs.

In parallel with the development of the SU–76, the construction group produced a prototype 122 mm howitzer carriage based on the T–34 tank, which was designated the SU–122. In 1942 Stalin ordered the mass-production of this vehicle, and by January 1943 they were formed into the first regiment of self-propelled artillery. The SU–122 consisted of the Model 1938 122 mm field-artillery howitzer mounted on the chassis of the T–34 tank. It was designed to provide artillery fire support to tank divisions and had little effect against armoured vehicles; it was withdrawn in the autumn of 1943. The gun was mounted in a fixed super-structure, the hull, running gear and automotive components being identical to the T–34/76 Model C tank, the superstructure was rectangular in shape, fully enclosed, and located forward of the chassis. It was constructed of rolled armour plate with welded seams. Handrails on both sides of the hull were for use by infantry. The armour was well arranged and heavily sloped so that good protection was afforded. The vehicle commander was situated in the left front corner and was provided with a periscope and radio. The howitzer was laid by a panoramic telescope. SU–122s were organized in platoons of 3 SUs each.

In early 1943, the Chelyabinsk construction group under Kotin built a prototype heavy 152 mm gun motor carriage,

designated SU–152, which was designed and built within 25 days. The SU–152 mounted the Model 1937 152 mm corps gun/howitzer of the KV–II tank on the KV–IS tank chassis; it entered mass-production during February 1943 and first saw action at Kursk in the same year. The new vehicles began to enter Soviet units during the spring of 1943. The SU–152 became the only standardized self-propelled mounting based on the KV chassis until 1944, when the SU–122 was built. The gun had a muzzle velocity

240. 36 × 80 mm M–8 rocket-launcher on ZIS–6; 241. 16 × 130 mm M–13 rocket-launcher on ZIS–6; 242. Second observed model of the SU–76 gun motor carriage. Note the slightly cut-away compartment rear; 243. SU–122 122 mm howitzer motor carriage based on the T–34; 244. SU–152. 152 mm howitzer motor carriage based on the KV tank.

240

243

241

242

244

of 1,900 fps and a range of 19,000 yards. A direct-laying telescope was fitted left of the gun above the recoil mechanism housing. Traverse was about 10°. The shell weighed about 95 lbs and was semi-fixed (case and projectiles separately loaded), only 28 rounds being carried. An interrupted thread breechblock was used instead of the wedge type of other SUs. The commander was situated to the right, and the driver in front and to the left. Handrails were fitted for tank-borne infantry. The vehicle weighed about 50 tons and could ford up to the track guards. In the combats with the German heavy tanks the SU–152 proved of particular value and became highly regarded by Soviet soldiers—they called it the 'Zveroboy' (Conquering Beast'). The SU–152 was removed from service in 1954.

During the second half of 1943 further self-propelled mountings were developed. Units received the SU–37 anti-aircraft support tank—of which there were two models: a single-barrelled 37 mm mounting designated SU–37–1, and a twin-barrelled 37 mm mounting designated SU–37–2. Very few of the latter models were produced. Both mounted the 37 mm Model 39 fully-automatic anti-aircraft gun in an open-topped fully rotating turret mounted at the rear of a modified T–70 light tank chassis. It is interesting to note that no subsidiary armament was mounted on this vehicle, although a sub-machine-gun was carried for each crew member. The SU–37–2 twin 37 mm and SU–37–1 single 37 mm SPs appeared in the 7th Kantemirovka Tank Division Tankman's Day Parade in Moscow during 1946 and have not been since seen. The vehicles were designed to provide anti-aircraft protection for mobile units but could not have been very successful since they were eventually withdrawn from service at the end of that year.

The Russians also reworked captured German tanks, armoured cars and half-tracks into self-propelled mountings, the most significant of which was the conversion of the Stu.G–III to mount the 76·2 mm M–1942/43 anti-tank gun. This vehicle was designated the SU–76i and was produced throughout 1942–3. It weighed 22·5 tons and had a crew of 4 men. The vehicle retained the original German Maybach 300 hp twelve-cylinder tank engine giving it a speed of 50 kph. 98 rounds of ammunition were carried. As far as SPs are concerned, from the Lend-Lease arrangement the Russians received only 650 of the US T–48 57 mm SP half-track mountings, 52 M–10 gun motor carriages, and took only 5 M–18s for tests (since they now had their own SPs). They also received 100 M–15s and 1,000 M–17s.

Several SPs were built in competition with the IS tank series (see heavy tank section). Amongst these was the KV–7 on the KV–1 heavy tank chassis which mounted one 76 mm and 2 × 45 mm guns. Another SP had twin 76 mm guns.

In August 1943 engineers Machonin, Gorlick and Trojanov designed the new SU–85 tank destroyer. Towards the end of 1943 the Uralmashzavod and Chelyabinsk combines built 100 SU–85s, but during the following year a significant increase in the production of this vehicle took place. The SU–85 gained respect during the fighting with German tanks in the Ukraine and Dniepner offensives of 1944. It took over the tank-destroyer role from the SU–76, which now became relegated to providing artillery fire support to infantry units. The SU–85 closely resembled the older SU–122 in hull configuration, with the gun mounted in a fixed superstructure on the T–34 tank chassis. The gun was a tank adaptation of the 85 mm anti-aircraft gun M–1939. With the introduction in 1944 of the T–34/85 tank, the SU–85 became obsolescent and was reworked with the

245

246

247

85 mm gun D5–S85A (M–1944) anti-tank gun and issued to satellite armies. There was no visible difference between the two guns, although the M–1944 had a greater range and greater armour penetration. In September 1944 the SU–85 started to be replaced by the SU–100, and by early 1945 it disappeared altogether from the Soviet Army. 500 of the new SU–100 tank destroyers were manufactured during early 1944. Garret Underhill wrote:

With the advent in 1944 of the SU–100, with the new 100 mm gun (adapted from the prewar naval 100/56 high velocity dual-purpose gun) the SU version of the T–34 received far more firepower than its turreted counterpart. As with the SU–85 the gun was laid with a tank-gun type telescope: no panoramic telescopes were provided. No machine-gun was mounted, even for anti-aircraft use. The SUs always had both intercom sets and radio; the

248

249

250

245. *SU–37–1. Single 37 mm AA mounting on T–70 light tank chassis;* **246.** *SU–76i. 76 mm gun motor carriage based on captured German Stu.G–III chassis;* **247.** *SU–57. 57 mm A/Tk guns mounted on Lend-lease U.S. half-tracks;* **248.** *SU–85. 85 mm A/Tk mounting based on the T–34 tank;* **249.** *SU–100. 100 mm A/Tk mounting based on the T–34 tank;* **250.** *SU–122. 122 mm gun motor carriage based on the KV heavy tank chassis.*

intercom was more necessary on the SU than on the early T–34 medium, since the former's driver was separated from the vehicle commander. In the T–34/76 both commander and driver were on the left; the commander could use foot signals on the driver's shoulder. In the SUs the commander was off to the right, and on the SU–76 was separated from the driver by the engine and transmission.[249]

The superstructure was very similar to that of the SU–85, and the hull, running-gear and automotive components were identical to the T–34/85 tank. The armament consisted of the 100 mm field/anti-tank gun Model 1944 (D–10S). As with the SU–85, no secondary armament was carried. The 100 mm gun had a greatly improved performance over that of the 85 mm gun, firing a 35 lb HE shell to a range of 21,000 yards. It also fired a 434 lb AP round.

The SU–100 normally carried, on each side towards the rear, two extra fuel tanks. A single headlamp was mounted on the left over the track for night driving. Spare track links were often bolted on the front, together with a long wire towing cable. In action, the rear of the chassis behind the crew compartment was usually piled with wooden ammunition boxes, and stowage. The short whip aerial could be folded to the rear along the side.

In addition to the distinctive long gun, the SU–100 could be distinguished by the differently-shaped mantlet and the circular cupola which was attached to the right-hand side of the superstructure top. This vehicle remained the standard support gun for mechanized and armoured divisions until their reorganization in 1957, when it was replaced by the ISU–122 (A–19S) gun motor carriage on the IS tank chassis. Obsolete vehicles were subsequently supplied to Bulgaria, Communist China, Czechoslovakia, East Germany, Poland, Rumania and the United Arab Republic.

Concurrent with the production of the SU–100 were those of the SU–122, self-propelled 122 mm gun designed for fighting heavy tanks, and the SU–152, self-propelled 152 mm gun/howitzer, both based on the KV tank chassis. The SU–122 consisted of the long Model 1931–7 122 mm gun (muzzle-velocity 2,625 fps) mounted on the modified chassis of the KV tank (interchangeable with the 152 mm M–37 howitzer to form the SU–152). Only 35 of the SU–122s were produced during 1943, and these were not widely used; production stopped when the Stalin tank appeared.

The SU–76, 85, 100, 122 and 152 were attached to regiments and divisions of armoured artillery, infantry divisions and armoured corps.

1944 saw the replacement of the earlier ZIS–6 and GAZ–AA rocket launcher mountings by those mounted on the new GAZ–63 trucks (e.g., the M–8, M–13 and M–31 rocket launchers). In addition, large quantities of T–60 and T–70 chassis (as well as tracked prime-movers) were fitted with Katyusha rocket launchers.

Following the introduction of the new IS heavy tank series, those self-propelled mountings formerly built around KV tank components were transferred to this new

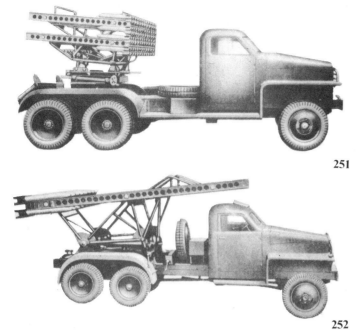

251

253

252

254

251. *48×82 mm rocket launcher M–8 on GAZ–63;*
252. *16×130 mm rocket launcher M–13 on GAZ–63;*
253. *12×300 mm rocket launcher M–31 on GAZ–63;*
254. *ISU–122 (A–19). 122 mm gun motor carriage based on the IS tank chassis;* **255.** *ISU–152. 152 mm howitzer carriage on the IS tank chassis;* **256.** *12×240 mm rocket launcher BM–24 on ZIL–151 (lightweight);* **257.** *16×140 mm rocket launcher BM–14 on ZIL–151;*

255

256

257

tank. The older SU–122 and SU–152 carriages were removed from service during the autumn of 1943 and replaced by the ISU–122 and ISU–152 mountings during 1944, both based on the IS heavy tank.

On these new SUs the crew compartment was made higher and more rectangular with side armour less-sloped. KV hatches were replaced by tank and SU–100 cupolas then in production. The hatches were fitted with the new wartime simplified standard periscope of which there was one in the front right, and one in the front left hatch. No cupola was fitted. The ISU–122 mounted the 122 mm M–1944 L/45 A–19 gun having a wedge breech block, and fired a 55 lb shell to a range of 14,200 yards. 2,510 were produced during 1944. Further ISU–122s were provided with the 122 mm tank gun D–25S L/43 (distinguished by

258. 4 × 200 mm rocket launcher BMD–20 on ZIL–151;
259. 12 × 300 mm rocket launcher BM431–12 on armoured GAZ–63.

258

259

its muzzle-brake), which had slightly greater armour penetration. The ISU–152 mounted the original M–37 152 mm (modified ML–20) howitzer firing an HE shell weighing 96 lbs to a range of 9,800 yards. It also fired a 107 lb AP round. Garret Underhill wrote:

The ISU–152 fired an HE shell weighing over 95 lbs, thereby bringing artillery support down to tank company level. Despite its slow rate of fire the ISU–152 was intended to engage armour with AP and shot weighing even more than its HE, and to get in its opening rounds at phenomenal ranges.[250]

The effectiveness of the ISU–152 was greatly hampered by only carrying 20 rounds of ammunition. A machine-gun was mounted on the right side of the superstructure for close-in protection. The vehicle was identical to the ISU–122 (A–19S) apart from the gun. It was used as a support weapon to accompany medium tanks in the motorized rifle and tank divisions, as well as in independent units. The Russians stated that the only reason for continuing production of the ISU–122 while the ISU–152 was in service was because a large number of artillery pieces were in stock for this model.

The major differences between the ISU and the original SU series were its lower suspension system and a higher, less sharply-sloped superstructure. Also the vehicle mounted a new, heavy, two-piece mantlet mounted on the right-hand side. The inner section of the mantlet was bolted to the superstructure while the outer section was moveable, allowing the gun to be elevated and traversed. The lower suspension gave the impression that the fighting compartment had been heightened. Several modifications were observed in the ISU–152 such as provision for skirting armour, sponson boxes and redesigned track-guards.

During the war SP guns fought enemy tanks and anti-tank artillery, accompanied motorized infantry and tank units, and provided air-cover for troops. All these vehicles were manned by tank personnel.

Postwar development. Although very little further development of tracked self-propelled vehicles took place before the 1950s, the development of rocket-weapons received a tremendous impetus. Since the war the Soviets have re-arranged their entire artillery rocket launcher system. A new series of truck-mounted and tracked multi-barrelled launchers appeared, firing new types of rocket. Over 1946–7 appeared the M–13 rocket launcher mounted on the ZIS/ZIL–150/151 6 × 4 truck chassis, and the M–31 rocket launcher mounted on the ZIL–151 truck. There was also an 82 mm mounting on the ZIL–151 truck. In 1953 the BM–24 240 mm 12-tube open rocket launcher appeared, mounted on the ZIL–151 truck. Two armoured covers were hinged to the car roof which were folded over the windscreen during firing. This mounting was introduced to replace the obsolete short-range 300 mm M–31 rocket launcher.

In the same year the RM–130 130 mm 32-round rocket launcher appeared, also mounted on the ZIL–151. This vehicle was the first of its type to have self-contained ammunition stowage facilities, and 66 rounds of ammunition could be carried in the special compartment. Refinements incorporated in the design of this mounting did away with the requirement for armoured shields over the crew cab, and for stabilizing jacks at the rear of the chassis. 1944 saw the appearance of three further mountings: the ZIL–151 140 mm 16-round BM–14 (since removed), the ZIL–151 200 mm 4-round launcher, and the GAZ–63 armoured BM–31 12-round launcher. In 1957 a rocket launcher appeared mounted on the AT–S full-tracked prime-

260. 12×240 mm rocket launcher BM–24 on AT–S tractor; 261. 6×280 mm rocket launcher BMD–28 on YaAZ–214; 262. 310 mm gun motor carriage on IS tank chassis; 263. 400/420 mm gun motor carriage on IS tank chassis; 264. FROG 1 ICBM on ISU tank chassis; 265. FROG 2 on PT–76 light tank chassis; 266. SCUD A on ISU chassis; 267. ASU–57. Air-portable 57 mm SP anti-tank gun. Earliest observed version with long barrel and bore-evacuator; 268. ASU–57. Second observed model with unusual muzzle-brake; 269. ASU–57. Third observed version with double-baffle muzzle-brake.

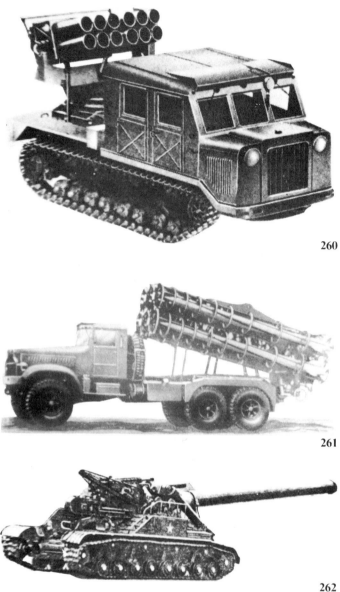

260

261

262

263

264

265

mover, the 240 mm 12-tube BM–24. In this vehicle, the equipment could be elevated or traversed by manual or power operation. The rockets were electrically fired and spin-stabilized, the spin being imparted by angled venturis at the base of the rockets. This vehicle provided the Soviet Army with a highly mobile, multi-round rocket launcher which can accompany armoured units on all missions. Modifications to the vehicle included removal of the cargo deck and the provision of hinged blast screens on the windows around the personnel compartment. In the same year, a further wheeled launcher appeared, the YAZ–214 280 mm rocket launcher 6-tube BMD–25. Like the majority of other wheeled mountings, this was based on an open chassis. Spiral rocket vanes were used to give spin stabilization. The launcher consisted of a series of concentric rings.

This has been the largest multi-round rocket launcher used by the Soviet Army. Although the rocket is exceeded in calibre by the 300 mm type, the great weight and length of the 280 mm round surpassed that of the 300 mm. Perhaps the most significant development in rocketry during that year was the introduction of several weapons with a nuclear capability. Firstly, there were two interim vehicles based on the IS heavy tank chassis and components—a 310 long-barrelled gun firing a ram-jet nuclear missile and a 400 mm self-propelled mortar. Both equipments were designed to be fired from rear areas and consequently had a minimum of armour protection; and from photographs taken during parades they appeared to be mechanically unstable. The vehicle itself had no conventional self-propelled gun superstructure, the area above the chassis being

266

267

268

Luna in Russia—or Free-Rocket-Over-Ground I on the IS tank chassis, and secondly the FROG-2 on the PT–76 light amphibious tank chassis. The first vehicle had a large segmented housing to protect the rocket which also served as a temperature conditioning device for its solid propellant. Another IS chassis carried missile was the SCUD–A (1958), also known as the T–7A missile. The entire framework is elevated for launching by means of a hydraulic cylinder on either side of the vehicle near the rear of the cab. The modified chassis was identical to that used for the 310/400 mm vehicles. The FROG-2 on the PT–76 chassis was designed to fulfil the nuclear artillery role in the mobile arms. The turret was removed and an elevating launching ramp was rigidly attached to the superstructure deck. Two support jacks were located at the chassis rear for cross-levelling and stabilizing the equipment.

1957 also saw the introduction of three self-propelled gun mountings, two of which were standardized and taken into service. An experimental 122 mm mounting was produced on the chassis of the T–54 medium tank: the vehicle mounted a modified 122 mm D–74 field-gun in a fixed superstructure together with a dual purpose machine-gun. This vehicle was not, however, taken into service. The two standardized mountings were the ASU–57 (Avisdesantnaya Samochodnaya Ustanovka) and the ZSU–57–2 (Zanitnaya Samochodnaya Ustanovka). The ASU–57 consisted of the 57 mm M–55 anti-tank gun Model 1943 mounted in a fixed superstructure on a small, light-weight chassis of new design (which was, in fact a modified T–70 light tank chassis). It was designed primarily as an air-portable assault gun. Two models appeared in 1957; one mounted a 57 mm gun with double-baffle muzzle-brake while the other mounted a modified 57 mm gun with a fume extractor. The superstructure was fixed and box-shaped, open at the top and located to the rear of the chassis. The hull was armoured and had a sloping front plate, vertical sides and a tapering rear plate. The suspension was of a torsion bar type with the drive sprocket at the front, where the engine and transmission were also housed. The armour was very light, varying from 15 mm on the front to 10 mm on the sides. Ammunition for the gun was stowed under the crew seats located along the sides and rear of the superstructure. The engine was mounted on the right-hand side of the chassis next to the driver. Two companies, each of ten vehicles, were assigned to anti-tank battalions of the airborne divisions. The ZSU–57–2 is a special anti-aircraft derivative of the T–54 tank, mounting twin 57 mm anti-aircraft guns Model S–68. The T–54 suspension has been modified by reducing the number of road-wheels to four and then respacing them. A large, square, open-topped turret with

occupied by the trunnions, breech assembly and other components required for artillery pieces of this calibre. A small cab for the driver was situated at the front on the right side of the chassis. The modified IS chassis was approximately 6 feet longer and 1 foot wider than the original, and had eight (rather than six) road wheels on each side. The 310 mm gun could fire an atomic shell as well as conventional ammunition, and could be traversed approximately 2–4°, and elevated from −2° to +42° Neither of these weapons was adopted in quantity, since nuclear rounds could be fired from conventional guns, and several other nuclear rockets were eventually introduced into service. In this year two nuclear rocket launchers were provided with high-mobility chassis and introduced into service with the Soviet Army; firstly, the FROG—referred to as

269

270

272

271

273

274

275

276

360° traverse has been mounted centrally along the hull length. On the rear of this turret is a wire-mesh cage for storing spent cartridge cases and baggage. Six of these vehicles were deployed in each battery of an anti-aircraft regiment, and 18 attached to each armoured division. The vehicle was designed to provide anti-aircraft protection for moving columns as well as to deliver direct fire in support of ground forces.

A further anti-aircraft vehicle appeared in 1958, in the form of the BTR–152 6 × 6 armoured personnel carrier. This vehicle mounted quadruple DShK machine-guns on a revolving mount at the rear of the chassis. Two other wheeled anti-aircraft vehicles appeared during the following year—both conversions of the standard armoured wheeled personnel carriers. First was the BTR–40 4 × 4 armoured personnel carrier mounting twin ZPU–2 14·5 mm machine-guns, and secondly a similar mounting on the BTR–152. A further artillery-rocket launcher was introduced during 1959 based on the GAZ–63 truck. This was the 140 mm 17-round M–1959, and was essentially a lighter vehicle mounting of the BM–14. In 1960 a new version of the SP 420 mm mortar appeared. This version had extensive modifications to both weapons and vehicle. The tube is longer, the re-located equilibriators are longer but smaller in diameter. The altered vehicle now has large additional shock-absorbers. The Soviets redesigned the cab and repositioned it from the right-hand side to directly behind the barrel.

The sixties. In 1960 a modified version of the Frog-2 on the PT–76 chassis appeared, designated Frog-3. The main change in this system was in the warhead; technology of nuclear engineering allowed a decreased warhead diameter as compared with the former Frog-2 missile. The system was otherwise identical. In 1961 a new version of the IS SCUD mounting appeared designated SCUD–B.

In 1962 an improved version of the PT–76 Frog mounting appeared, designated FROG-4, as well as a truck-mounted anti-aircraft missile designated the SA–2 mounted on a ZIL 157.

Two new self-propelled conventional mountings were introduced during 1962: the ASU–85 airborne mounting—replacing the older ASU–57, and the new SU–100 on the T–54 chassis. The ASU–85 employed the chassis and components of the PT–76 light tank, although no means seems to have been incorporated for amphibious use. This vehicle mounted the 85 mm gun L/53 in a fixed armoured superstructure, and had the engine at the rear. It is not known why the Russians produced the SU–100 on the T–54 chassis, although it may have been produced solely for satellite armies.

During 1963 a further wheeled, self-propelled rocket launcher appeared—the 140 mm BM–14 eight-tube launcher mounted on the GAZ–63 truck. 1964 saw the

270. *ZSU–57–2. SP twin-barrel 57 mm anti-aircraft gun;* **271.** *BTR–152 fitted with 360 degree traverse twin 14·5 mm AAMG mounting;* **272.** *BTR–40 fitted with 360 degree traverse twin 14·5 mm AAMG mounting;* **273.** *FROG 3 on PT–76 light tank chassis;* **274.** *FROG 4 on PT–76 light tank chassis;* **275.** *SU–100. 100 mm gun motor carriage based on T–54 medium tank chassis;* **276.** *17 × 140 mm rocket launcher BM–14–17 on GAZ–63;* **277.** *SA–2 AA missile GOA on ZIL–157;* **278.** *GANEF AA guided missile system on modified ASU–85 chassis;* **279.** *BRDM armoured car with Snapper ATGWs;* **280.** *FROG 5 on PT–76 light tank chassis.*

281

282

283

284

introduction of two further rocket launchers: the 110/140 mm 40-tube rocket launcher on the Ural 375 6 × 6 truck, and the 115 mm BM–115/40 (M–64) 40-tube launcher, also on the Ural–375 truck. Two anti-aircraft guided missile launcher vehicles appeared during this year, one wheeled and one tracked. The wheeled system, mounted on the ZIL–157 truck, consisted of two GOA anti-aircraft missiles on a traversable mount, and the tracked system, mounted on a lengthened (and slightly modified) ASU–85 gun motor carriage chassis, consisted of two Ganef anti-aircraft missiles. The first Soviet mobile anti-tank guided missile systems were introduced in 1964, both mounted on wheeled chassis. 'Snapper' anti-tank missiles were mounted on both the GAZ–69 4 × 4 reconnaissance vehicle (unarmoured) and the BRDM armoured amphibious scout car. In this role the BRDM became designated the BARN. On the GAZ–69 four of these wire-guided missiles are mounted facing to the rear, whilst on the BARN only three are mounted on a retractile launcher arm fitted within the crew compartment. In 1965 a whole new series of self-propelled weapons were introduced into the Soviet Army and a swing was observed from tracked carrier vehicles to a new series of high-mobility wheeled carriers. The Frog-6 system was mounted on the ZIL–157 6 × 6 wheeled vehicle, the Frog-4 on the new 8 × 8 MAZ–543 high-mobility carrier, and the Frog-7 on the new 8 × 8 ZIL–135. These new vehicles have electro-hydraulic launcher assembly systems. Four larger missiles appeared during this year, all mounted on modified IS–1V/T–10 chassis—the SS–4 'Sandal', the SS–5 'Skean', the 'Scrooge' and the 'Scamp' (NATO code names). All of these are believed to be either ICBMs or FROGS and have a nuclear capability. Also in 1965, two anti-tank guided missile versions of the BRDM appeared, both basically similar to the original Barn but employing new guided weapons, the 'Swatter' and the 'Sagger'. In the former case the missile stowage was increased to 4 and in the latter to 6. The Swatter was radio controlled and the Sagger wire-guided. The last vehicle in this class to appear, during 1965, was a new radar controlled anti-aircraft machine-gun system based on the PT–76 light amphibious tank chassis. This vehicle is designated ZSU–23–4, and mounts four 23 mm machine-guns in a fully-rotating turret. The chassis, which has been slightly modified, does not seem to include the hydra-jet propulsion ports of the parent vehicle, indicating that it is not amphibious. In 1965 a new truck-mounted rocket-launcher appeared—the BM–28 on the YaAZ 6 × 4 truck. In 1966 the swing to wheeled launcher vehicles was further demonstrated by the adaptation of the SCUD–B missile to the new MAZ–543 twin-cab 8 × 8 high mobility wheeled carrier. Since 1967 only one new vehicle in this category seems to have been introduced, an armoured anti-aircraft rocket ('Gainful') vehicle based on the PT–76 chassis, to supplement the ZSU–23–4 system in defending armoured and other mobile units against low-flying aircraft. Three missiles are mounted lengthways along the vehicle.

It appears that the self-propelled assault gun is now becoming obsolete in the Soviet Army except for use by airborne units.

281. *SCROOGE on IS/T–10 chassis;* **282.** *BRDM armoured car with Swatter ATGWs;* **283.** *ZSU–23–4. SP quad mount 23 mm AA mounting on modified PT–76 chassis;* **284.** *SCUD B on MAZ–543.*

5 Wheeled (Armoured) & Tracked Supporting Vehicles

This chapter is concerned with the development of armoured wheeled vehicles, armoured and unarmoured military tracked vehicles, and non-commercial unarmoured wheeled vehicles employed by the Soviet Army.

It has been shown in Part 1 that several wheeled tank and armoured car projects were explored at the turn of the century, but none of these were adopted. In 1904, at the time of the Russo-Japanese War, Nakaszidze put forward an armoured car project to the Commander-in-Chief of the Russian Imperial Army, and the French firm of Charron, Girardot et Voigt was commissioned to build three prototypes. In 1905 this order was completed and the vehicles were sent to Russia by rail, via Germany. Only one, however, eventually arrived.

Early armoured cars. The production of armoured cars in Russia took place soon after the beginning of World War I in 1914. The first Russian-built armoured cars, armoured at the Izhorski Factory at Kolpino, were assembled at the Russo-Baltic firm in St Petersburg. These were four-wheeled cars with pneumatic tyres, and were armed with three 7·62 mm machine-guns in a fixed turret; their armour ranged from 6 to 12 mm. These cars were formed into an armoured car company which was first employed on the North-Western Front on 19 October 1914.

During 1914 several armoured cars were purchased from abroad (principally England). Austin, Sheffield-Simplex, Armstrong-Whitworth and Fiat types formed the major part of the 100 armoured cars employed by the White Russians; but the Russians had little faith in the effectiveness of these foreign vehicles. Mostovenko wrote:

The delivery of English armoured cars showed poor quality of manufacture, and nearly all the vehicles proved unsuitable for combat. Towards the end of spring 1916, armoured cars arrived in Russia; 25 Sheffield-Simplex, 36 Armstrong-Whitworth-Fiat, and 30 Garret. These proved useless for combat employment. In a telegram from a Russian war correspondent to England on June 30th 1916, it was stated that the Armstrong-Whitworth armoured cars were unsuitable for employment on the Front, owing to their poor quality of manufacture (spoked wheels, brake failures, overloaded chassis, numerous faults in the transmission and running gear, unreliability resulting from the use of poor quality materials, etc). . . . In a document dated 30th June 1916, addressed to a War Correspondent in England on the occasion of a further delivery of armoured cars, it was stated '. . . all armoured cars Sheffield and Armstrong, dispatched to Petrograd, of the present type are unsuitable for use on the Front. . . .' Dependence upon foreign capitalists seriously hampered the supply of armoured vehicles to the Russian Army. After several deliveries to the State of armoured cars from England, the Russian War Ministry decided to purchase automobile chassis only, and to armour these in Russian factories. However, English and American firms did not fulfil the contract, which seriously hampered construction work—particularly at the Putilov and Izhorskiy plants—of armoured cars for the Russian Army. As a result, even a small order of 200 armoured cars per year proved impossible to fulfil. . . .[251]

The Pierce-Arrow armoured car. Introduced in 1914, this heavy armoured car was based on a commercial lorry chassis and armoured with 9 mm plates. This car, which was controlled only in a forward direction, was armed with a 57 mm gun. The original turreted cars were found to be too heavy and most of them were remodelled in Russia by removing the turrets and building up the side armour. Some of these vehicles had naval 3-pounder guns in shields at the rear of the chassis.

In the autumn of the same year the Putilov firm was organized for undertaking the manufacture of a new gun armoured car, called the Putilov-Garford. This vehicle was based on the chassis of the American Garford heavy truck and weighed about nine tons. It was armed with either a 57 or 76·2 mm gun plus one machine-gun in the turret, and two further machine guns mounted in side sponsons. The vehicle proved to be top-heavy and could be controlled only in a forward direction. Its maximum speed was 20 kph. A number were built and considerable use was made of them: they could be adapted to run on railway lines. The Germans reported these vehicles as still in use in 1936 as armoured trains.

Another car employed during 1914 was the Sheffield-Simplex which weighed about 6 tons. It was based on the English Sheffield-Simplex passenger-car chassis and was armoured in Russia. The car was powered by a 60 hp engine and could reach a speed of 30 mph. It had a crew of 5 men, and two turrets (side by side) each of which mounted a 7·62 mm water-cooled Maxim machine-gun. In 1914 negotiations were completed with the Armstrong-Whitworth firm to build an experimental armoured car. One was built and delivered to the Russians, being a four-wheeled vehicle with dual, solid rubber-tyred wheels at the rear with a revolving turret. Another English armoured car used in Russia during 1914 was the 'Peerless'. This consisted of a truck chassis with a box-like hull, armoured over the engine, with a small cylindrical turret mounting one water-cooled 7·62 mm Maxim machine-gun. The four

was not successful. In 1915 another version of the Austin armoured car appeared, designated the Austin-Putilov in which the armour was increased to 7 mm. Some cars had armour of 5 mm chrome-steel. The original English Austin cars could be steered only from the front, and the Russians specified additional steering from the rear. A rear steering wheel operated by a drum and cable passing to the normal steering controls was tried, but later duplicated steering wheels connected to the front wheels were added, and finally an auxiliary gear. Owing to commitments in England, the Austin Company was unable to furnish Russia with sufficient numbers of completed cars and hence the Russians decided to buy chassis in England and armour them at the Putilov works. The cars were similar except that the hulls were slightly modified and that the turrets were placed diagonally across the hull tops.

Over the period 1914–15 two types of Fiat passenger car were armoured and fitted with diagonally placed turrets. These cars carried two Maxim 7·62 mm water-cooled machine-guns, and sometimes were referred to as the Fiat 60 × 90. About the same time, two other armoured cars were built completely by the Russians; one designed by Captain of Cavalry Mgebrov on the chassis of the Renault M–1915 armoured car, and the other by Staff Captain Poplavko. Mostovenko wrote:

In the application of armour to these early cars, Russian engineers showed a great deal of ingenuity and creative ability. Note, for example, one type of armoured car built in 1915, the armour of which was designed by Staff Captain Mgebrov. He achieved good protection by employing inclined armour plates on this and other armoured cars produced between 1914 and 1918.

285

286

wheels had solid rubber tyres. A further three machine-guns were located in the hull, one at either side and one at the rear. Unlike the earlier types, this vehicle had dual controls for steering forwards or backwards. The car weighed 7½ tons, was about 20 feet long, 7 feet wide, and 9 feet high. It had armour 8 mm thick and was manned by a crew of 5. Perhaps the most important armoured car introduced during 1914 was the Austin. The first Austin armoured car was four-wheeled with pneumatic tyres and had 5 mm armour. Two Maxim 7·62 water-cooled machine-guns formed the armament, and these were located in two turrets mounted side-by-side across the hull. The early models had tyre covers, but later the Russians introduced solid rubber tyres. Experiments were carried out at St Petersburg Military Automobile School with pneumatic tyres filled with a mixture of gelatine and glycerine, but this

Talented designer Staff Captain Mgebrov (who was killed on the Front in 1915) also designed for his armoured cars bullet-proof glass and several other features.[252]

The Renault-Mgebrov armoured car was unusual looking owing to the Renault hood which made possible the forward-sloping armour on this car. The Russian placement of armour was skilful in its application in that it provided an angled surface against enemy fire to a far greater degree than similar designs in other countries. This car did not go into production until 1924.

In December 1915 an officer of the 7th Avtobronie Battalion on the South-Western Front, Staff-Captain Poplavko, put forward a proposal for a new armoured car. The armoured hull was designed for overcoming barbed-wire obstacles. To increase mobility he decided to use a

287

288

289

291

chassis with four-wheel drive (Jeffery). An armoured car of this type was built shortly afterwards and subsequently tested. Owing to the special hull shape, the car—whilst travelling at 5–6 mph—could break and deflect barbed-wire coils, and, with the aid of a special bridge, could cross ditches and trenches. Poplavko was summoned to St Petersburg, where he directed the manufacture of his armoured car. The vehicle was again tested during July 1916 at the Izhorskiy Proving Grounds. Trials were carried out on damp clay and peat, and the armoured car overcame barbed-wire obstacles 5 rows deep (with a coil height of 1–2 metres). Following a successful conclusion of the trials, the War Ministry ordered 30 of these cars which were formed into a special Avtobronie battalion during October 1916 and despatched to the South-Western Front.

Poplavko also designed another armoured car based on the Jeffery chassis, called the Poplavko-Jeffery armoured car (AB–9). This car weighed 8 tons and had a crew of eight. Its most outstanding features were its four-wheel drive and double steering with a high-speed reverse. It was armoured with 16–18 mm plates and mounted two 7·62 mm water-cooled Maxim machine-guns. Another unusual feature was that it was powered by two engines. It was a low vehicle with flat armour plate and had a superstructure built around the crew seats. Solid rubber tyres were used, and double controls were provided for driving in either direction. The gearbox provided 5 speeds forward or backwards. The car was about 19 ft 4 in long, 7 ft 9 in wide and about 9 ft 6 in high.

During 1915 the Russians produced their first semi-track armoured car, which was designed by an engineer named Gulkevitch (see Part 1). The car, based on the Lombard

285. *Pierce-Arrow 1917 Armoured Car;* **286.** *Putilov-Garford Armoured Car;* **287.** *Sheffield-Simplex Armoured Car;* **288.** *Fiat Model A Armoured Car;* **289.** *Renault Mgebrov Armoured Car;* **290.** *Larsky-Eberhardt Armoured Car 1915;* **291.** *Poplavko-Jeffery AB–9 Armoured Car.*

truck chassis and armoured at the Putilov Works, had steel tracks and was not very satisfactory. Another semi-tracked armoured car was built in the following year based on the Austin-Putilov armoured car. Two types were made: with diagonally arranged turrets or with turrets arranged in juxtaposition (as with the original Austin cars). Sixty of these cars were made and issued to units. Some cars were fitted with rollers at the front to improve their obstacle ability.

290

During 1917 several other armoured cars were introduced. The Packard heavy armoured car M–1917 consisted of the Packard truck chassis with flat armour plates riveted on, and armed with one Maxim machine-gun on a pedestal mount with a shield. Several others were built with better armour arrangement and an additional Maxim machine-gun in the hull rear. These cars had armour 6 mm thick and solid rubber tyres. In addition, the Russians employed Belgian 'Minerva' armoured cars, English 'Lanchester' armoured cars (which differed from the English model in having a small observation turret above the main one) and French White armoured passenger cars, which closely resembled the English Austins.

Armoured cars between the wars. No further armoured car development took place until the introduction of the First Five-Year Plan during 1927, when the production of

292. *Packard Armoured Car 1917;* 293. *BA–27 Armoured Car;* 294. *Bronieford FA–1 Armoured Car;* 295. *Bronieford FA–2 Armoured Car;* 296. *BA–10 heavy armoured car.*

armoured cars was undertaken on a large scale. The Red Army received its first 1927 armoured car series based on the GAZ–A 4-seater, 4-cylinder engined car. Ford vehicles were called BA (Bronieavtomobil—or armoured automobile).

The four-wheeled armoured car was called the BA–27 which, in original form, had a riveted hull and turret (the same as that used on the MS–III light tank). In the turret were mounted a 37 mm gun, and to the right of this a ball-mounted 7·62 mm air-cooled tank machine-gun. Some of these cars had radio equipment. In 1930 two other armoured cars were placed in mass-production, the light four-wheeled Bronieford and the heavy BA–10. Like the BA–27, the Bronieford was also based on the Model A chassis and had a single turret with a DT machine-gun. This turret was so small that turret armour (as well as the driver's position) was domed to provide room for the crew. Some vehicles had no turret and in this form were designated FA–2. The turreted model was designated FA–1. The car was a modernized BA–27 with angled side armour, new turret and hull armour, and spoked wheels as opposed to the solid type employed on the BA–27. The turret mounted a single machine-gun. The car was four-wheeled with drive on the rear axle only. The turretless version (FA–2) was also known as the Bronieford armoured saloon: it had an open top with a pedestal-mounted 7·62 mm DT tank machine-gun. The BA–10 was a heavy armoured car based on the GAZ–AAA 6-wheeled commercial truck chassis. The

297

298

301

299

300

6-wheeled lorry chassis was reinforced for cross-country work, and had improvements in the suspension system. Three versions of this car were produced between 1930 and 1940. The first model had riveted armour (ranging from 10–15 mm) and a small turret mounting either a 37 mm gun or a 12·7 mm DShK heavy machine-gun. A further 7·62 mm machine-gun was placed in the hull to the right of the driver. The wheels were provided with pressed-steel hubs, and when travelling across country tracks could be attached to the rear wheels to improve the performance. The car was built at the Gorki works.

A redesigned version of the Bronieford appeared in 1931, designated the BA–20 (sometimes erroneously referred to as the BA–7). When GAZ began to turn out their M–1 Ford car in 1931, the V–8 chassis was used for the BA–20. This was a modified Bronieford with a new turret, single

297. *BA–20 Armoured Car;* 298. *BA–20(V). Commander's Model of BA–20;* 299. *BA–32–1 heavy armoured car;* 300. *BAZ heavy amphibious armoured car;* 301. *ZIS–33 semi-track.*

machine-gun, domed cupola and, in some cases, a frame aerial around the hull (in this latter case the vehicle was called the BA–20V). Some early production BA–20s had the old BA Bronieford turrets.

In 1932 a modernized version of the BA–10 appeared, designated the BA–32–1. This vehicle had a square-cut welded hull with a new turret, taken from the T–26B light tank. Some cars had the turret of the BT–3 tank. All models mounted a 37 mm semi-automatic anti-tank gun. This car had a whip type aerial and a standard all-round periscope located in the turret top for the commander. It was employed during the Spanish Civil War and some were sold to Turkey. The vehicle has also been referred to as the BAF. In the same year an amphibious version of the BA–10 appeared, designated the BAZ. This vehicle was based on the German Büssing-NAG amphibious armoured car tested at Kazan. Not very many of these BAZ cars were made.

During 1932 two unarmoured semi-tracks appeared—the YaSP and the ZIS–33. The YaSP, built by the Yaroslavl combine, was a half-tracked lorry (a modified Ya G–5 Komits) fitted with a T–26 light tank type suspension system at the rear. The vehicle had a load capacity of 2 tons, and was sometimes fitted with skis for use in snow. The ZIS–33 was built around a modified ZIS–5 truck. Both vehicles were widely used as gun tractors and personnel carriers.

302

306

303

307

304

308

305

302. BA–32–2 heavy armoured car; 303. Komintern full-tracked artillery tractor; 304. VM Pikap semi-track; 305. BA–32–3 heavy armoured car; 306. BA–20M armoured car; 307. Voroshilovets full-tracked artillery tractor; 308. STZ Komsomolets (gun crew carrier version); 309. STZ Komsomolets (Ammunition carrier version).

309

In 1934 a further model of the BA–10 armoured car appeared, designated the BA–32–2. This vehicle had the same hull as the earlier type but had a turret originally designed for the T–30 experimental light tank (round welded) which mounted a 45 mm semi-automatic tank gun. The vehicle was also provided with two 7·62 mm DT machine-guns.

Several unarmoured semi- and fully-tracked artillery prime-movers appeared in 1936. Amongst the fully-tracked types were the STZ–3, KhTZ, ChTZ, Kirovets and Komintern—all of which were placed in production for the Army. Five semi-tracks were produced during this year—'Vezdekhods' Models VM Pikap, a half-tracked version of the ZIS–6, V–M, a half-tracked 2½-ton staff car based on the GAZ–A car, and finally the ZIS–22, 2½-ton experimental half-track.

In 1937 a final model of the BA–32 6-wheeled armoured car was produced, the BA–32–3, having a pressed and welded hull, and the same turret as the previous model with a 45 mm gun. All the BA 6-wheeled models could have tracks fitted around the rear wheels for cross-country work. A newer model of the BA–20 also appeared, designated the BA–20M. This car was welded throughout and had an aerial on the left-hand side of the hull, in place of the large frame type previously used on the BA–20V.

In 1937 two other fully-tracked prime-movers were manufactured—an unarmoured model designated the Voroshilovets and an armoured version called the Komsomolets. The Voroshilovets resembled the earlier prime-movers, but employed the quarter-elliptical spring suspension peculiar to the T–26 tank. The armoured Komsomolets tractor was built in two basic versions; a gun tractor with seats for the personnel, and an ammunition and cargo-carrying version. The troop-carrying version had three bucket seats on each side for the gun crew, and an armoured compartment at the front for the driver and hull machine-gunner. A ball-mounted DT machine-gun was mounted at the right front, with the driver on the left. An aerial was mounted above the gun crew compartment which also served as the frame for a large canvas hood. The gun crew sat back-to-back over the engine at the rear. The suspension consisted of four bogie wheels per side with inverted semi-elliptical springs. There were two return rollers on each side, and the drive was at the front. This vehicle was designated the STZ. The ammunition carrier version had a canvas hood flush with the top of the armoured crew compartment, and had the bucket seats removed; it was otherwise identical.

An unarmoured version of the Komsomolets was produced, known as the Pioneer tractor, and this had a pressed mild-steel engine compartment at the front. The gun tractor versions were often employed to tow the 76·2 mm anti-tank gun, or the M–38 infantry howitzer. 1937 also saw the introduction of four further semi-tracked artillery prime-movers: the 'Vezdekhods' Model B (a 1¼-ton semi-track), BM (a 1½-ton semi-track), V–2 (a 2-ton semi-track), and finally the VM Pikap (a modified M–1 car).

During 1939 two experimental tracked amphibians were produced, designated VL–1 and VL–3 (there was probably also a VL–2) but little is known about them. In 1940 the Kharkov KhTZ–3 full-tracked artillery prime-mover appeared and was placed in mass-production for the Army.

310. *Pioneer artillery tractor;* 311. *VZ semi-track;* 312. *GAZ–60(Ad) semi-track;* 313. *STZ–5–2TB full-tracked artillery tractor.*

310

311

312

313

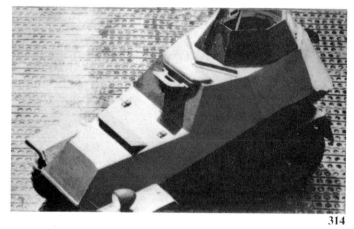

314

318

315

319

316

320

321

317

322

323

Wartime developments. From 1942 onwards, the Russians employed gutted BA–10 and BA–32 armoured cars as armoured personnel carriers. They also introduced two new semi-tracked vehicles—the ZIS–42 2½-ton semi-tracked weapons carrier, and the GAZ–60 (Ad) semi-tracked troop carrier. This latter vehicle was made from the GAZ–63 truck employing captured German half-track suspension systems (taken from Sd.Kfz–251 and 18-ton Famo semi-tracks). A further full-tracked artillery tractor was introduced during this year based on the Komsomlets chassis and designated the STZ–5–2TB. This was a cab-over-engine design and represented the first of the new line of Soviet tracked prime-movers.

In 1943 a new four-wheeled armoured car was placed in production at the GAZ factory, and was designated the BA–64. This was a two-man car designed mainly for liaison, but under wartime conditions was used as a reconnaissance car and as an armoured personnel carrier. The design of this car was based on the captured German Sd.Kfz–222 series armoured cars, which it closely resembled. 1943 also saw the employment of US and British armoured cars, and US artillery tractors provided under the Lend-Lease agreement.

During 1944 the Soviets introduced a number of new full-tracked prime-movers. These included the KT–12, Ya–12 and Ya–13f. The latter pair were practically identical vehicles, except that the Ya–12 was powered by a petrol, and the Ya–13f by a diesel engine; being externally distinguishable only by the type of bogie-wheels employed. (Some sources erroneously refer to the Ya–13f as the M–2.) Torsion-bar suspension was used on these vehicles.

1944 also saw the conversion of several existing tanks and self-propelled gun chassis to armoured recovery and artillery tractors. Tanks mainly converted were old T–34 and KV models and discontinued SU–76 gun motor carriages.

Postwar vehicles. During the 1946 reorganization of the Soviet Army, two new regimental armoured personnel carriers were introduced, the BTR–40 and the BTR–152. (The latter did not in fact go into full-scale production until later.) These vehicles were based on the German Sd.Kfz–247 4- and 6-wheeled models respectively. The term BTR, introduced to distinguish between armoured cars and armoured personnel carriers, was a contraction of Bronietransporter (or armoured carrier). The BTR–40 employed the chassis of the GAZ–63A 4 × 4 truck, whilst the BTR–152 was based on the ZIL–151 6-wheeler truck. The BTR–40 carried 8 men, whilst the BTR–152 could carry up to 16 men. Originally intended as an artillery prime-mover and weapons carrier, the BTR–152 was standardized in all armoured and mechanized units during 1958 as an armoured personnel carrier. The original BTR–152 went into production during 1950 and was based on the chassis of the ZIL–151 truck but provided with a more

powerful engine (110 hp 6-cylinder in-line petrol ZIL–123). It also had larger single tyres in place of the dual tyres used on the rear wheels of the original truck.

Also during 1946 IS and ISU chassis were converted into a new range of armoured recovery vehicles and troop carriers. For a long time the Soviet Army employed simple unsophisticated ARVs, generally referred to as 'armoured prime-movers' by the Russians. In the medium field they used turretless T–34 tanks or disarmed SU–85 gun motor carriages. In the heavy field, old KV and newer IS–2 tank chassis, as well as disarmed ISU gun motor carriages were employed. All these were simply towing vehicles without cranes or specialized equipment. The first specialized vehicle was the SKP–5, which consisted of a T–34 chassis with a special 360° traverse crane of 5-tons capacity. Among these original ARVs were included the SU–100–T, IS–2–T, T–34–T (Model A) and the SU–85–T. The SU–100–T was converted from various SU–100 gun motor carriages to form a medium tank recovery vehicle. Very few such conversions were carried out. The IS–2–T was one of the early heavy tank recovery vehicles, frequently based on the modified, late model IS–2 tank chassis, which had a different glacis plate and sloped side boxes on the track guards. The Russians classed the T–34–T (Model A) as a medium recovery vehicle and basically it was a T–34 medium tank with the turret removed and the fighting compartment stripped of ammunition racks and other equipment pertaining to a fighting tank.

The T–34–T (Model A) varied in appearance due to the presence or absence of a cupola or other superstructure on the armour plate, which was welded over the turret-ring. A large number of SU–85 assault guns were converted into SU–85–T medium ARVs by the removal of the main armament and associated equipment. Covering the glacis plate was a sheet of welded armour plate.

During 1948 two further tracked prime-movers entered production at the Yaroslavl plant—the Ya–14 and the Ya–14f. Both were improved versions of the Ya–13 and 13f respectively, and remained the standard light prime-movers until 1953 when they were replaced by the AT–L and AT–S respectively. The diesel version was powered by a 150 hp 4-cylinder in-line diesel (model YaAZ–204) which gave it a speed of 30 mph.

The fifties. During 1950 two new tracked amphibians were introduced: the K–61 tracked DUKW (also known as the GPT) and the Penguin arctic tractor. The K–61 was a large unarmoured amphibious tractor which was used extensively to transport cargo, equipment and personnel in river crossing operations. Water propulsion was achieved via

314. BA–64 armoured car; 315. Ya–12 tracked artillery tractor; 316. BTR–152 armoured personnel carrier; 317. BTR–40 armoured personnel carrier; 318. SKP–5 Armoured Recovery Vehicle (based on T–34); 319. SU–100–T Armoured Recovery Vehicle (based on SU–100); 320. IS–2–T Armoured Recovery Vehicle (based on IS tank); 321. T–34–T Armoured Recovery Vehicle Model A (based on T–34); 322. SU–85–T Armoured Recovery Vehicle (based on SU–85); 323. KV–1–T Armoured Recovery Vehicle (based on KV–1); 324. Ya–14 Tracked Artillery Tractor.

324

325. *K–61 Tracked amphibian;* **326.** *AT–T Tracked prime-mover;* **327.** *Pinguin amphibious load carrier;* **328.** *T–34–T Armoured Recovery Vehicle Model B (based on T–34);* **329.** *ISU–T Armoured Recovery Vehicle Model A (based on ISU).*

the AT–T had a truck body with a driver's cab and cargo/personnel space. The suspension system was that of the T–54 medium tank with 5 bogie rollers per side: it differed, however, in that the drive sprocket was at the front. This vehicle has since been used as prime-mover for tactical missiles, the BAT dozer, and the BTM trench-digging device. It was powered by a 41 hp V–12 diesel model V–401 giving it a speed of 22 mph.

During 1953 the AT–L artillery tractor was adopted; in its initial form it had 6 small roadwheels and 3 track-support rollers. It replaced the earlier Ya–14 and Ya–14f artillery tractors in their lighter role. Powered by a 135 hp 4-cylinder in-line diesel (model YaAZ–M204VKr) this vehicle could carry 11 men and 4,500 lbs load at a speed of 26 mph.

It was about this time that the Soviets introduced new ARVs into the Army. They fitted both T–34 and ISU recovery vehicles with specialized equipment such as dismountable cranes, boxes for spare parts and winches, some also having pushing-bars. This range included the T–34–T (Model B), ISU–T (Model A), ISU–T (Model B). The T–34 (Model B) was an improved version of the ARV on the T–34 chassis. Changes included the addition of a radio set, a rigging assembly, a loading platform, and a jib crane.

two large, three-bladed propellers located at the rear of the vehicle. It had torsion-bar suspension, and with an unladen weight of 21,000 lbs the K–61 could carry up to 11,000 lbs of equipment or 40 men. It was powered by a 135 hp 4-cylinder in-line diesel (model YaAZ–M204VKr) and could attain a speed on land of 22 mph, and 6 mph in water. The Penguin was a 12-ton tracked amphibian capable of transporting a 2½-ton payload over snow and across water obstacles. Its chassis was later used for the PT–76 light tank.

1950 also saw the introduction of a new tracked prime-mover, the AT–T, which became the largest artillery tractor in use with the Soviet Army. Like the other lighter tractors,

The rear deck of the vehicle had a cargo platform of 2½ tons capacity, designed for carrying equipment and tank accessories. The ISU–T (Model A) was one of the most numerous Soviet heavy tank recovery vehicles, and was created by stripping the main armament and associated equipment from either the ISU–122 or ISU–152 heavy gun motor carriages. The ISU–T (Model B) was similar to the Model A but was provided with a cargo platform, rigging equipment, and a jib crane similar to that used on the T–34–T (Model B).

From investigations of US and British vehicles supplied under the Lend-Lease Agreement of World War II, two

330

331

333

An improved model, designated BAV–A has since appeared in service with the Soviet Army. This is based on the ZIL–157 truck and has internal air-lines on somewhat larger tyres as well as other modifications. The second amphibian, based on the US $\frac{1}{4}$-ton amphibian truck GPA (Duckling) was designated the MAV (GAZ–46). This was built on the chassis of the standard 4 × 4 GAZ–69 or 49 truck. Propulsion in water was achieved by a large, three-bladed propeller located centrally at the rear of the vehicle. The vehicle was entirely unarmoured and carried no armament. Its crew consisted of 5 men (including the driver), it had a road speed of 60 mph, and a water speed of 4 knots. It was principally for engineer reconnaissance.

From 1954 onwards the BTR–152 was modified into various new models. Firstly the BTR–152V appeared, marked chiefly by the use of a tyre inflation/deflation

332

334

330. *BAV (ZIL–485) wheeled amphibian;* 331. *MAV (GAZ–46) wheeled amphibian;* 332. *BTR–152V1 Armoured Personnel Carrier;* 333. *BTR–152V2 Armoured Personnel Carrier;* 334. *BTR–152V3 Armoured Personnel Carrier.*

new Soviet wheeled amphibians appeared during 1954. An amphibious 2$\frac{1}{2}$-ton truck, closely resembling the American DUKW was produced by the ZIL factory, designated the BAV (ZIL–485), and based on the ZIL–151 truck. In comparison with the original US vehicle, the rear was extended giving a larger cargo space, and a tail-gate was added for ease of loading. The vehicle was propelled in water by a large-three-bladed propeller located at the rear in the centre. It carried 25 to 30 men, 2$\frac{1}{2}$ tons of payload or the 85 mm divisional gun. Its speed on land was 40 mph, in water, 5 knots. It was principally operated by engineer units to ferry troops and equipment making rapid assault crossings.

device. The early models were built on the ZIL–151 truck chassis and had an external air-line system, but later models built on the ZIL–157 truck chassis had an internal air-line system. Four models of the BTR–152V have been produced as follows:

BTR–152V1: external air-lines and fitted with a winch.

BTR–152V2: internal air-lines and no winch (converted BTR–152).

BTR–153V3: internal air-lines, with winch, and IR driving lights.

BTR–152K : similar to BTR–152V3 but provided with overhead cover.

335

337

336

338

An armoured command version of the BTR–152 was adopted, designated the BTR–152U. This was a standard BTR–152V (either V1 or V3) with a built-up back and fitted with overhead cover.

A new amphibious $\frac{1}{4}$-ton truck also appeared during 1954 designated the P2S (or MAV 69). This was a more streamlined version of the earlier MAV (GAZ–46). In the tracked vehicle line there appeared the AT–P light armoured artillery prime-mover and the BTR–50P amphibious armoured personnel carrier. The AT–P was based on the ASU–57 gun motor carriage chassis and was designed to tow 85 and 100 mm anti-tank guns, although it was also used to tow 120 mm mortars and 122 mm howitzers. With the reduction in 85 and 100 mm towed artillery, this vehicle became less common.

It had an armoured crew compartment at the front with a 7·62 mm tank machine-gun ball-mounted on the right-hand side of the glacis plate. The crew were seated in an open-topped armoured compartment at the rear. It was, in fact, a modern form of the old Komsomolets armoured tractor. A modified version has been seen provided with overhead cover on the rear crew compartment. Powered by a 110 hp 6-cylinder in-line ZIL–123 engine the vehicle could attain a speed of 40 mph. A command version of the AT–P was built which differed from the tractor in having permanently mounted stowage boxes on the track guards, overhead armour for the troop compartment, and a higher circular fully-rotating cupola for the commander. The exhaust also has been moved to the top of the vehicle. A further modification of the AT–P, with a large full-width troop compartment has also been observed. The BTR–50P was the first of a long line of special infantry vehicles

developed from the PT–76 light amphibious tank. It resembled the tank very closely, except that the turret was removed, and the hull centre was built up into an armoured box to protect the personnel. The armoured personnel version could carry 12 fully-equipped men in addition to the 3-man crew. A 6-cylinder 237 hp in-line V–6 diesel engine gave the vehicle a land speed of 25 mph, and a water speed of 6 knots, over a range of about 160 miles. Hydrojets propelled the vehicle in water, as on the original light tank. The maximum armour thickness was about 14 mm. Other variations of this vehicle have since been produced with overhead cover (designated BTR–50PK) and as commander's vehicles designated BTR–50PU. Apart from the addition of overhead cover the BTR–50PK has an improved vision device mounted on the right-hand side of the frontal armour which is able to rotate. Some of these vehicles have an IR searchlight as well as IR driving lights. Two versions of the BTR–50PU have been observed; the first model differs from the second in having only one projecting bay (cupola) on the glacis plate, while the second has two bays. Both models have overhead cover, but the hatch arrangement differs from that of the BTR–50PK, in that there is a hatch on the left projecting bay, a central rotating cupola just behind the driver, two oval shaped hatches on the roof, and two dome ventilators. There are also mountings for five aerials. Both models have various boxes on the rear deck for extra batteries and other equipment necessary for the radio equipment. The first model has a medium sized IR searchlight mounted to the right of the driver. Recently BTR–50Ps have been observed as portees for 57 mm anti-tank guns M–1943, which, although not a permanent fixture, may be fired from the vehicle.

339

341

340

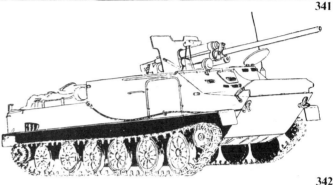

342

343

During 1954 the AT–S artillery prime-mover appeared. It took over the heavier roles of the Ya–14, and later many of the lighter roles of the AT–T tractor. Its main role was a prime-mover for 152 mm gun/howitzers and 100 mm anti-tank guns, and it had a unique suspension with torsion bars in place of the usual volute spring type. The vehicle has also been employed as the prime-mover for an artillery rocket launcher, and the dozer equipment OST. Powered by a 250 hp V–12 cylinder diesel Model V–54–T, the vehicle can achieve a road speed of 22 mph.

During 1955 the BTR–40 became relegated to auxiliary roles such as a carrier vehicle for two ZPU–2 machine-guns, an armoured radio/command vehicle and an armoured ambulance. There was also a chemical reconnaissance vehicle designated the BTR–40–rkh.

The special AA version of the BTR–40 was provided with a small, fully-rotating turret mounting twin 14·5 mm machine-guns. This vehicle went into production and was employed for supporting armoured units against aircraft and ground targets. A similar installation has since been installed on the BTR–152 6-wheeled armoured personnel carrier.

It was during 1956 that the AT–L(mod) appeared, becoming the standard light artillery tractor of the Soviet forces. It received a new suspension system consisting of 5 large roadwheels instead of the 6 small roadwheels and 3 track support rollers as found on the original tractor.

Also in 1956 an armoured amphibious cargo/personnel carrier appeared, this being the GAZ–47 (also known as the GT–S). This vehicle was propelled in the water by its tracks only, and utilized suspension and automotive components of the AT–P armoured tractor. It was powered by a 74 hp

344

335. *BTR–152 converted to mine-laying role;* 336. *BTR–152U Armoured Command Vehicle;* 337. *AT–P Armoured Artillery Tractor;* 338. *AT–PU Armoured Command Vehicle;* 339. *BTR–50P Amphibious Armoured Personnel Carrier;* 340. *BTR–50PK Armoured Personnel Carrier with overhead cover;* 341. *BTR–50PU Model 2 Armoured Command Vehicle;* 342. *BTR–50P carrying 57 mm A/Tk gun M–1943;* 343. *AT–S artillery tractor;* 344. *AT–L (modified) artillery tractor.*

345

348

346

349

347

6-cylinder in-line petrol engine (model GAZ–61) and weighed 8,000 lbs. It could carry 11 men or 2,000 lbs of equipment at 22 mph on land and 2½ mph in water.

A new amphibious armoured car was introduced during 1959, designated the BRDM (also known as the BTR–40A or BTR–40P) or the Bronevaya Razvedyvatelnaya Dosornaya Maschina. This vehicle has a boat-shaped hull and front-mounted engine and was propelled in water by a single propeller at the rear. Later vehicles had hydro-jet propulsion. The most interesting feature of this vehicle was that there were four auxiliary wheels which could be lowered and used as required; they were chain driven from the main gearbox. The four main wheels had a tyre inflation/deflation device. Originally open-topped, some of these cars have since been covered in and redesignated

350

BTR–40PK. The vehicle is used for tactical and chemical reconnaissance of water obstacles, and as a carrier vehicle for anti-tank guided-weapon systems and radio equipment. There is also a chemical/radiological reconnaissance vehicle designated BTR–40P-rkh.

During the late fifties various new tank recovery vehicles were identified in Soviet use. Three variants of the ISU–T appeared. The Model C is essentially the same as the ISU–T (model B), with the addition of an earth anchor, and is in use with medium as well as heavy tank units. The Model D is a further modification of the ISU–T (Model C). The most important additions are the provision for deep water fording by means of a chimney snorkel, and the two pushing bars mounted on the front of the vehicle. This vehicle supports fording operations by medium tank units, along

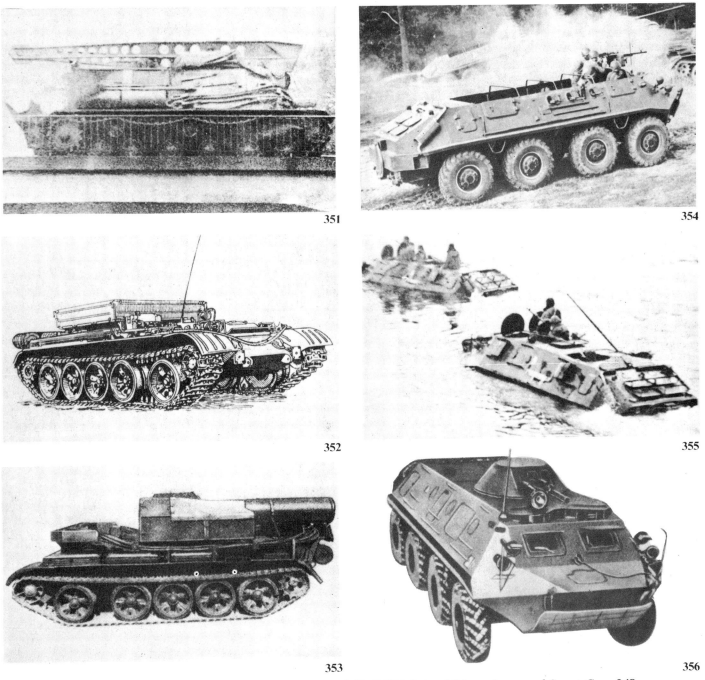

351

354

352

355

353

356

345. *GAZ–47 (GTS) Amphibious Armoured Carrier;* **346, 347.** *BRDM Amphibious Armoured Scout Car;* **348.** *BTR–40PK Armoured Scout Car with overhead cover;* **349.** *BTR–40–rkh Armoured Chemical Reconnaissance Car;* **350.** *ISU–T ARV Model D (based on ISU gun motor carriage);* **351.** *ISU–T Model E (based on ISU gun motor carriage);* **352.** *T–54–T ARV (based on T–54);* **353.** *T–54–T ARV with snorkel;* **354.** *BTR–60P Wheeled Armoured Amphibious Personnel Carrier;* **355.** *BTR–60PK Wheeled Armoured Amphibious Personnel Carrier with overhead cover;* **356.** *BTR–60PB Wheeled Amphibious Armoured Personnel Carrier with turret and heavy MG.*

with the medium vehicle T–54–T and non-snorkelling recovery vehicles. The most recent ISU–T variant, the Model E, is basically a Model C equipped with a large A-frame as well as a dismountable jib-crane. The A-frame is capable of lifting heavy loads, and armoured maintenance units employ it to remove tank turrets. The most modern ARVs of the Soviet Army are based on the T–54 The T–54–T has all of the features of the improved T–34–T (Model B)

mounted on the standard T–54 tank chassis. In addition it has a large spade mounted on the rear of the vehicle and a large chimney snorkel which allows the vehicle to engage in deep fording operations. Later models have more powerful engines than the original gun tanks. A non-amphibious T–54 recovery vehicle has also been identified, but the true designation is as yet unknown.

The new ATS–59 tracked prime-mover entered service

during 1959 to replace the AT–S. This vehicle is more streamlined and has a new suspension, more powerful engine and greater top speed. The engine is a 300 hp V–12 diesel giving a sustained speed of 25 mph.

The sixties. A new wheeled armoured amphibious infantry vehicle appeared during November 1961. This was the BTR–60P 8 × 8 amphibious armoured personnel carrier. In this vehicle the water-cooled engine a 180 hp V–8 ZIL–375 petrol engine was mounted at the rear. On land all 8 wheels are driven, but only the forward pairs are for steering. Water propulsion comes from a hydro-jet system similar to that used on the BRDM. The vehicle has IR driving lights and an IR commander's searchlight. The tyres have inflation/deflation devices. The speed on land is 50 mph and in water 6 mph. Besides the two-man crew,

14 fully-equipped riflemen may be carried. Originally issued to Soviet marines this vehicle has gradually been superceding the BTR–152 in motor-rifle regiments of the Soviet Army. Two further models have since been developed, one with overhead cover (designated BTR–60PK), and another with a small turret mounting a 14·5 mm machine-gun (designated BTR–60PB). Both incorporate a number of changes, some of which are minor, others more pronounced: on the BTR–60PK, besides the provision of overhead cover, the most noticeable difference is the location of the forward machine-gun mount, which is now somewhat towards the centre of the vehicle. Like the BTR–60P this vehicle may mount up to three 12·7 mm or 7·62 mm machine-guns, but normally it carries a single 7·62 mm Goryunov machine-gun. The BTR–60PB has the same turret as the BTR–40PB. Unusual for a wheeled vehicle is the fact that the BTR–60P series has torsion-bar suspension. In keeping with previous Soviet APC development, it would not be surprising to see a command version of the BTR–60P introduced into the Soviet Army.

During 1961 overhead cover versions of the BTR–40 and the BTR–152 appeared. So modified, the BTR–40 was retained for the reconnaissance role and became known as the BTR–40K, differing from the basic vehicle in having an armoured roof with two sets of hinged doors so that troops can get in and out of the vehicle rapidly and man their weapons more effectively. When closed down, the crew can fire their small-arms only through the firing ports on the sides and rear of the vehicle. The modified BTR–152 (as mentioned previously) now became based on the ZIL–157 chassis, and designated the BTR–152K (some sources call this vehicle the BTR–152D). Both these vehicles were intro-

357

357. A motorized rifle section dismount from their BTR–60P; 358. BTR–60PKs in action. These vehicles have overhead armour cover; 359. BTR–152K Armoured Personnel Carrier with overhead cover; 360. GAZ–48 full-tracked amphibious armoured carrier; 361. GSP full-tracked amphibious load carrier; 362. full-tracked amphibious bridging vehicle; 363. PV–A full-tracked amphibious load carrier.

duced to provide some form of protection from nuclear and chemical contamination.

During 1963 two further tracked amphibians were introduced: the GAZ–48, an armoured personnel and load carrier (similar to the older GAZ–47) and a heavy 15-ton raft and load carrier (unarmoured) designated the GSP. The GAZ–48 was a larger, more powerful version of the GAZ–47, having a fully-enclosed cargo compartment making it suitable for arctic operations. With an unladen weight of 8,800 lbs this vehicle can carry a payload of 3,500 lbs at a top speed of 23 mph. The engine is a GAZ–53 V–8

developing 115 hp. The GSP utilized components of the PT–76 light tank, with a slightly extended running gear. Also known as the PT–S, this vehicle had two propellers, each in a rear stern tunnel. This has been the largest amphibious vehicle observed in Soviet use. A complete ferry consists of two of these vehicles, a right hand section and a left-hand section: each vehicle moves the pontoon into a float position and the vehicles are joined. The resulting self-propelled ferry can carry medium tanks. With an unladen weight of 33,000 lbs, the vehicle is powered by a 180 hp 6-cylinder pancake diesel giving it a speed on land

364. *BTR–40PB armoured amphibious scout car;* **365.** *BTR–40PB armoured cars of a modern Soviet reconnaissance unit;* **366.** *BMP–76PB armoured amphibious personnel carrier.*

of 25 mph and in water of 6 mph. It has a load capacity of 33,000 lbs afloat.

A further new amphibious vehicle is the PVA which uses the same suspension and water propulsion system as the PT–76 light tank, but has wider tracks.

During 1964 the Russians introduced a new front-engined version of the BRDM, based on similar derivatives developed in Czechoslovakia and East Germany. This vehicle had a conical turret which mounted 1 or 2 7·62 mm machine-guns and either a 14·5 mm machine gun or a light mortar. It has been designated the BTR–40PB.

In 1965 a new armoured amphibious prime-mover appeared; this is probably a GAZ vehicle, but as yet nothing is known about it in detail.

Recently the Soviet press has portrayed a number of vehicles which are at the moment in the experimental stage, but may well be developed for the Army. One of these is the GPI–37 light tracked transporter. This is a prototype ultra-light amphibian based on the Moskvitch–407 passenger car and weighing about 1 ton. It can carry a half-ton pay-load at a speed of 22 mph. The engine is a 45 hp in-line petrol type (probably GAZ).

The latest development in the armoured carrier field to be exhibited by the Russians is a new tracked armoured personnel carrier, equipped with a small turret mounting a guided weapon launcher and a 76 mm gun, designated BMP–76PB (Boyevaga Mashina Piechoty). This was seen for the first time during the 1967 parades. The vehicle employs certain components and design features of the PT–76 light tank and carries half a section (8 men). It is amphibious but has no hydro-jet propulsion system; it is propelled and steered in water by its tracks. The engine is mounted at the right front with the driver on the left. The one-man turret mounts a smooth-bore 76 mm gun which may possibly fire a fin-stabilized hollow-charged round (at high velocity) to a range of 1,000 metres. Coaxial with the gun is a 7·62 mm machine-gun. Also attached to the mantlet is a single guide-rail for a Sagger anti-tank guided-weapon. A periscope sight is attached at the left front of the turret. The riflemen are each provided with a firing port, and the vehicle crew appear to have IR facilities.

APPENDICES

Data Tables
Light Tanks

	KS–1/2/3	MS–1/2/3/3A
Crew	2	2
Weight, combat (tons)	6·9	5·4–6·7
Length, overall (ft)	12·1/16·5[1]	11·8/14·3[1]
length ex. gun (ft)	12·1/16·5[1]	11·8/14·3[1]
Width, overall (ft)	5·75	5·75
over tracks (ft)	5·70	5·70
Track centres (ft)	4·50	4·70
Height, overall (ft)	7·50	6·90
Ground clearance (in)	16·5	15·5
Ground contact (ft)	6·8	8·0
Max speed, road (mph)	8·3	10·6–14·0
cross-country (mph)	5	8
cruising (mph)	2–4·5	6
Fuel capacity (gal)	19·85	19·85
Range, road (miles)	37·5	37·5–68
cross-country (miles)	22	20–40
Turning circle (ft)	pivots	pivots
Power : weight ratio	6·5	6·5–6·0
Ground pressure (psi)	5·69	6·1–6·5
Trench crossing (ft)	5·9	4·25
Vertical step (ft)	1·9	1·9
Grade ability (°)	38	35
Fording, unprep. (ft)	1·7	2·35
Engine: model	A.M.O.	Fiat 'transverse)
type	Flat 4 cyl	Flat 4 or 6 cyl
output (hp/rpm)	33·5–45/1500	35–40/1500
cooling	thermo-syphon	water/air[3]
Transmission	sliding gear	sliding gear
Gear ratios (fwd/rev)	4/1	4/1
Steering	clutch and brake	simple differential (manual)
Tracks: type	flat steel plates	skeleton, cast double spud
width (in)	16	11·8
pitch (in)	10	5·9
shoes per track	32	54
Suspension	pivoted dble arms & dble bogies; coil & leaf springs	vertical helical springs additional bogie at front
wheels per side	4 double bogies per side with single bogie each side behind idler[5]	
Armament: main	KS–1, 3: 37 mm Hotchkiss L/21	37 mm Puteaux A/Tk gun
auxiliary	KS–2, 3: 7·62 mm Hotchkiss MG	1 or 2 7·62 mm Hotchkiss MGs
traverse (°)	360	360
elevation (°)	—5+35	—10+30
Ammunition: main	250	250
auxiliary	3000	3000
Communications	flag	flag[4]
Armour: turret (mm)	8–16	8–22
hull side, front (mm)	8	8
hull side, rear (mm)	8	8
hull front (mm)	16	16
hull rear (mm)	8	8
hull floor (mm)	6	6
hull roof (mm)	6	6

T-27	T-27A/T-27B*	T-37 (3-2T)	T-37/T-37A*	T-38/T-38-M2*
2	2	2	2	2
1·7	2·68/1·9*	3·18	3·5/3·9*	3·28/3·8*
7·5	8·5/8·1*	12·26	12·26	12·35
7·5	8·5/8·1*	12·26	12·26	12·35
5·1	6·0/5·5*	6·51	6·51	7·65
5·0	5·5	6·5	6·5	7·5
4·55	5·0	5·5	5·5	6·9
3·6	4·76/4·5*	5·5	5·91	5·33/5·15*
9·5	9·5/11·0*	11·8	11·8	11·8/10*
4·5	4·8/4·76*	5·15	5·15	6·25/6·5*
28	25	26	40	28/40*
20	20	12	20	15/25*
15	15	2·5[7]	2·5[8]	3·75/4·4*[8]
8	8·0/9·85*	24	22	26·5/35*
100	53/100*	153	143/115*	156/160*
42	37·5	72	64/60*	137/140*
12·0	13·1	19·6	19·6	20·0
11·9	8·21/11·58*	12·55	18·5/17·9*	12·2/13·2*
8·6	10·7/7·6*	7·5	7·83/9·48*	8·0/9·25*
3·75	4·0	5·25	5·25	5·5
1·25	1·6	1·6	1·6	1·6
49	40/45*	30–40	30–40	40
1·8	1·6/2·15*	floats	floats	floats
GAZ (Ford) AA	GAZ (Ford) AA	GAZ (Ford) AA	GAZ (Ford) AA	GAZ (Ford) AA/M1*
4 cyl (petrol)	4 cyl (petrol)	4 cyl (petrol)	4 cyl (petrol)	4 cyl (petrol)
22/1700	40/2200	40/3000	65/2200	(40/50*) 2200
water	water	water	water	water
epicyclic	epicyclic	epicyclic	epicyclic	epicyclic
3/1	3/1	4/1	4/1	4/1
clutch and brake	clutch and brake	simple differential	simple differential	clutch and brake
drop-forged	drop-forged	drop-forged	drop-forged	drop-forged
5·5	5·5	8·26	8·26	7·5
1·7	1·7	3·5	3·5	2·5
100	108/106*	90	90	146
Vickers-Carden-Loyd	Vickers-Carden-Loyd	Horstman (modified)	coil spring	coil spring
	6 bogies per side	4 wheels per side	4 wheels per side	4 wheels per side
—	—	—	—	—
7·62 mm DT MG	7·62 mm DT MG[2]	7·62 mm DT MG	7·62 mm DT MG or 12·7 mm DShK	7·62 mm DT MG
20	20	360	360	360
—10+10	—10+10	—5+5	—5+5	—5+5
	—	—	—	
2520	2520	585	585	1512
flag	flag[7]	flag	flag[9]	flag[10][11]
9[5]	10[6]	4–6	4–6	4–6
9	10	7	7/10*	9
8	9	7	7/10*	9
9	10	9·5	9·5/10*	9·5
8	9	6	6	6
4	4	4	4/5–7*	4
6	6	4	4/5*	4

1: w.o./with tail 2: some vehicles were fitted with a 12·7 mm DShK MG instead of the 7·62 mm DT. 3: MS–1/remainder 4: Some fitted with radio 5: MS–I had three track support rollers. Remainder had four track support rollers 6: Hull and turret integral 7: Commander's

	T–26A (series)	T–26V–1	T–26V	OT–26
Crew	3	2	3	2
Weight, combat (tons)	7–8·5	7·0	8·1–8·6[14]	7·0
Length, overall (ft)	15·76	15·76	15·76	15·76
length ex. gun (ft)	15·76	15·76	15·76	15·76
Width, overall (ft)	7·85	7·85	7·85	7·85
over tracks (ft)	7·66	7·66	7·66	7·66
Track centres (ft)	6·95	6·95	6·95	6·95
Height, overall (ft)	6·75	6·75	6·75	6·75
Ground clearance (in)	1·2	1·2	1·2	1·2
Ground contact (ft)	9·75	9·75	9·75	9·75
Max speed, road (mph)	22	22	20	22
cross-country (mph)	15	15	15	13
cruising (mph)	10	10	10	10
Fuel capacity (gal)	40	40	40	40
Range, road (miles)	87	87·5	87·5	87·5
cross-country (miles)	60	60	60	60
Turning circle (ft)	42·5	42·5	42·5	42·5
Power : weight ratio	12·6–10·3	12·6	11–10·3[14]	12·6
Ground pressure (psi)	8·96–11·0	8·96	10·4–11·0[14]	8·96
Trench crossing (ft)	5·85	5·85	5·85	5·85
Vertical step (ft)	2·4	2·4	2·4	2·4
Grade ability (°)	32	32	32	32
Fording, unprep. (ft)	2·85	2·85	2·85	2·85
Engine: model	GAZ T–26 (Armstrong-Siddeley licence)			
type	8 cyl (petrol) horizontally opposed			
output (hp/rpm)	88–91/2200			
cooling	air			
Transmission	epicyclic	epicyclic	epicyclic	epicyclic
Gear ratios (fwd/rev)	5/1	5/1	5/1	5/1
Steering	clutch and brake	clutch and brake	clutch and brake	clutch and brake
Tracks: type	drop-forged	drop-forged	drop-forged	drop-forged
width (in)	10·2	10·2	10·2	10·2
pitch (in)	3·625	3·625	3·625	3·625
shoes per track	95	95	95	95
Suspension	quarter-elliptic; double arms with double bogies; both base arms and bogie arms sprung			
wheels per side	4 wheels per side			
Armament: main	—	20 mm cannon[13]	27 mm or 37 mm gun[13]	OT–26 flame-gun[13]
auxiliary		—	7·62 mm DT MG	—
traverse (°)	See text for	360	265	360
elevation (°)	model variations	−10+10	−10+40	−10+10
Ammunition: main		1000	180	14·3 (galls)
auxiliary		—	3000	—
Communications	flag	radio	radio	flag
Armour: turret (mm)	6–15[12]	6–15	6–15[12]	6–15
hull side, front (mm)	15	15	15	15
hull side, rear (mm)	15	15	15	15
hull front (mm)	15	15	15	15
hull rear (mm)	15	15	15	15
hull floor (mm)	10	10	10	10
hull roof (mm)	6	6	6	6

model fitted with radio—designated T–27V 8: Speed in water 9: Commander's model fitted with radio—designated T–37V 10: Commander's model fitted with radio—designated T–38V 11: Commander's model fitted with radio—designated T–38M2V 12: Each of two turrets

T–26B–1/1V*	AT–26	T–46	T–26B–2	OT–130
3	3	3	3	3
9·2/9·6[14]	10·1	10·2	9·55	9·3
15·76	15·76	18·0	15·0	15·1
15·76	15·76	18·0	15·0	15·1
7·85	7·85	7·66	8·05	8·05
7·66	7·66	7·5	7·66	7·66
6·95	6·95	6·69	6·66	6·66
7·95	8·25	7·5	8·33	8·33
1·2	1·2	1·15	1·15	1·15
9·75	9·75	12·0	9·1	9·1
17·5	17	35/36	17·5	17·5
13	13	20	13	13
10	10	20	10	10
63	63	74	63·5	63
140	140	224/310[15]	215	215
110	110	180/250[15]	109	110
42·5	42·5	47·5	42·5	42·5
9·9/9·5*[14]	8·7	8·7	9·6	9·46
11·8/12·3*[14]	10·1	8·96	12·3	8·95
5·85	5·85	6·85	5·66	5·66
2·4	2·4	2·46	2·33	2·4
32	32	40	32	32
2·85	2·85	3·1	2·85	2·5
GAZ T–26 (Armstrong-Siddeley licence)			GAZ T–26 (Armstrong-Siddeley licence)	
8 cyl (petrol) horizontally opposed			8 cyl (petrol) horizontally opposed	
88–91/2200			88–91/2200	
air			air	
epicyclic	epicyclic	epicyclic	epicyclic	epicyclic
5/1	5/1	5/1	5/1	5/1
clutch and brake	clutch and brake	clutch and brake	clutch and brake	clutch and brake
drop-forged	drop-forged	drop-forged	drop-forged	drop-forged
10·2	10·2	10·25	10·2	10·2
3·625	3·625	10	3·625	3·625
95	95	72	95	95
quarter-elliptic; double arms with double bogies; both base arms and bogie arms sprung		Christie (independent)	quarter-elliptic	quarter-elliptic
4 wheels per side		4 wheels per side	4 wheels per side	4 wheels per side
37 mm/45 mm L46* A/Tk gun, 7·62 mm DT MG	76·2 mm L/16·5 gun	45 mm L/46 A/Tk gun	45 mm L/46 A/Tk. gun	OT–130 flame-gun
—	7·62 mm DT MG	7·62 mm DT MG	2×7·62 mm DT MG	7·62 mm DT MG
360	360	360	360	360
—10+40	—10+60	—10+40	—10+40	—10+40
100/92*	32	165	165	28·6/32·2 (galls)*
3000	3000	3654	3654	2000
flag/radio*	radio	radio	radio[16]	radio
6–15	6–15	6–15	10–25 mm	10–25
15	15	15	16	16
15	15	15	16	16
15	15	15	13	13
10	10	10	10	10
6–10	6–10	6–10	7–11	7–11

13: Right-hand turret 14: Depending on converted model 15: Tracks/wheels 16: Fitted only to very late production models 17: Lengths with and w.o. bridge. 18: Optional 19: Commander's model fitted with radio—designated T–40V

	T–26S	OT–133	T–26MU (IT–26)	DT–26
Crew	3	3	1	2
Weight, combat (tons)	10·3	9·5	8·6	6·8
Length, overall (ft)	15·25	15·0	21·1	15·75
length ex. gun (ft)	15·25	15·0	15·0[17]	15·75
Width, overall (ft)	8·0	7·95	8·0	7·85
over tracks (ft)	7·66	7·66	7·66	7·66
Track centres (ft)	6·98	6·98	6·98	6·98
Height, overall (ft)	7·65	7·65	6·85	6·75
Ground clearance (in)	1·15	1·15	1·18	1·15
Ground contact (ft)	9·75	9·75	9·75	9·75
Max speed, road (mph)	16·8	17·5	20	25
cross-country (mph)	13	13	5	15
cruising (mph)	10	10	10	10
Fuel capacity (gal)	64·5	64·5	68	40
Range, road (miles)	215	130	150	90
cross-country (miles)	109	105	120	60
Turning circle (ft)	42·5	42·5	42·5	42·5
Power : weight ratio	8·9	9·57	10·23	12·8
Ground pressure (psi)	9·36	12·3	11·0	8·7
Trench crossing (ft)	5·66	5·85	5·85	5·85
Vertical step (ft)	2·33	2·45	2·45	2·45
Grade ability (°)	32	32	32	32
Fording, unprep. (ft)	2·5	2·85	2·85	2·85
Engine: model	GAZ T–26 (Armstrong-Siddeley licence)			
type	8 cyl (petrol) horizontally opposed			
output (hp/rpm)	88–81/2200			
cooling	air			
Transmission	epicyclic	epicyclic	epicyclic	epicyclic
Gear ratios (fwd/rev)	5/1	5/1	5/1	5/1
Steering	clutch and brake	clutch and brake	clutch and brake	clutch and brake
Tracks: type	drop-forged	drop-forged	drop-forged	drop-forged
width (in)	10·2	10·2	10·2	10·2
pitch (in)	3·625	3·625	3·625	3·625
shoes per track	95	95	95	95
Suspension	quarter-elliptic	quarter-elliptic	quarter-elliptic	quarter-elliptic
wheels per side	4 wheels per side	4 wheels per side	4 wheels per side	4 wheels per side
Armament: main	45 mm L/46 A/Tk gun	OT–133 flame-gun	—	2 × sulphuric acid smoke generators
auxiliary	2 × 7·62 mm DT MG	7·62 mm DT MG	—	7·62 mm DT MG
traverse (°)	360	360	—	360
elevation (°)	−10+40	−10+40	—	−10+10
Ammunition: main	165	32·2 (galls)	—	42·7 (galls)
auxiliary	3654	3000	—	250
Communications	radio	radio	radio	flag
Armour: turret (mm)	10–25	10–25	—	6–15
hull side, front (mm)	16	16	15	15
hull side, rear (mm)	16	16	15	15
hull front (mm)	25	25	15	15
hull rear (mm)	16	16	15	15
hull floor (mm)	10	10	10	10
hull roof (mm)	10	10	6–10	6

T–50	T–40/T–40A*	T–40S	T–60/T–60A*	T–70
4	2	2	2	2
13·5	5·5/6·2*	6·1	5·75/6·4*	9·05
17·0	13·5/14·0*	13·85	13·1/13·65*	15·28
17·0	13·5/14·0*	13·85	13·1/13·65*	14·1
8·1	7·65	7·65	7·5/7·66*	7·68
8·1	6·18	6·18	7·18	7·5
6·6	5·65	5·65	6·65	5·2
7·1	6·48	6·38	5·75/5·85*	6·78
1·1	1·18	1·18	1·0	11·75
9·5	7·66	7·66	7·5	10·25
32·5	28/26*	26	27·5/26·2*	32
25	17	17	20	14
20	3·1[8]	5·0	15	20
77	45·5/45·5*	45·5	70·5	101
220	222/210*	216	384/375*	279
172	115/100*	110	197/188*	186
45	39·6	39·6	39·6	41
23·2	15·45/13·7*	13·9	12·2/13·3*	7·74
8·12	6·55/7·4*	7·25	6·55/7·8*	9·53
7·15	5·65	5·65	5·65	5·95
2·25	2·15	2·1	1·65	2·18
35	34	34	29	34
3·6	floats	floats	2·85	2·95
GAZ V–4	GAZ–202	GAZ–202	GAZ–202	2 × ZIS–202
6 cyl (diesel)	6 cyl (petrol)	6 cyl (petrol)	6 cyl (petrol)	each 6 cyl (petrol)
300/2000	85/3600	85/3600	(70/85*)/(2800/3600*)	each 70/2800
water	water	water	water	water
epicyclic	sliding gear	sliding gear	sliding gear	sliding gear
5/1	4/1	4/1	4/1	4/1
clutch and brake	clutch and brake	clutch and brake	clutch and brake	clutch and brake
cast manganese steel	cast manganese steel	cast manganese steel	cast manganese steel	cast manganese steel
17·0	7·0	7·0	7·0	17·5
2·5	2·5	2·5	2·5	3·25
110	70	70	70	91
torsion-bar	torsion-bar	torsion-bar	torsion-bar	torsion-bar
(independent)	(independent)	(independent)	(independent)	(independent)
6 wheels per side	4 wheels per side	4 wheels per side	4 wheels per side	5 wheels per side
45 mm L/46 A/Tk gun	12·7 mm DShK or 20 mm cannon	12·7 mm DShK or 20 mm cannon	20 mm ShVAK cannon	45 mm L/46 A/Tk gun
7·62 mm DT MG	7·62 mm DT MG[18]	7·62 mm DT MG[18]	7·62 mm DT MG	7·62 mm DT MG
360	360	360	360	360
−10+40	−10+40	−10+40	−10+40	−6+20
150	550	550	780	66–70
4000	2016	2016	945	945
radio-telephone	flag[19]	radio	radio and intercom	radio and intercom
15–37	7–14	7–14	7–15/25*	10–60
37	13/14*	14	15/25*	16
25	13/14*	14	15/25*	16
37	10–13/14*	14	14–20/35*	35–40
25–37	10/12*	12	10–13/25*	25
12–15	6–10/10*	10	7–10/13*	10
12–15	6–10/10*	10	7–10/13*	10

	T–70A	T–80	T–34	PT–76
Crew	2	3	3	3
Weight, combat (tons)	10·0	11·6	8·94	14·7
Length, overall (ft)	15·48	15·49	12·25	24·85
length ex. gun (ft)	14·48	14·5	12·0	22·66
Width, overall (ft)	8·1	8·47	7·5	10·33
over tracks (ft)	7·85	8·20	7·35	10·1
Track centres (ft)	6·76	6·98	5·98	9·1
Height, overall (ft)	6·66	7·15	6·5	7·33
Ground clearance (in)	11·75	11·75	11·0	14·0
Ground contact (ft)	10·25	10·25	6·18	13·48
Max speed, road (mph)	28	25	30	25
cross-country (mph)	14	14	15	18
cruising (mph)	20	18	20	6[8]
Fuel capacity (gal)	101	97·5	101	55
Range, road (miles)	260	200	224	155
cross-country (miles)	175	145	112	110
Turning circle (ft)	41	41	41	40
Power : weight ratio	8·5	7·3	9·5	16·3
Ground pressure (psi)	10·05	11·4	9·48	6·7
Trench crossing (ft)	5·98	5·98	5·0	7·5
Vertical step (ft)	2·18	2·18	2·0	3·5
Grade ability (°)	34	34	34	38
Fording, unprep. (ft)	2·98	2·98	3·0	floats
Engine: model	2×GAZ–203	2×GAZ–203	2×GAZ–202	T–54V–2
type	6 cyl (petrol)	6 cyl (petrol)	6 cyl (petrol)	6 cyl (diesel)
output (hp/rpm)	85/3600	85/3600	85/3600	240/1200
cooling	water	water	water	water
Transmission	sliding gear	sliding gear	sliding gear	sliding gear
Gear ratios (fwd/rev)	4/1	4/1	4/1	5/1
Steering	clutch and brake	clutch and brake	clutch and brake	clutch and brake
Tracks: type	cast manganese steel	cast manganese steel	cast manganese steel	cast manganese steel
width (in)	17·5	17·5	17·5	12·0
pitch (in)	3·25	3·25	3·25	2·5
shoes per track	91	91	95	108
Suspension	torsion-bar (independent)	torsion-bar (independent)	torsion-bar (independent)	torsion-bar (independent)
wheels per side	5 wheels per side	5 wheels per side	3 wheels per side	6 wheels per side
Armament: main	45 mm L/46 A/Tk gun	45 mm L/46 A/Tk gun	57 mm ZIS–1 or 45 mm L/46	76·2 mm D–56T G.P. gun
auxiliary	7·62 mm DT MG	7·62 mm DT MG	7·62 mm DT MG	7·62 mm SGMT MG
traverse (°)	360	360	360	360
elevation (°)	−6+20	−6+20	−5+30	−4+30
Ammunition: main	94	94	50	40
auxiliary	1008	1008	1008	1008
Communications	radio and intercom	radio and intercom	radio and intercom	radio and intercom
Armour: turret (mm)	10–70	20–70	10–70	10–45
hull side, front (mm)	16	16–25	16	10–15
hull side, rear (mm)	16	16–25	16	10–15
hull front (mm)	35–45	50	34	15–20
hull rear (mm)	25	25	25	10
hull floor (mm)	10	15	10	10
hull roof (mm)	10	15	10	10

Medium Tanks

	T–24	BT–1/BT–2 (early)*
Crew	5	3
Weight, combat (tons)	18·5	10·2
Length, overall (ft)	21·5	18·0
length ex. gun (ft)	21·18	18·0
Width, overall (ft)	9·85	7·33
over tracks (ft)	9·66	7·16
Track centres (ft)	7·75	6·33
Height, overall (ft)	9·20	7·25
Ground clearance (in)	2·0	9/10·5[2]
Ground contact (ft)	9·85	10·66
Max speed, road (mph)	13·75	69[3]
cross-country (mph)	8	39
cruising (mph)	10	40
Fuel capacity (gal)	20·8	88
Range, road (miles)	42	187[3]
cross-country (miles)	25	125
Turning circle (ft)	pivots	40
Power : weight ratio	13·5	34·3
Ground pressure (psi)	9·2	8·96
Trench crossing (ft)	8·10	6·85
Vertical step (in)	2·18	8/29·4[2]
Grade ability (°)	30	40
Fording, unprep. (ft)	2·25	3·95
Engine: model	M–5 (modified Aero)[1]	Liberty Aero
type	12 cyl (petrol)	12 cyl V (petrol)
output (hp/rpm)	250/1800	343–400/2000
cooling	water	water
Transmission	sliding gear	sliding gear
Gear ratios (fwd/rev)	4/1	4/1
Steering	clutch and brake	as BT–2 (late)–BT–IT
Tracks: type	laminated steel plates	drop-forged
width (in)	23	10·25
pitch (in)	10	10
shoes per track	73	73
Suspension	helical springs	Christie independent type
wheels per side	8 double bogies per side	4 large bogie wheels per side
Armament: main	45 mm gun M–1920	—
auxiliary	4×7·62 mm Hotchkiss MGs	2×7·62 mm air-cooled MGs
traverse (°)	360	360
elevation (°)	−5+30	−10+10
Ammunition: main	30–45	—
auxiliary	3000	4000
Communications	flag	flag
Armour: turret (mm)	8·5–20	10–13
hull side, front (mm)	8	10–13
hull side, rear (mm)	8	10–13
hull front (mm)	20	13
hull rear (mm)	8	10
hull floor (mm)	8	6–10
hull roof (mm)	8	6–10

	BT–2 (late)	BT–3/4*	BT–5/5A*	BT–IT
Crew	3	3	3	1
Weight, combat (tons)	11·0	10·2	11·5/11·7*	12·7
Length, overall (ft)	18·1	18·0	18·1/18·0*	21·33[8]
length ex. gun (ft)	18·0	18·0	18·0	18·0
Width, overall (ft)	7·33	7·33	7·33	7·33
over tracks (ft)	7·18	7·18	7·18	7·16
Track centres (ft)	6·33	6·33	6·33	6·33
Height, overall (ft)	7·25	7·25	7·25	7·25
Ground clearance (in)	9/10·5[2]	9/10·5[2]	9/10·5[2]	9/10·5[2]
Ground contact (ft)	12·0	12·0	12·0	12·0
Max speed, road (mph)	69[3]	69[3]	69[3]	69[3]
cross-country (mph)	39	39	39	5
cruising (mph)	40	40	40	40
Fuel capacity (gal)	88	88	88	88
Range, road (miles)	187[3]	187[3]	187[3]	187[3]
cross-country (miles)	125	125	125	125
Turning circle (ft)	40	40	40	40
Power : weight ratio	32·6	34·3	30·4	30
Ground pressure (psi)	8·96	8·96	9·3	10·4
Trench crossing (ft)	6·85	6·85	8·85	20·0[8]
Vertical step (in)	8/29·8[2]	8/29·8[2]	8/29·8[2]	8/30[2]
Grade ability (°)	40	40	40	40
Fording, unprep. (ft)	3·98	3·98	3·98	3·98
Engine: model	Liberty Aero (modified aircraft engine)		M–5 modified Aero engine	
type	12 cyl V (petrol)		12 cyl V (petrol)	
output (hp/rpm)	343–400/2000		350/2300	
cooling	water	water	water	water
Transmission	sliding gear	sliding gear	sliding gear	sliding gear
Gear ratios (fwd/rev)	4/1	4/1	4/1	4/1
Steering	steering wheel controlling front pair of bogie wheels/clutch and brake*			
Tracks: type	drop-forged	drop-forged	drop-forged	drop-forged
width (in)	10·25	10·25	10·25	10·25
pitch (in)	10	10	10	10
shoes per track	73	73	73	73
Suspension	Christie independent type			
wheels per side	4 large bogie wheels per side			
Armament: main	37 mm M–1930 A/Tk gun	45 mm L/46 A/Tk gun 27 mm gun[4]*	45 mm L/46 A/Tk gun 76·2 mm L/16·5 gun*	
auxiliary	7·62 mm DTMG	7·62 mm DTMG	7·62 mm DTMG	7·62 mm DTMG
traverse (°)	360	360/265*	360	−5+5
elevation (°)	−4+40	−4+40/−5+25*	−4+40	−5+5
Ammunition: main	96	96/180*	72/115[7]	—
auxiliary	2709	2709	2394	2394
Communications	flag	flag/flag[6]*	flag/radio[7]	—
Armour: turret (mm)	10–13	10–13/6–15*	10–13	—
hull side, front (mm)	10–13	10–13	10–13	10–13
hull side, rear (mm)	10–13	10–13	10–13	10–13
hull front (mm)	13	13	13	13
hull rear (mm)	10	10	10	10
hull floor (mm)	6–10	6–10	6–10	6–10
hull roof (mm)	6–10	6–10	6–10	6–10

1: later production models had M–6 engine developing 300HP 2: wheels/tracks 3: wheels 4: right-hand turret 5: left-hand turret 6: intended as commander's tank—production models were to have had radio equipment 7: with/w.o. radio equipment 8: with bridge

BT–5–OT	T–28/28A* (T–28V)	BT–7–1/BT–7–1V*	BT–7–2/BT–7A*	T–29
2	6	3	3	6
11·6	28·5/31*	13·8 13·6	13·8	24·0
18·0	24·25/23·62*	18·65	18·65	23·10
18·0	24·45/23·62*	18·65	18·65	23·10
7·33	9·20	7·98	7·98	9·5
7·16	9·0	7·18	7·18	9·33
6·33	7·85	6·33	6·33	9·5
7·25	9·25/9·0*	7·5	7·5	8·69
9/10·5²	1·78	10·5/12²	10·5/12²	1·78
12·0	19·18/21·25*	12·0	12·0	19·0
69³	23	45·6³	45·6³	50·0³
39	14	33	33	36
40	14	40	40	30
88	143	174	174	143
187³	137/112*	310³	310³	100³
125	100/90*	220	220	75
40	—	40	40	46
30·4	17·6/16·1*	32·6	32·6	21
9·3	10·25/10·6*	10·2	10·2	10·4
6·85	8·85	6·0	6·0	8·5
8/30²	3·18	8/30²	8/30²	11/39²
40	142/43*	32	32	42
3·98	2·62/2·65*	3·98	3·98	2·66
M–5 modified Aero engine	M–17L Liberty⁹	M–17T Liberty		M–17L Liberty
12 cyl V (petrol)	12 cyl V (petrol)	12 cyl V (petrol)		12 cyl V (petrol)
350/2300	500/1450	450/1750		500/1450
water	water	water	water	water
sliding gear	sliding gear	sliding gear	sliding gear	sliding gear
4/1	5/1	3/1	3/1	4/1
(as for previous BT vehicles)	clutch and brake	(as for previous BT		
drop-forged	drop-forged	drop-forged	drop-forged	drop-forged
10·25	14·0	10·25	10·25	10·25
10	6·8	10·0	10·0	10·0
73	76	73	73	80
Christie independent type	Vickers standard vertical plunger type	Christie independent type		
4 large bogie wheels per side	6 double bogies per side	4 large bogie wheels per side		
OT–130 flame-gun	76·2 mm L/16·5+ 7·62 mm DT MG¹⁰	45 mm L/46 A/Tk gun	45 mm L/46 A/Tk gun 76·2 mm L/16·5 gun*	76·2 mm L/26 gun (model L–10)
7·62 mm DT MG	either 47 mm gun or 7·62 mm DT MG¹¹	2×7·62 mm DT MGs	2×7·62 mm DT MGs 1×7·62 mm DT MG*	3×7·62 mm DT MGs
360	see note 11	360	360	360
−10+40	−10+40	−4+40	−4+40	−10+40
28·6 (galls)	70/35¹²	172–188⁷	(132–146/172–188⁷)/40–50*	70
2394	7938	2394	2394	7938
radio	radio	flag	flag/radio⁷	radio
10–13	11–20+20	10–13	10–15	11–40
10–13	20	13	13	20
10–13	20	13	13	20
13	30	22	22	35
10	20	13	13	20
6–10	10–15	6–10	6–10	10–15
6–10	10–15	6–10	6–10	10–15

9: some early tanks fitted with 345HP Hispano-Suiza engine   10: together in main turret—360° traverse   11: in right-hand subsidiary turret, further   DT MG in left-hand subsidiary turret; minor turrets have 90° traverse   12: 76·2/47 mm guns   13: w.o./with L/41·2 gun   14: w.o./with additional

	BT–7M (BT–8)	T–28B (T–28M)/C*	IT–28	OT–28
Crew	3	6	3	6
Weight, combat (tons)	14·65	31/32*	26·5	32·0
Length, overall (ft)	18·65	24·45	24·45	24·45
length ex. gun (ft)	18·65	24·45	24·45	24·45
Width, overall (ft)	7·98	9·20	9·20	9·20
over tracks (ft)	7·18	9·0	9·0	9·0
Track centres (ft)	6·33	7·85	7·85	7·85
Height, overall (ft)	7·5	9·25	11·5	11·5
Ground clearance (in)	10·5/12[2]	1·78	1·78	1·78
Ground contact (ft)	12·0	21·25	21·25	21·25
Max speed, road (mph)	54[3]	14·4	14·4	14·4
cross-country (mph)	39	14	6	14
cruising (mph)	40	14	14	14
Fuel capacity (gal)	174	143	143	143
Range, road (miles)	440[3]	110	110	110
cross-country (miles)	375	85	85	85
Turning circle (ft)	40	—	—	—
Power : weight ratio	35	15·6	18·8	15·6
Ground pressure (psi)	10·4	10·95	10·4	10·95
Trench crossing (ft)	6·85	8·85	38·0	8·85
Vertical step (in)	8/30[2]	3·18	3·18	3·18
Grade ability (°)	32	43	43	43
Fording, unprep. (ft)	3·25	2·65	2·65	2·65
Engine: model	V–2	M–17L Liberty		
type	12 cyl V (diesel)	12 cyl V (petrol)		
output (hp/rpm)	500/2200	500/1450		
cooling	water	water	water	water
Transmission	sliding gear	sliding gear	sliding gear	sliding gear
Gear ratios (fwd/rev)	3/1	5/1	5/1	5/1
Steering		clutch and brake	clutch and brake	clutch and brake
Tracks: type	drop-forged	drop-forged	drop-forged	drop-forged
width (in)	10·25	14·0	14·0	14·0
pitch (in)	10·0	6·8	6·8	6·8
shoes per track	73	76	76	76
Suspension	Christie independent type	Vickers standard vertical plunger type	Vickers standard vertical plunger type	Vickers standard vertical plunger type
wheels per side	4 large bogie wheels per side	6 double bogies per side	6 double bogies per side	6 double bogies per side
Armament: main	76·2 mm L/26 gun (model L–10)	76·2 mm L/26 gun (model L–10)	—	76·2 mm L/26+ (7·62 mm DT MG[10]
auxiliary	2×7·62 mm DT MGs	3×7·62 mm DT MGs	2×7·62 mm DT MGs	OT–130 flame-gun) (see note 11)
traverse (°)	360	360	90	360
elevation (°)	—10+40	—10+40	—5+5	—10+40
Ammunition: main	40	70	—	70
auxiliary	2394	7938	7938	7938/28·6 (galls)
Communications	radio	radio	radio	radio
Armour: turret (mm)	10–15	11–20+20/20–70+10*	—	20–70+10
hull side, front (mm)	13	20/50*	50	50
hull side, rear (mm)	13	20/50*	50	50
hull front (mm)	22	35/50–80*	50–80	50–80
hull rear (mm)	13	20	50	50
hull floor (mm)	6–10	10–15/23*	23	23
hull roof (mm)	6–10	10–15/23*	23	23

fuel tanks   15: commanders' models fitted with L/41·2 gun   16: first 115 produced had additional MG in turret rear   17: as for 13   18: commanders' tanks had radio equipment   19: wider tracks may be fitted to reduce ground pressure   20: w.o/with snorkel   21: 7·62/12·7 mm

BT–IS	A–20/A–30*	T–32	T–34/76A	T–34/76B
3	4	4	4	4
15·6	19·8/20·86*	19·0	26·3	28·0
18·98	17·85	17·85	20/21·6[13]	21·6
18·98	17·85	17·85	20·0	20·0
7·5	8·85	8·85	9·8	9·8
7·18	7·18	7·18	9·6	9·6
6·33	6·33	6·33	8·1	8·1
7·5	7·85	7·85	8·0	8·0
10·5/12[2]	10·5/12[2]	12·0	1·25	1·25
12·0	12·0	12·0	12·2	12·2
70[3]	40[3]/38[3]*	38	31	31
40	40/35*	35	25	25
40	40/35*	35	25	25
174	174	174	90/123[14]	92/123[14]
430[3]	430[3]/400[3]*	400	188/280[14]	188/280[14]
370	370/350*	350	130/240[14]	130/240[14]
40·0	40·0	40·0	25	25
32·0	25·2/24·0*	23·6	19·0	17·9
11·0	12·8/13·1*	9·2	9·1	9·3
6·85	6·85	6·85	9·8	9·8
8/30[2]	8/30[2]	2·5	3·0	2·4
32	30	30	35	35
3·25	3·25	3·25	3·6	4·6
V–2	V–2	V–2	V–2–34	
12 cyl V (diesel)	12 cyl V (diesel)	12 cyl V (diesel)	12 cyl V (diesel)	
500/2200	450/2200	450/2200	500/1800	
water	water	water	water	water
sliding gear	sliding gear	sliding gear	sliding gear	sliding gear
3/1	3/1	3/1	4/1	4/1
(as for previous BT vehicles)		clutch and brake	clutch and brake	clutch and brake
drop-forged	drop-forged	drop-forged	cast manganese steel (horn on each alternate track plate)	
10·25	10·25	10·25	19·1	19·1
10·0	10·0	10·0	6·8	6·8
80	80	80	72	72
Christie independent type		(As for A–30)	Christie independent type	
4 large bogie wheels per side		5 large bogie wheels per side	5 large bogie wheels per side	
45 mm L/46 A/Tk gun	45 mm L/46 A/Tk gun	76·2 mm L/30·5 (Mod 38) dual purpose gun	76·2 mm L/30·5 (Mod 38) dual-purpose gun[15]	76·2 mm L/41·2 (Mod 40) dual-purpose gun
	76·2 mm L/30·5 A/Tk gun			
7·62 mm DT MG	2×7·62 mm DT MGs	2×7·62 mm DT MGs	2×7·62 mm DT MGs[16]	2×7·62 mm DT MGs
360	360	360	360	360
−10+40	−10+40/−5+35*	−5+35	−3+30	−3+30
132	132/40*	40	80/77[17]	77
2394	2394	2394	2394	2394
radio	radio	radio	flag[18]	radio
10–30	16–60	16–60	16–45	16–45+25/20–70*
15	45	16	45	45
15	45	16	40	40–45
30	45	32	45	45+15
15	40	10	40	45
6–10	15	10	15–20	20
6–10	20	10	18–22	18–22

	T-34/76B (ATO-41)	T-34/76C/(D, E, F)*	T-43	T-34/85-I, II
Crew	4	4	4	5
Weight, combat (tons)	30·2	30·9	31	31·5
Length, overall (ft)	24·65	21·6	22·5	24·6
length ex. gun (ft)	23·05	20	19·7	19·7
Width, overall (ft)	9·8	9·8	9·8	9·8
over tracks (ft)	9·6	9·6	9·6	9·6
Track centres (ft)	8·1	8·1	8·1	8·1
Height, overall (ft)	8·0	8·45/8·0*	8·5	7·8
Ground clearance (in)	1·25	1·25	1·25	1·3
Ground contact (ft)	12·2	12·2	12·25	12·2
Max speed, road (mph)	30	31	31	31
cross-country (mph)	25	25	25	25
cruising (mph)	15	20	20	20
Fuel capacity (gal)	92/130[14]	92/130[14]	140/170[14]	140/170[14]
Range, road (miles)	170/260[14]	180/270[14]	186/220[14]	186/220[14]
cross-country (miles)	120/220[14]	125/230[14]	130/210[14]	130/210[14]
Turning circle (ft)	25	25	25	25
Power : weight ratio	16·5	16·2	16·1	15·6
Ground pressure (psi)	19·1	10·0/10·2[19]	10·2[19]	11·2[19]
Trench crossing (ft)	9·8	8·2	8·2	8·2
Vertical step (ft)	2·4	2·8	2·8	2·4
Grade ability (°)	35	30	30	30
Fording, unprep. (ft)	4·6	4·3	4·3	4·3
Engine : model	V-2-34			
type	12 cyl V (diesel)			
output (hp/rpm)	500/1800			
cooling	water	water	water	water
Transmission	sliding gear	sliding gear	sliding gear	sliding gear
Gear ratios (fwd/rev)	4/1	4/1	5/1	5/1
Steering	clutch and brake	clutch and brake	clutch and brake	clutch and brake
Tracks : type	cast manganese steel (horn on each alternate track plate)			
width (in)	19·1	19·1	19·1	19·1
pitch (in)	6·8	6·8	6·8	8·8
shoes per track	72	72	72	72
Suspension	Christie independent type			
wheels per side	5 large bogie wheels per side			
Armament : main	76·2 mm L/41·2 and ATO-41 flame-gun	76·2 mm L/41·2 (Mod 40) dual-purpose gun	76·2 mm L/41·2 (Mod 40) dual purpose gun	85 mm M-1944 ZIS-S53 L/51·5 dual-purpose gun
auxiliary	1 × 7·62 mm DT MG	2 × 7·62 mm DT MGs	2 × 7·62 mm DT MGs	2 × 7·62 mm DT MGs
traverse (°)	360	360	360	360
elevation (°)	—3+30	—3+30	—3+30	—5+25
Ammunition : main	45	77	77	55
auxiliary	2394	2394	2394	2394
Communications	radio	radio	radio	radio ..
Armour : turret (mm)	20–70	20–70	20–70	20–75
hull side, front (mm)	45	45	45–47	45–47
hull side, rear (mm)	40–45	45	45	45
hull front (mm)	45+15	45–47	70–110	47–45+15
hull rear (mm)	45	45	45	45
hull floor (mm)	20	20	18–22	18–22
hull roof (mm)	18–22	18–22	22	18–22

T-44/85/T-44/100*	T-54/T-54(M)	T-54A/T-54A(M)	T-54B	T-55-1/T-55-2
4	4	4	4	4
31·9/34*	35·0	35·4	35·4	35·0
25·1/26·5*	29·65	29·65	30·1	27·95
19·85	21·85	21·85	21·85	19·75
10·2	10·75	10·75	10·75	10·75
10·2	10·33	10·33	10·33	10·33
8·6	8·66	8·66	8·66	8·66
7·85	7·85	7·85	7·85	7·85
1·65	1·35	1·35	1·35	1·35
12·65	12·65	12·65	12·65	12·65
32	31	31	31	34·4
16·7	20	20	20	20
15	15	15	15	15
132/228[14]	158/240	158/344	158/344	158/344
145/189[14]	220/310	220/477	220/477	220/477
122/155[14]	185/300	185/430	185/430	185/430
25	26·3	26·3	26·3	26·3
16·0	16·3	16·1	16·1	16·5
11·58[19]	11·4	11·8	11·8	11·4
8·2	8·95	8·95	8·95	8·75
3·25	2·65	2·65	2·65	2·65
32/30*	30	30	30	30
4·3	4·65/18·0[20]	4·65/18·0[20]	4·65/18·0[20]	5·5/18·0[20]
V-2-44	V-2-54	V-2-54	V-2-54	V-2-55
12 cyl V (diesel)	12 cyl V (diesel)	12 cyl V (diesel)	12 cyl V (diesel)	12 cyl V (diesel)
512/2000	570/2000	570/2000	570/2000	580/2200
water	water	water	water	water
sliding gear	sliding gear	sliding gear	sliding gear	sliding gear
5/1	5/1	5/1	5/1	5/1
clutch and brake	clutch and brake	clutch and brake	clutch and brake	clutch and brake
cast manganese steel, centre guide; horn on alternate track plate				
19·8	19·8	19·8	19·8	19·8
6·9	6·9	6·9	6·9	6·9
72	74	74	74	74
Modified Christie type (torsion-bar)	modified Christie type (torsion bar), shock absorbers on 1st and 5th stations			
5 large bogie wheels per side	5 large bogie wheels per side; larger gap between first and second pair			
85 mm M-1944 ZIS-S53 L/51·5 dual-p. gun	100 mm D-10T L/54 dual-purpose gun	100 mm D-10TG L/54 dual-purpose gun	100 mm D-10TS L/54 dual-purpose gun	100 mm D-10T2S L/54 dual-purpose gun
3×7·62 mm DT MGs	12·7 mm DShK AAMG	12·7 mm DShK AAMG	12·7 mm DShK AAMG	1×7·62 mm DT MG
	2×7·62 mm DT MGs	2×7·62 mm DT MGs	2×7·62 mm DT MGs	
360	360	360	360	360
-5+25/-5+18*	-5+18	-5+18	-5+18	-5+18
58/34*	34	34	34	43
1890	3000/500[21]	3000/500[21]	3000/500[21]	2200
radio	radio and intercom	radio and intercom	radio and intercom	radio and intercom
25-120*	30-210	30-210	30-210	30-210
75	80	80	80	80
75	80	80	80	80
70-90	100	100	100	100
30	60	60	60	60
20	20	20	20	20
15-20	30	30	30	30

T–62

Crew	4
Weight, combat (tons)	37·5
Length, overall (ft)	31·0
length ex. gun (ft)	21·6
Width, overall (ft)	11·0
over tracks (ft)	10·33
Track centres (ft)	8·8
Height, overall (ft)	7·3
Ground clearance (in)	1·33
Ground contact (ft)	12·5
Max speed, road (mph)	34·4
cross-country (mph)	20
cruising (mph)	15
Fuel capacity (gal)	158/344
Range, road (miles)	190/300
cross-country (miles)	140/190
Turning circle (ft)	28·8
Power : weight ratio	18·6
Ground pressure (psi)	11·6
Trench crossing (ft)	8·85
Vertical step (ft)	2·65
Grade ability (°)	30
Fording, unprep. (ft)	5·5/18·0
Engine: model	V–2–62
type	12 cyl V (diesel)
output (hp/rpm)	700/2200
cooling	water
Transmission	sliding gear
Gear ratios (fwd/rev)	5/1
Steering	clutch and brake
Tracks: type	cast manganese steel, centre guide; horn on alternate track plate
width (in)	19·8
pitch (in)	6·9
shoes per track	74
Suspension	modified Christie type (torsion bar) shock absorbers on 1st and 5th stations
wheels per side	5 large bogie wheels per side; large gaps between 3rd, 4th and 5th pairs
Armament: main	115 mm smooth-bore tank gun
auxiliary	1 × 7·62 mm DT MG
traverse (°)	360
elevation (°)	−5+20
Ammunition: main	45
auxiliary	2200
Communications	radio and intercom
Armour: turret (mm)	30–210
hull side, front (mm)	80
hull side, rear (mm)	80
hull front (mm)	100
hull rear (mm)	60
hull floor (mm)	20
hull roof (mm)	30

Heavy Tanks

	T–32	T–35–1/T–35–2*
Crew	10	10/7*
Weight, combat (tons)	44·8	45
Length, overall (ft)	30·5	31·5/31·9*
length ex. gun (ft)	30·5	31·5/31·9*
Width, overall (ft)	10·5	10·5
over tracks (ft)	10·35	10·33
Track centres (ft)	9·18	9·18
Height, overall (ft)	10·0	11·25/10·5*
Ground clearance (in)	1·75	1·75
Ground contact (ft)	26·1	26·1
Max speed, road (mph)	18	18/19*
cross-country (mph)	12	12
cruising (mph)	14	14
Fuel capacity (gal)	130	130
Range, road (miles)	94	94
cross-country (miles)	50	50
Turning circle (ft)	?	?
Power : weight ratio	7·7	11·1
Ground pressure (psi)	11·1	11·1/10·2*
Trench crossing (ft)	15·0	15·0/15·1*
Vertical step (ft)	3·90	3·9
Grade ability (°)	40	40/35*
Fording, unprep. (ft)	3·95	3·95
Engine: model	M–17L (Hispano-Suiza)	M–17M
type	12 cyl V (petrol)	12 cyl V (petrol)
output (hp/rpm)	345/2000	500/2200
cooling	water	water
Transmission	hydraulic (hydrostatic)	sliding gear
Gear ratios (fwd/rev)	infinitely variable	4/1
Steering	hydraulic steering clutches	clutch and brake
Tracks: type	cast; webbed and spudded small pitch; centre guide	
width (in)	12·18	12·18
pitch (in)	6·8	6·8
shoes per track	?	?
Suspension	pivoted bogies, scissors type with compression springs	
wheels per side	6 large bogie wheels per side grouped in pairs	8 small wheels per side, grouped in pairs
Armament: main	76·2 mm L/16·5 (main turr.) 2×37 mm (sub. turrets)	76·2 mm L/16 or 24 (main) 2×45 mm (subsidiary)
auxiliary	6×7·62 mm DT MGs	5×7·62 mm DT MGs
traverse (°)	360 (main turret)	360 (main turret)
elevation (°)	—5+25 (main turret)	—5+25 (main turret)
Ammunition: main	96/220[1]	96/220[1]
auxiliary	8230	10,000
Communications	flag[2]	flag[2]/radio*
Armour: turret (mm)	11–20 (main turret)	11–20/11–35*
hull side, front (mm)	20	20/25*
hull side, rear (mm)	20	20/25*
hull front (mm)	25	30/35*
hull rear (mm)	20	20
hull floor (mm)	11	11
hull roof (mm)	14	14

	SMK/T–100*	KV–1	KV–1A	KV–1B (cast turret)
Crew	7/6*	5	5	5
Weight, combat (tons)	45/56*	46·35	43·5	47·5
Length, overall (ft)	31·5/29·3*	22·6	22·3	22·3
length ex. gun (ft)	31·5/29·3*	22·6	22·15	22·15
Width, overall (ft)	10·5/9·75*	10·65	10·93	10·93
over tracks (ft)	10·5/9·75*	10·65	10·65	10·65
Track centres (ft)	8·8	8·66	8·66	8·66
Height, overall (ft)	10·5/10·7*	8·75	8·88	10·65
Ground clearance (in)	1·35	1·0	1·7	1·47
Ground contact (ft)	?	14·2	13·8	13·8
Max speed, road (mph)	20/18·7*	22	22	22
cross-country (mph)	10	7·5	7·5	7·5
cruising (mph)	14	15	15	15
Fuel capacity (gal)	130	131	121	121
Range, road (miles)	94	140	140	140
cross-country (miles)	50	94	94	94
Turning circle (ft)	?	1·0	31·0	31·0
Power : weight ratio	11·1/8·9*	11·9	12·6	11·6
Ground pressure (psi)	11·8/12·0*	10·9	10·8	11·0
Trench crossing (ft)	14·25	8·85	9·2	9·2
Vertical step (ft)	4·0	3·9	3·0	3·0
Grade ability (°)	30	36	36	36
Fording, unprep. (ft)	3·75	4·75	4·75	4·75
Engine: model	BD–2	V–2K	V–2K	V–2K
type	12 cyl V (petrol)	12 cyl V (diesel)	12 cyl V (diesel)	12 cyl V (diesel)
output (hp/rpm)	400/2000	550/2150	550/2150	550/2150
cooling	water	water	water	water
Transmission	sliding gear	sliding gear	sliding gear	sliding gear
Gear ratios (fwd/rev)	5/1	5/1	5/1	5/1
Steering	clutch and brake	clutch and brake	clutch and brake	clutch and brake
Tracks: type	cast; webbed and spudded small pitch; centre guide	cast manganese steel; centre guide horn on alternate track plates		
width (in)	27·5	27·5	27·5	27·5
pitch (in)	6·25	6·25	6·25	6·25
shoes per track	?	87–90	87–90	87–90
Suspension	torsion bar (independent)	single torsion bar to each bogie, equally spaced on each side of trailing arms		
wheels per side	8 wheels per side	6 dual wheels per side		
Armament: main	76·2 mm L/24 (main) 45 mm L/46 (subsidiary)	76·2 mm M–1938/39 L/30·5 dual purpose gun	76·2 mm M–1940 L/41·5 dual purpose gun	76·2 mm M–1938/39 L/30·5 dual purpose gun
auxiliary	3 × 7·62 mm DT MGs	3 × 7·62 mm DT MGs	3 × 7·62 mm DT MGs	3 × 7·62 mm DT MGs
traverse (°)	360 (main); 180 (sub	360	360	360
elevation (°)	−5 + 25 (main turret)	−4 + 24·5	−4 + 24·5	−4 + 24·5
Ammunition: main	50/100[1]	111	111	111
auxiliary	8230	3024	3024	3024
Communications	radio	radio and intercom	radio and intercom	radio and intercom
Armour: turret (mm)	30–60	30–75 + 25	35–75 + 35	35–75 + 25
hull side, front (mm)	45	77	77	75–75 + 35
hull side, rear (mm)	45	75	75	75
hull front (mm)	60	75 + 31	75 + 35	75 + 35
hull rear (mm)	30	75	75	75
hull floor (mm)	30	32–40	35	35
hull roof (mm)	45	30–40	35	35

1: main/subsidiary armament   2: commanders' tanks fitted with radio
3: 45 mm ammunition/flame-thrower fuel   4: 7·62 mm/12·7 mm

KV–1B (bolted turret)	KV–1C	KV–1s	KV–8	KV–85
5	5	5	5	4
47·5	47·0	42·5	46	46
22·3	22·3	22·1	22·15	27·85
22·15	22·15	21·6	22·15	22·3
10·93	10·93	10·7	10·93	10·66
10·65	10·65	10·65	10·65	10·65
8·66	8·66	8·45	8·66	8·66
10·65	10·65	9·8	10·65	9·5
1·47	1·47	1·5	1·47	1·3
13·8	13·8	13·8	13·8	14·4
22	18·4	25	22	22
7·5	7·5	12	7·5	7·5
15	15	20	15	15
121	121	121	121	121
156	156	156	140	156
110	110	110	94	93
31·0	31·0	31·0	31·0	31·0
11·6	11·7	14·1	12·0	13·0
11·0	11·4	10·4	10·9	11·4
9·2	9·2	9·2	9·2	8·85
3·0	3·0	3·0	3·0	3·9
36	36	36	36	36
4·75	4·75	4·75.	4·75	5·25
V–2K	V–2K	V–2K–s	V–2K	V–2K–s
12 cyl V (diesel)	12 cyl V (diesel)	12 cyl V (diesel)	12 cyl V (diesel)	12 cyl V (diesel)
550/2150	550/2150	600/1900	550/2150	600/1900
water	water	water	water	water
sliding gear	sliding gear	sliding gear	sliding gear	sliding gear
5/1	5/1	5/1	5/1	5/1
clutch and brake	clutch and brake	clutch and brake	clutch and brake	clutch and brake
	cast manganese steel; centre guide horn on alternate track plates			
27·5	27·5	28·0	27·5	28·0
6·25	6·25	6·25	6·25	6·25
87–90	87–90	87–90	87–90	87–90
single torsion bar to each bogie, equally spaced on each side of trailing arms				
6 dual wheels per side				
76·2 mm M–1938/39 L/30 d. purpose gun	76·2 mm M–1940 L/41·5 dual-purpose gun	7·62 mm M–1940 L/41·5 dual-purpose gun	45 mm L/46 gun ATO–41 flame-gun	85 mm M–1943 D–5T85 L/51·5 d.p. gun
3×7·62 mm DT MGs	3×7·62 mm DT MGs	3×7·62 mm DT MGs	4×7·62 mm DT MGs	3×7·62 mm DT MGs
360	360	360	360	360
—4+24·5	—4+24·5	—4+24·5	—4+35	—4+23
114	114	102	40/22 galls[3]	71
3024	3024	3042	6000	3276
radio and intercom	radio and intercom	radio and intercom	radio and intercom	radio and intercom
40–110	40–120	30–82	35–75+25	30–110
75–110	90+40	60	75–75+35	65
75	90	60	75	60
110	75+35	75	75+35	60–75
75	75	60	75	60
35	35	35	35	30
35	40	35	35	30

	KV–IIA	KV–IIB	IS–I (IS–85)	IS–I (IS–122)
Crew	6	6	4	4
Weight, combat (tons)	53	57	44	44·5
Length, overall (ft)	22·3	22·3	27·3	31·5
length ex. gun (ft)	22·2	22·2	21·75	21·75
Width, overall (ft)	10·93	10·93	10·25	10·25
over tracks (ft)	10·65	10·65	10·0	10·0
Track centres (ft)	8·66	8·66	8·15	8·15
Height, overall (ft)	12·0	13·7	8·9	8·9
Ground clearance (in)	1·3	1·47	1·2	1·2
Ground contact (ft)	14·4	14·4	14·3	14·3
Max speed, road (mph)	16	16	23	23
cross-country (mph)	7·5	7·5	12	12
cruising (mph)	14	14	15	15
Fuel capacity (gal)	131	131	115	115
Range, road (miles)	100	100	150	150
cross-country (miles)	84	84	130	130
Turning circle (ft)	31·0	31·0	skid turns	skid turns
Power : weight ratio	10·4	9·7	11·6	11·5
Ground pressure (psi)	12·3	12·3	10·7	11·0
Trench crossing (ft)	8·85	9·2	8·15	8·15
Vertical step (ft)	3·0	3·0	3·25	3·25
Grade ability (°)	34	34	36	36
Fording, unprep. (ft)	4·75	4·75	4·75	4·25
Engine: model	V–2K	V–2K	V–2–IS (V2K)	V–2–IS (V2K)
type	12 cyl V (diesel)	12 cyl V (diesel)	12 cyl V (diesel)	12 cyl V (diesel)
output (hp/rpm)	550/2150	550/2150	513/2000	513/2000
cooling	water	water	water	water
Transmission	sliding gear	sliding gear	syncromesh	syncromesh
Gear ratios (fwd/rev)	5/1	5/1	4/1	4/1
Steering	clutch and brake	clutch and brake	regenative (2-stage) with skid turn	
Tracks: type	cast manganese steel; centre guide horn on alternate track plates			
width (in)	27·5	27·5	25·63	25·63
pitch (in)	6·25	6·25	6·25	6·25
shoes per track	87–90	87–90	87–90	87–90
Suspension	single torsion bar to each bogie, equally spaced on each side of trailing arms			
wheels per side	6 dual wheels per side	6 dual wheels per side	6 dual wheels per side	6 dual wheels per side
Armament: main	152 mm M–1938/40 L/20 (M–10) howitzer	152 mm M–1938/40 L/20 (M–10) howitzer	85 mm M–1943 D–5T85 L/51·5 dual-purpose gun	122 mm D–25 M–1943 L/43 dual-purpose gun
auxiliary	2×7·62 mm DT MGs	2×7·62 mm DT MGs	3×7·62 mm DT MGs 12·7 mm DShK AAMG	3×7·62 mm DT MGs 12·7 mm DShK AAMG
traverse (°)	360	360	360	360
elevation (°)	−4+24·5	−4+24·5	−4+23	−3+20
Ammunition: main	36	36	71	28
auxiliary	3087	3087	1330/945[4]	2330/945
Communications	radio and intercom	radio and intercom	radio and intercom	radio and intercom
Armour: turret (mm)	35–100	35–100	30–100	30–102
hull side, front (mm)	77	75+35	90	90
hull side, rear (mm)	75	75	89	89
hull front (mm)	75+35	75+35	120	120
hull rear (mm)	75	75	22–64	22–64
hull floor (mm)	35	35	19	19
hull roof (mm)	35	35	25	25

IS–II (IS–122)	IS–III	T–10	T–10M
4	4	4	4
45·0	45·8	49·0	45·5
31·5	32·75	32·33	33·85
21·75	21·85	23·95	25·18
10·25	10·5	11·66	11·5
10·0	10·0	10·86	10·86
8·15	8·15	8·5	8·5
8·9	8·9	7·9	7·9
1·2	1·48	1·5	1·5
14·3	14·1	15·0	15·0
23	23	31	31
12	12	12	12
15	15	22	22
115	106	185	185
150	130	217	217
130	94	140	140
skid turns	skid turns	skid turns	skid turns
11·3	11·3	14·1	15·1
11·25	11·25	10·1	10·1
8·15	8·15	9·85	9,85
3·25	3·25	3·25	3·25
36	36	32	32
4·25	4·25	4·25	4·25
V–2–IS (V2K)	V–2–IS (V2K)	V–2–IS (V2K)	V–2–IS (V2K)
12cyl V (diesel)	12 cyl V (diesel)	12 cyl V (diesel)	12 cyl V (diesel)
513/2000	519/2200	690/2000	690/2000
water	water	water	water
syncromesh	synchromesh	syncromesh	syncromesh
4/1	4/1	5/1	5/1

regenerative (2-stage) with skid turn

cast manganese steel; centre guide, horn on alternate track plates

IS–II (IS–122)	IS–III	T–10	T–10M
25·63	25·63	28·3	28·3
6·25	6·25	16·3	16·3
87–90	97–90	?	?

single torsion bar to each bogie, equally spaced on each side of trailing arms

6 dual wheels per side   7 dual wheels per side

122 mm D–25 M–1943 L/43
dual-purpose gun

122 mm D–25 M–1943 L/43 (improved)
dual-purpose gun (D–74)

IS–II (IS–122)	IS–III	T–10	T–10M
3×7·62 mm DT MGs	2×7·62 mm DT MGs	2×14·5 mm KPV MGs	
12·7 mm DShK AAMG	12·7 mm DShK AAMG	12·7 mm DShK AAMG (optional)	
360	360	360	360
—3+20	—3+20	—3+17	—3+17
28	28	30	50
2330/945	1000/945	1000/945	1000/0
radio and intercom	radio and intercom	radio and intercom	radio and intercom
30–102	25–230	25–230	25–230
90	90	120	120
89	60	80	80
120	110–120	110–273	110–273
22–64	60–90	60	60
19	20–35	20	20
25	25–45	20–35	20–35

Soviet AFV Production

Year	Vehicle Type	Yearly Output	Total in Service
1930	German 18-ton tanks	—	15
	T–24 Medium tanks	25	(not known)
	German leichter tractors	—	5
	Austrian wheel/track	—	1
	German armoured cars	—	6
	Vickers Medium tanks Mk II	—	15
	CL Mk VI Machine-Gun Carriers	—	26
	CL Amphibious tanks	—	8
	VA 6-ton tanks	—	15
	VA Tractor trucks	—	12
	Renault/KS light tanks	—	116
	Whippet light tanks	—	8
	Mk V Heavy tanks	—	25
	MS Light tanks	—	300
	Armoured cars (foreign)	—	150
	Russian tank prototypes	—	20
	Czech KH–50 wheel/track	—	1
	Fiat 3000B light tank	—	1
	Total		724
1931	BA–27 Armoured cars	100	824[1]
1932	Tanks (all types)	3300	3700
1933	Tanks (all types)	3442	7142
1934	Tanks (all types)	3371	10,513
1935	Tanks (all types plus 400 French AMRs)	3139	14,052
1936	Tanks (all types)	3139	16,391
1937	Tanks (all types)	3139	19,430
1938	Tanks (all types)	1500	20,930
1939	Tanks (all types)	3000	23,930
1940	Tanks (all types plus 115 T–34s and 243 KVs)	2794	24,000 (est.)
1941	Tanks (all types plus 1110 T–34s and 393 KVs)	6590[2]	24,000 (est.)
1942	Tanks (all types plus 13,500 T–34s)	24,668	(not known)
1943	Tanks and SP Guns	24,000[3]	(not known)
1944	Tanks and SP Guns plus Lend Lease Tanks	29,000 + 10,898[4]	(not known)
1945	Tanks and SP Guns	25,448	(not known)
1946-67	Tanks and SP Guns	35,025	(not known)

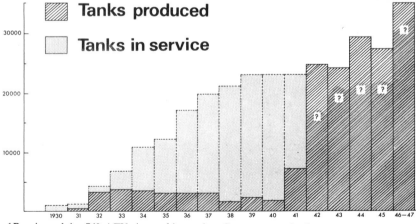

[1] Russians claim 740 AFVs in working order; Germans put the figure at 250 tanks and 100 armoured cars.
[2] This includes 48 T–50s and 1548 T–60s.
[3] This includes 35 ISU–122s and ISU 152s and 283 T–34/85 tanks.
[4] This includes 11,778 T–34/85s, 2250 ISs, 500 SU–100s, and 2510 ISU–122 and 152s.

T-34 and KV-1

Drawings depicting the interior layout of the two principal Soviet tank models—the T–34 and the KV–1. Very generally, these are indicative of the basic style of other Soviet vehicles in their respective classes. (For permission to reproduce these drawings the author wishes to acknowledge the Armour School, Bovington Camp, Dorset.)

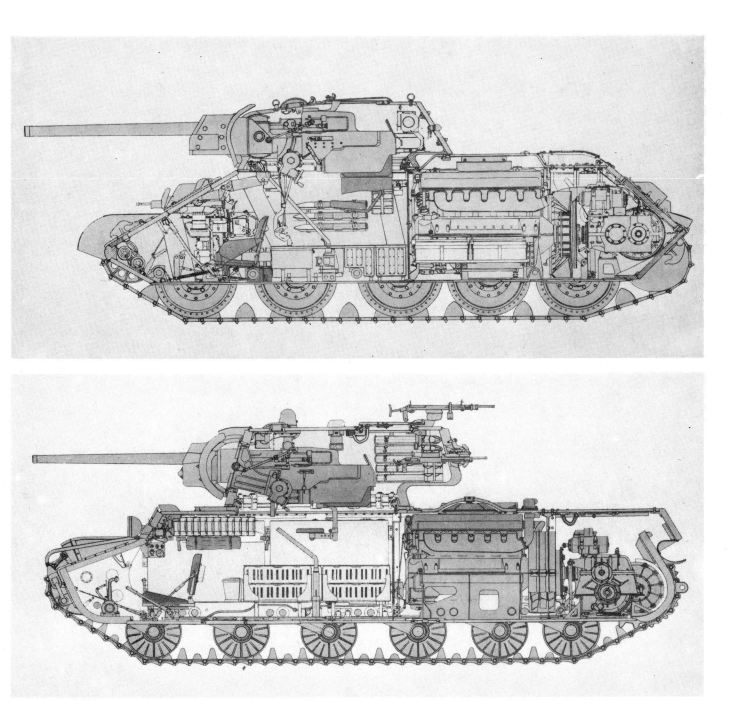

Notes and References

1 Mostovenko, Colonel V. D., *Tanki* (Tanks), Voenizdat, Moscow 1958.
2 *Artilleriyskiy Zhurnal*, No. 2, 1900, p. 789.
3 Ibid., No. 4, 1901, p. 1022
4 Mostovenko, op. cit.
5 Ibid.
6 Antonov, A. S., et. al., *Tank*, Voenizdat, Moscow, 1947.
7 Mostovenko, op. cit.
8 N.I.V.A., No. 24, 1906, pp. 380–382.
9 Mostovenko, op. cit.
10 Ibid.
11 Ts.GVIA (Central State War-History Archives), p. 2000.
12 Mostovenko, op. cit.
13 Ibid.
14 Ibid.
15 Icks, Lieutenant-Colonel R. J., *Tanks and Armored Vehicles*, Duell, Sloan and Pearce, New York, 1945.
16 Mostovenko, op. cit.
17 One verst is equal to 3,500 ft.
18 Mostovenko, op. cit.
19 Ts.GVIA, p. 802.
20 *The History of the CPSU(b)*, Voenizdat, Moscow, 1945.
21 Bibergan, D., 'K Istoriy Otechestvennogo Tankostroeniya 1914–1925' (The History of the Soviet Tank Industry 1914–1925), *Avto-Bronetankovi Zhurnal*, No. 7, July 1939.
22 Ibid.
23 Ibid.
24 Ibid.
25 Mostovenko, op. cit.
26 Ibid.
27 Ibid.
28 Ibid.
29 Antonov, op. cit.
30 Ibid.
31 Mostovenko, op. cit.
32 Ibid.
33 Ibid.
34 Ibid.
35 Antonov, op. cit.
36 Ibid.
37 Watyn-Watyniecki, Inz J., 'Ewolucja Sprzetu Pancernego Armji Czerwonej' (The Evolution of Armoured Fighting Vehicles in the Red Army), *Przeglad Wojskowo Techniczny*, No. 6, June 1934.
38 Mostovenko, op. cit.
39 Ts.GVIA, p. 802.
40 Ibid.
41 Ibid.
42 Mostovenko, op. cit.
43 Ibid.
44 Ibid.
45 Ibid.
46 Ibid.
47 Ibid.
48 Ibid.
49 Ibid.
50 Ibid.
51 Ibid.
52 Ibid.
53 Ibid.
54 Ibid.
55 Ibid.
56 Ibid.
57 Ibid.
58 *The History of the CPSU(b)*, Voenizdat, Moscow, 1945.
59 Underhill, Colonel G., 'The Story of Soviet Armor' (Part I),

Armor, No. 1, January-February 1949.

60 Magnuski, J., *Wozy Bojowe* (Armoured Vehicles), Polish Defence Ministry, 1964.
61 Ibid.
62 Mostovenko, op. cit.
63 Bibergan, op. cit.
64 Ibid.
65 Mostovenko, op. cit.
66 Bach, H., 'Die Tankwaffe Sowjetrusslands' (The Tank Arm of Soviet Russia), *Wehrtechnische Monatshefte*, No. 8, August 1936.
67 Mostovenko, op. cit.
68 Sokolovski, Marshal V. D., *Military Strategy*, Praeger, New York, 1963.
69 Erickson, J., *The Soviet High Command 1918–1941*, Macmillan, London, 1962.
70 Mostovenko, op. cit.
71 Bach, op. cit.
72 Bibergan, op. cit.
73 Chief of the German Army Command from March 1920 to October 1926.
74 Erickson, op. cit.
75 Ibid.
76 Mostovenko, op. cit.
77 Ibid.
78 Bibergan, op. cit.
79 Magnuski, op. cit.
80 Underhill, op. cit., (Part II), *Armor*, No. 3, May-June 1949.
81 *United States Cavalry Journal*, 1926.
82 Bibergan, op. cit.
83 Ibid.
84 Ibid.
85 Ibid.
86 Ibid.
87 Svietshin, *Strategy*, Gosizdat, Moscow, 1927.
88 Bibergan, op. cit.
89 Underhill, op. cit.
90 Mostovenko, op. cit
91 Erickson, op. cit.
92 Ibid.
93 Voroshilov, Marshal K. E., *Report on the Ceremonial Anniversary Meeting in the Bolshoi Theatre, 23rd February 1933*, 15th Anniversary of the Red Army, 1933.
94 Mostovenko, op. cit.
95 Erickson, op. cit.
96 Ibid.
97 *Soviet Military Review*.
98 Webb, S., et. al., *Soviet Communism—a New Civilisation?*, London, 1935.
99 Werner, M., *The Military Strength of the Powers*, Victor Gollancz, London, 1939.
100 Eimannsberger, L. Ritter von, *Der Kampfwagenkrieg* (The Tank War), Lehmann, Munich, 1935.
101 Mostovenko, op. cit.
102 Mostovenko, op. cit.
103 Wheldon, J., *Machine Age Armies*, Abelard-Schuman, London, 1968.
104 Erickson, op. cit.
105 Voroshilov, Marshal K. E., *Speech to the 16th Party Congress*, 1930.
106 Bach, op. cit.
107 Guderian, General H., *Panzer Leader*, Michael Joseph, London, 1952.
108 Underhill, op. cit., (Part I), *Armor*, No. 1, January-February, 1949.
109 Erickson, op. cit.

110 Underhill, op. cit.
111 Erickson, op. cit.
112 Ibid.
113 *Polska Zbroina*, 4 August, 1931.
114 Zacharoff, L., *We Made a Mistake—Hitler*, Grosset & Dunlap, New York, 1941.
115 Mostovenko, op. cit.
116 Antonov, op. cit.
117 Mostovenko, op. cit.
118 *Yessu*, 1932.
119 Magnuski, op. cit.
120 Mostovenko, Colonel V. D., 'Razvitie Sovetskich Tankov v Godi Velikoi Otechestvennoy Voyni' (The Development of Soviet Tanks During the Great Patriotic War), *Voenno-Istoricheskiy* Zhurnal, No. 9, September 1961.
121 Voroshilov, Marshal K. E., *Report on the Ceremonial Anniversary Meeting in the Bolshoi Theatre, 23rd February 1933*, 15th Anniversary of the Red Army, 1933.
122 Werner, op. cit.
123 Mostovenko, Colonel V. D., *Tanki* (Tanks), Voenizdat, Moscow, 1958.
124 Werner, op. cit.
125 Ibid.
126 Erickson, op. cit.
127 *Sovier Military Review*.
128 *Temps*, 25 March 1934.
129 Bach, op. cit.
130 Werner, op. cit.
131 Watyn-Watyniecki, op. cit.
132 Ibid.
133 *Militär-Wochenblatt*, 18 October 1934.
134 Werner, op. cit.
135 *Militär-Wochenblatt*, 1935.
136 *Krasnaya Zvezda*, 17 September 1935.
137 *Voina I Revolutsia*, March-April 1932.
138 Antonov, op. cit.
139 Werner, op. cit.
140 *Pravda*, 14 September 1936.
141 Liddell Hart, Captain B. H., *The Tanks*, Cassell, 1959.
142 *Pravda*, 14 September 1936.
143 Ibid.
144 Werner, op. cit.
145 *Field Service Regulations*, Gosizdat, Moscow, 1934.
146 Werner, op. cit.
147 Krivoshein, *Taktik Sneller Verbände*, (Tactics of Fast Units), Voggenreiter-Verlag, Potsdam, 1934.
148 Bach, op. cit.
149 Begerchuk, I., 'Vzaimodeistvie Pechoti, Tankov i Artilleriy v Nastupatelinom Bou' (The Co-operation between Infantry, Tanks and Artillery in Offensive War), *Avto-Bronetankovi Zhurnal*, No. 7, July 1939.
150 Begishev, Reserve Colonel A., 'Primenenie Tankov Nero-sredstvennoy Podderzhki Pechoti v Nastupatelinich Operatsiyach Velikoy Otechestvennoy Voyni' (The Employment of Tanks in Direct Infantry Support During the Offensive Operations of the Great Patriotic War), *Voenno-Istoricheskiy Zhurnal*, No. 6, June 1962.
151 Bach, op. cit.
152 Ibid.
153 Ibid.
154 Garforth, R., *How Russia Makes War*, Allen & Unwin, London, 1954.
155 Underhill, op. cit., (Part IV), *Armor*, No. 6, November-December, 1952.
156 *Wehrtechnische Monatshefte*, August, 1936.
157 *Notes on the Red Army, 1940* (MI2b) London, 1940.

158 Werner, op. cit.
159 Garforth, op. cit.
160 Clark, A., *Barbarossa—The Russian German Conflict, 1941-1945*, Penguin, 1965.
161 Erickson, op. cit.
162 *Avto-Bronetankoviy Zhurnal*, 1936.
163 Hooper, Major A. S., *The Soviet Fighting Forces*, Frederick Muller, London, 1941.
164 Wheldon, op. cit.
165 Clark, op. cit.
166 Wheldon, op. cit.
167 Liddell Hart, Captain B. H., *The Soviet Army*, Weidenfeld & Nicolson, London, 1956.
168 Clark, op. cit.
169 *The Draft Field Service Regulations, 1939*, Voenizdat, Moscow, 1939.
170 Werner, op. cit.
171 Erickson, op. cit.
172 Mostovenko, op. cit.
173 Ibid.
174 Reynaud, P., *Le Probleme Militaire Francais* (The French Military Problem), Paris, 1937.
175 Bibergan, op. cit.
176 Werner, op. cit.
177 Ibid.
178 Haudann, Dr E., *Das Motorisierungspotential der Sowjet-Union* (The Motorization Potential of the Soviet Union), Hamburg, 1937.
179 Erickson, op. cit.
180 Hooper, op. cit.
181 Hooper, Major A. S., *The Soviet-Finnish Campaign*, Frederick Muller, London, 1940.
182 Hooper, Major A. S., *The Soviet Fighting Forces*, Frederick Muller, London, 1941.
183 Antonov, op. cit.
184 Garforth, op. cit.
185 Mostovenko, Colonel V. D., 'Razvitie Sovetskich Tankov v Godi Velikoi Otechestvennoy Voyni' (The Development of Soviet Tanks During the Second World War), *Voenno-Istoricheskiy Zhurnal*, No. 9, September 1961.
186 Mostovenko, Colonel V. D., *Tanki* (Tanks), Voenizdat, Moscow, 1958.
187 Ibid.
188 Kerr, W., *The Russian Army*, Victor Gollancz, London, 1944.
189 Liddell Hart, Captain B. H., *Defence of the West*, Cassell, London, 1950.
190 Begishev, op. cit.
191 Ibid.
192 *Voennyi Vestnik*, No. 18, September 1945.
193 Mellenthin, General F. W. von, *Panzer Battles*, Cassell, 1955.
194 Ibid.
195 Begishev, op. cit.
196 Mellenthin, op. cit.
197 Mostovenko, Colonel V. D., 'Razvitie Sovetskich Tankov v Godi Velikoi Otechestvennoy Voyni' (The Development of Soviet Tanks During the Great Patriotic War), *Voenno-Istoricheskiy Zhurnal*, No. 9, September 1961.
198 *Neue Zuercher Zeitung*, July 1941.
199 Underhill, op. cit., (Part III), *Armor*, No. 2, March-April 1950.
200 Clark, op. cit.
201 Begishev, op. cit.
202 Ibid.
203 Garforth, op. cit.
204 Underhill, op. cit., (Part IV), *Armor*, No. 1, January-February 1953.
205 Begishev, op. cit.
206 Ibid.
207 Martel, Lieutenant-General Sir G. Le Q., *Our Armoured Forces*, Faber, 1945
208 Clark, op. cit.
209 Begishev, op. cit.
210 Ibid.
211 Ibid.
212 Ibid.
213 Ibid.
214 Mellenthin, op. cit.
215 Ibid.
216 Mostovenko, op. cit.
217 Liddell Hart, op. cit.
218 Martel, op. cit.
219 *Armor*, No. 6, November-December 1952.
220 Liddell Hart, Captain B. H., *The Soviet Army*, Weidenfeld & Nicolson, London, 1956.
221 Garforth, op. cit.
222 *Krasnaya Zvezda:*
223 Ogorkiewicz, R. M., *Armour*, Stevens & Sons, London, 1960.
224 *Krasnaya Zvezda*.
225 Ibid.
226 Ibid.
227 Liddell Hart, Captain B. H., *Defence of the West*, Cassell, London, 1950.
228 *Krasnaya Zvezda*.
229 Ibid.
230 Mostovenko, Colonel V. D., *Tanki* (Tanks), Voenizdat, Moscow, 1958.
231 Ibid.
232 Ibid.
233 Ibid.
234 Mostovenko, Colonel V. D., 'Razvitie Sovetskich Tankov v Godi Velikoi Otechestvennoy Voyni' (The Development of Soviet Tanks During the Great Patriotic War), *Voenno-Istoricheskiy Zhurnal*, No. 9, September 1961.
235 Ibid.
236 *Starshina Zhergeant*, 1967.
237 Mostovenko, Colonel V. D., *Tanki* (Tanks), Voenizdat, Moscow, 1958.
238 Ibid.
239 Ibid.
240 Ibid.
241 Mostovenko, Colonel V. D., 'Razvitie Sovetskich Tankov v Godi Velikoi Otechestvennoy Voyni' (The Development of Soviet Tanks During the Great Patriotic War), *Voenno-Istoricheskiy Zhurnal*, No. 9, September 1961.
242 Ibid.
243 Underhill, op. cit.
244 Mostovenko, op. cit.
245 Underhill, op. cit.
246 Mostovenko, op. cit.
247 Ibid.
248 Mostovenko, Colonel V. D., *Tanki* (Tanks), Voenizdat, Moscow, 1958.
249 Underhill, op. cit.
250 Ibid.
251 Mostovenko, op. cit.
252 Ibid.

Bibliography

Ammossov, 'Tanks in the Breakthrough Operation', *Voina I Revolutsia*, No. 5, September-October, 1932.

— 'The Application of a Tank Company in the Defence of a Rifle Regiment against an Attacking Enemy Equipped with Tanks' *Voennyi Vestnik*, No. 13, July 1932.

Ananiev, Colonel I., 'Tank Armies in Offensive Operations', *Military Review*, No. 1, January 1963.

Andronikov, N., *Bronetankovye I Mekhanizirovannye Voiska Sovetskoi Armii* (Tank and Mechanized Troops of the Soviet Army), Voenizdat, Moscow, 1958.

— Mostovenko, Colonel V. D., *Die Roten Panzer*, Lehmanns, Munich, 1962.

Antonov, A. S. et. al., *Tank*, Voenizdat, Moscow, 1947.

Bach, H., 'Die Tankwaffe Sowjetrusslands' (The Tank Arm of Soviet Russia), *Wehrtechnische Monatshefte*, No. 8, August 1936.

Basseches, N., *The Unknown Army*, Heinemann, London, 1943.

Begerchuk, I., 'Vzaimodeistvie Pechoti, Tankov i Artilleriy v Nastupatelinom Bou' (The Co-operation between Infantry, Tanks and Artillery in Offensive Combat), *Avto Bronetankovi Zhurnal*, No. 7, July 1939.

Begishev, Reserve Colonel A., 'Primenenie Tankov Nerosredstvennoy Podderzhki Pechoti v Nastupatelinich Operatsiyach Velikoy Otechestvennoy Voyni' (The Employment of Tanks in Direct Infantry Support during the Offensive Operations of the Great Patriotic War), *Voenno-Istoricheskiy Zhurnal*, No. 6, June 1962.

Berchert, Oberstleutnant G., et. al., *Kleine Panzerkunde* (The Little Armour Guide), Deutscher Militärverlag, Berlin, 1967.

Berchin, M. and Berchin, E., *The Red Army*, Allen & Unwin, London, 1942.

Bibergan, D., 'K Istoriy Otechestvennogo Tankostroeniya 1914–1925' (The History of the Soviet Tank Industry 1914–1925), *Avto Bronetankovi Zhurnal*, No. 7, July 1939.

Bochkarev, K. S., *Programma KPSS o Zashchite Sotsialisticheskogo Otechestva*, (The CPSU Programme on the Defence of the Socialist Fatherland), Voenizdat, Moscow, 1963.

Boucher, Y., *The Armoured Arm in War*, Voenizdat, Moscow, 1956.

Bronin, Colonel Ya. G., et. al., *Bronetankovye I Mekhanizirovannye Voiska Sovetskoi Armii*, (Tank and Mechanized Troops of the Soviet Army), Voenizdat, Moscow, 1948.

Bubnov, A. S., *O Krasnoi Armii* (On the Red Army), Voenizdat, Moscow, 1958.

Bushe, Zh., *Bronetankovoe Oruzhie v Voiyne* (The Armoured-Tank Arm in War), Gosizdat, Moscow, 1956.

Carell, P., *Hitler's War on Russia*, Harrap, London, 1964.

Carr, E. H., *German-Soviet Relations between the Two Wars*, Baltimore, 1951.

Chalepski, I., 'Mechanization and Motorization in Modern Armies', *Bolshevist*, 15 July 1935.

Chibisov, Major General N., 'The Military Science of the Red Army, *Krasnaia Zvezda*, 12 November 1944.

Clark, A., *Barbarossa—The Russian-German Conflict 1941-45*, Penguin, 1965.

Cole, D., *The Red Army*, Rich and Cowan, London, 1942.

Davison, Lieutenant-Colonel M., 'A Survey of Soviet Armor', *Armor*, No. 2, March-April, 1951.

Dinerstein, H., *War and the Soviet Union*, Praeger, New York, 1959.

Dittmar, Lieutenant-General K., *The Red Army in the Finnish War*, Harcourt, Brace & Co., New York, 1956.

Eimannsberger, L. Ritter von, *Der Kampfwagenkrieg* (The Tank War, Lehmanns, Munich, 1935.

Ely, Colonel L. B., *The Red Army Today*, Military Service Publishing Co., Harrisburg, USA, 1953.

Erickson, J., *The Soviet High Command 1918–1941*, Macmillan, London, 1962; St Martins, Toronto, 1962.

Federov, Colonel, *The Red Army*, Cobbett Press, London, 1943.

Fitzgerald, Colonel C., 'Armor—Soviet Arm of Decision?',

Military Review, No. 3, March 1969.

Fomichenko, Major-General, *The Red Army*, Hutchinson, London, 1945.

Frentag, Oberleutnant, 'Taktische und Operative Verwendung Moderner Tanks in der Roten Armee' (Tactics and Operational Employment of Modern Tanks in the Red Army), *Militär-Wochenblatt*, No. 2, 1932.

Galaktinov, N., 'Tanks and Automobiles', *Voina I Revolutsia*, No. 4, July-August, 1932.

— 'Artillery and Tanks', *Voina I Revolutsia*, Nos. 11 and 12, 1932.

Garforth, R. L., *Soviet Military Doctrine*, Free Press, Glencoe, USA, 1953.

— *How Russia Makes War*, Allen & Unwin, London, 1954.

— *Soviet Strategy in the Nuclear Age*, Praeger, New York, 1958.

— *Soviet Military Policy*, Faber, 1966.

Gardner, M., *Histoire de l'armée soviétique*, Paris, 1959.

Garvysh, Colonel N., 'The Development of the Armoured Troops and Their Influence on the Military Art', *Voennaia Mysl*, No. 9, September 1955.

Gatovsky, L., 'The Industrial Foundation of the Military Might of the USSR', *Bolshevik* Nos. 17-18, September, 1944.

Grigoriev, Major A. S., *Sbornik Primerov po Takticheskoi Podgotovke Ekipazha Tanka*, (A Collection of Examples on the Tactical Training of Tank Crews), Voenizdat, Moscow, 1946.

Grigoriev, M. G., et. al., *Taktika I Vooryzheniye Pechotych Podrazdieleniy Inostrannych Armiy* (Tactics and Equipment of Infantry Units in Foreign Armies), Voenizdat, Moscow, 1963.

Gromychenko, A., *Ocherki Taktiki Tankovych Chastiey* (Outline of Tank Unit Tactics), Voenizdat, Moscow, 1935.

Gruzdev, N. I., *Tanki: Teoriia* (Tanks: Theory), NKTM, Moscow-Sverdlovsk, 1944.

Guderian, General H., *Panzer Leader*, Michael Joseph, London, 1952, 1970, Collins, Toronto, 1952.

Guillaume, General A., *Soviet Arms and Soviet Power*, Infantry Journal Press, Washington, 1949.

Gurov, A. A., *Teknicheskii Progress I Militarizm* (Technical Progress and Militarism), Voenizdat, Moscow, 1963.

Haudann, Dr E., *Das Motorisierungspotential der Sowjet-Union* (The Motorization Potential of the Soviet Union), Hamburg, 1937.

Heigl, F., *Taschenbuch der Tanks* (Handbook of Tanks), Lehmanns, 1926, 1935.

Heiman, L., 'In the Soviet Arsenal', *Ordnance*, No. 1, January-February 1968.

Hooper, Major A., *The Soviet-Finnish Campaign*, Frederick Muller, London, 1940.

— *The Soviet Fighting Forces*, Frederick Muller, London, 1941.

Huie, C., 'Soviet Army Bids for River-Crossing Mobility', *Army*, No. 12, December 1968.

Icks, Lieutenant-Colonel R. J., *Tanks and Armored Vehicles*, Duell, Sloan and Pearce, New York, 1945.

Ignatiev, Colonel A., 'Recent Developments in the Techniques and Tactics of Tank Units', *Voennyi Vestnik*, No. 8, April 1932.

— *Tanki V Obshchevoiskovom Boiu* (Tanks in Combined Troop Combat), Gosvoenizdat, Moscow, 1939.

Isserson, G., *The Evolution of Operative Tactics*, Gosizdat, Moscow, 1932.

Jukes, G., *Kursk—The Clash of Armour*, Purnell's History of the Second World War, Battle Book No. 7, Purnell, London, 1969; Ballantine, New York, 1969.

Just, A., *Militärmacht Sowjet-Union* (The Military Machine of the Soviet Union), Breslau, 1935.

— *The Red Army*, Figurehead, London, 1936.

Karatygin, P., *Mobilizatsia Promyshlennosti Dlia Nuzhd Voiny* (Mobilization of Industry for War Needs), Voenizdat, Moscow, 1925.

Katukov, Major-General of Tank Troops M., *Boevye Deistviia Tankov* (Combat Actions of Tanks), Voenizdat, Moscow, 1942.

Kerr, W., *The Russian Army*, Victor Gollancz, London, 1944.

Kiriaev, Major-General N. M., *KPSS i Stroitelistvo Sovetskikh Vooruzhennukh Sil* (The CPSU and the Development of the Soviet Armed Forces), Voenizdat, Moscow, 1965.

Kjellberg, S., *Russland im Krieg, 1920–1945* (Russia in War, 1920–1945), Europa Verlag, Zurich, 1945.

Kolganov, K., *Razvitie Taktiki Sovetskoi Armii v Gody Velikoi Otechestvennoi Voiny 1941–1945* (The Development of Tactics by the Soviet Army During the Great Patriotic War 1941–1945), Voenizdat, Moscow, 1958.

Kolkowicz, R., *The Soviet Military and the Communist Party*, Princeton University Press, Princeton, New Jersey, 1967.

Korch, Lt. S., 'Pansarmaterielens Utveckling Under Kriget 1939–43' (The Development of Armoured Equipment During the War 1939–1943), *Miltär Teknisk Tidskrift*, No. 3, 1943.

Korniuskym, P., et. al., *Sovietskiyo Tankisty* (Soviet Tankman), Voenizdat, Moscow, 1954.

Korobkov, Colonel-General of Tank Troops B., 'Tankmen of the Soviet Army', *Voennyi Vestnik*, No. 16, August, 1968.

Kournakoff, Captain S., *Russia's Fighting Forces*, Duell, Sloan & Pearce, New York, 1942.

Kovalev, Lieutenant-General of Tank Troops G., 'Tank and Mechanized Troops of the Red Army', *Voennyi Vestnik*, No. 18, September, 1945.

Krivoshein, *Taktik Schneller Verbände* (Tactics of Fast Units), Voggenreiter-Verlag, Potsdam, 1934.

Kruger, R., *Tanks*, Schmidt, Berlin, 1921.

Kryshanovski, 'Combat by Combined Arms', *Voina i Revolutsia*, Nos. 8 and 9, 1932.

Kuzniekov, T. P., *Taktika Tankogych Voysk* (Tactics of Tank Troops), Voeniedat, Moscow, 1940.

Laverty, Captain W., 'Soviet Tankman', *Armor*, No. 6, November-December 1963.

Lavrov, Colonel E., *Tankovaia Razvedka* (Tank Reconnaissance), Voenizdat, Moscow, 1940.

Liddell Hart, Captain B. H., *Defence of the West*, Cassell, London, 1950; Morrow, New York, 1950.

— *The Red Army*, Harcourt, Brace & Co., 1956.

— *The Soviet Army*, Weidenfeld & Nicolson, London, 1956.

Livshits, Ys., *Pervaia Gvardeiskaia Tankovaia Brigada v Boiakh za Moskvu* (First Guards Tank Brigade in the Battle of Moscow), Voenizdat, Moscow, 1948.

Losik, Major-General of Tank Troops O., 'An Important Condition for the High Mobility of Tank Troops', *Krasnaya Zvezda*, 30 March 1957.

Mackintosh, M., *Juggernaut*, Secker & Warburg, London, 1967.

Magnuski J., *Czolg Sredni T–34* (The T–34 Tank), Wydawnictwo Ministerstwa Obrony Narodowej, Warsaw, 1969.

—*Wozy Bojowe*, Polish Defence Ministry, 1960, 1964.

— and Mostovenko V. D., 'Historia Rozwoju Radzieckich Czolgow' (The History of Soviet Tanks): Part I (Up to 1932), *Wojskowy Przeglad Techniczny*, No. 2, 1968; Part II (1933–1941), *Wojskowy Przeglad Techniczny*, No. 1, 1969; Part III (1941–1945), *Wojskowy Przeglad Techniczny*, No. 9, 1969.

Makhine, Colonel T., *L'Armée Rouge* (The Red Army), Payot, Paris, 1938.

Martel, Lieutenant-General Sir G. Le Q., *Our Armoured Forces*, Faber, London, 1945.

McGuire, J., 'Soviet Army Transport Vehicles', *Army Digest*, No. 6, June 1962.

Mellenthin, General F. W. von, *Panzer Battles 1939–45*, Cassell, London, 1955; University of Oklahoma Press, 1955.

Miezhistan, Brigadier-General Y., 'Tanks During the Second World War', *Przeglad Wojsk Pancernych*, No. 2, February 1948.

Miller, M. J. Jr., 'Russian Combat Vehicles', *Ordnance*, No. 4, July-August 1966.

— 'Soviet Armoured Personnel Carriers', op. cit., No. 2, March-April 1969.

Milsom, J. F., 'The T–34 Story', *Airfix Magazine*, 6 parts, July-December 1968.

Mints, Professor I., *The Red Army*, International Publishers, New York, 1943.

Mironov, Colonel V., et. al., 'Armoured Troops of the Soviet Army', *Voennye Znaniya*, No. 7, July 1956.

Mostovenko, Colonel V. D., *Tanki* (Tanks), Voenizdat, Moscow, 1958.

— 'Razvitie Sovetskich Tankov v Godi Velikoi Otechestvennoy Voyni' (The Development of Soviet Tanks During the Great Patriotic War), *Voenno-Istoricheskiy Zhurnal*, No. 9, September 1961.

— *Tanks of the Past and Present*, German Military Press, 1961.

— 'The Development of the T–34 Tank', *Tekhnika i Vooryzheniye*, No. 9, September 1966.

— 'The History of the T–34 Tank', *Soviet Military Review*, No. 3, March 1967.

— 'Soviet Heavy Tanks', *Soviet Military Review*, No. 2, February 1968.

— 'Soviet Self-Propelled Gun Mounts', *Soviet Military Review*, No. 5, May 1968.

Moskovsky, Major-General V. P., *Sovremennaia Voennaia Tekhnika* (Soviet Military Technology), Voenizdat, Moscow, 1956.

Nozdrunov, Major-General, *Samochodnaya Artilleriya* (Self-Propelled Artillery), Voenizdat, Moscow, 1943.

O'Ballance, Major E., 'A New Look at the Soviet Military Forces', *Military Review*, No. 4, April 1961.

— *The Red Army*, Faber & Faber, London, 1964.

— 'Evolution of Soviet Armoured Doctrine', *The Army Quarterly*, No. 7, July 1966.

Odom, Captain W. E., 'Armoured Personnel Carriers in the Soviet Army', *Military Review*, No. 6, June 1965.

Ogorkiewicz, R. M., *Armour*, London and New York, 1960; revised edition *Armoured Forces* published 1970, Arms & Armour Press, London, and Arco, New York.

— *Design and Development of Fighting Vehicles*, Macdonald, London, 1968; Doubleday, New York, 1968.

— 'Soviet Armoured Formations', *The Army Quarterly*, No. 10, October 1955.

Perré, Captain, *Chars de Combat* (Tanks), Paris, 1937.

Perrett, B., *Fighting Vehicles of the Red Army*, Ian Allan, London, 1969; Arco, New York, 1970.

Piatnitsky, Colonel N., *The Red Army of the Soviet Union*, Paris, 1931.

— *Krasnaia Armiia* (Red Army), 2 vols, Paris, 1932.

Pinchuk, Major-General of Tank Troops P., 'The Armoured Forces of the Soviet Army', *Krasnaya Zvezda*, 9 September 1956.

Pokrovskii, Major-General G. I., *Nauka i Tekhnika v Sovremennykh Voinakh* (Science and Technology in Modern Wars), Voenizdat, Moscow, 1956.

— *Roli Nauki i Tekhniki Sovremennoi Voine* (The Role of Science and Technology in Modern Warfare), Znanie, Moscow, 1957.

Polyakov, A., *White Mammoths*, Dutton, New York, 1943.

Prochko, Lieutenant-General I. S., *Sovetskaia Artilleriya* (Soviet Artillery), Voenizdat, Moscow, 1948.

Prow, J. W., 'What of Soviet Armour?', *Ordnance*, No. 2, March-April 1967.

Redkin, M. G., *Bronetransporteri* (Armoured Carriers), Voenizdat, Moscow, 1962.

Riedel, R., 'Offensive Doctrine of the Soviet Army', *Military Review*, No. 11, November 1962.

Rivus, H., 'Die Wichtigen Kampfwagen der Roten Armee' (The Principal Tanks of the Red Army), *Deutsche Wehr*, 11 August 1932.

Rotmistrov, Marshal of Tank Troops P., 'The Role and Place of Self-Propelled Artillery in Modern Warfare', *Voennaia Mysl*, No. 5, May 1945.

— 'Tanks—The Decisive Force of the Attack', *Voennaia Mysl*, No. 8, August 1946.

Rozen-Zawadski, Captain, 'Soviet Armoured Vehicles', *Przeglad Wojsk Pancernych*, No. 2, March-April 1938.

Saitsev, Colonel, *The Red Army*, Berlin, 1934.

Sakhno, Major-General of Tank Troops M., 'The Armoured Corps in a Breakthrough', *Zhurnal Avto-Bronetankovykh i Mekhanizirovannykh Voisk*, No. 6, June 1945.

Saveliev, M., *Tankist* (The Tankman), Dosarm, Moscow, 1950.

Sediakin, A., 'Tanks and Anti-Tank Formations', *Voina i Revolutsia*, No. 6, November-December 1934.

Senger und Etterlin, Dr F. M., *Das Kleine Panzerbuch* (The Little Tank Book), Lehmanns, Munich, 1964.

— *Kampfpanzer* (Tank), Lehmanns, Munich, 1967.

— *Taschenbuch der Panzer*, Lehmanns, 1954, 1957, 1960 and 1969.

— 'The Evolution of the Soviet Battle Tank', 2 parts, *Armor*, January-February/March-April 1968.

— *The World's Armoured Fighting Vehicles*, Macdonald, London, 1962.

Shevchenko, Colonel K., 'A Brief History of the Origin and Development of Tanks', *Przeglad Wojsk Pancernych*, No. 1, January 1946.

Shtromberg, Major-General of Tank Troops A., *Tankovye Voiska v Sovremennoi Voine* (Tank Troops in Contemporary War), Gosizdpolit, Moscow, 1944.

Shvanebach, B., *Mechanichakya i Motorichakya Sovremennich Armiy* (Mechanization and Motorization in Modern Armies), Gosizdat, Moscow, 1933.

Sokolovski, Marshal V. D., *Military Strategy*, Praeger, New York, 1963.

Sovadina, Staff Captain, 'Tanks and the Principles of their Employment', *Voennyi Vestnik*, No. 8, April 1932.

Spielberger, W., et. al., *Armor on the Eastern Front*, Aero Publications, Fallbrook, California, 1968.

Stepnoy, K., *Sovremennoi Sredstva Bronevich Voysk* (Modern Capabilities of Armoured Troops), Voenizdat, Moscow 1933.

Svietshin, *Strategy*, Gosizdat, Moscow, 1927, 1937.

Todorskii, A. I., *Marshal Tukhachevskii*, Politizdat, Moscow, 1963.

Tukhachevsky, Marshal M., 'On the New Field Service Regulations of the RKKA', *Bolshevik*, No. 9, 1 May 1937.

Trutko, 'Material Security for the Operation of a Shock Army', *Voina i Revolutsia*, No. 12, 1932.

Turner, Lieutenant-Colonel F., 'Soviet River Crossing', *Military Review*, No. 9, September 1966.

Underhill, Colonel G., 'The Story of Soviet Armor': Part I—'The Early Years', *Armor*, No. 1, January-February 1949. Part II—'The Middle Ages', *Armor*, No. 3, May-June 1949. Part III—'The War Years', *Armor*, No. 2, March-April 1950. Part IV—'SUs: Assault Guns and SP Artillery', *Armor*, No. 6, November-December 1952, and No. 1, January-February 1953.

Vincent, C., 'L'Armée Rouge Est une Armée Entièrement Blindée' (The Red Army is an Entirely Armoured Army), *Revue Militaire Suisse*, No. 5, May 1950.

Voroshilov, Marshal K., *15 Years of the Red Army*, Gosizdat, Moscow, 1933.

— et. al., *The Red Army Today*, Moscow, 1939.

Watyn-Watyniecki, Inz. J., 'Ewolucja Sprzetu Pancernego Armji Czerwonej' (The Development of Armoured Fighting Vehicles in the Red Army), *Przeglad Wojskowo Techniczny*, No. 6, June 1934.

Werner, M., *The Military Strength of the Powers*, Victor Gollancz, London, 1939.

Wheldon, J., *Machine Age Armies*, Abelard-Schuman, London and New York, 1968.

White, J., *Red Russia Arms*, Burrup & Mathieson, London, 1932.

White, D. M., *The Growth of the Red Army*, Princeton University Press, Princeton, 1944.

Wiener, F., *Truppendienst Taschenbuch—die Armeen der Ostblockstaaten* (Troop-Service Handbook—The Armies of the Eastern Block States), Lehmanns, Munich, 1967.

Wollenberg, E., *The Red Army*, Secker & Warburg, London, 1938.

Yakovkin, Colonel V., 'Atomic Weapons and Anti-Atomic Defence of the Troops: Special Features of the Actions of Tank Troops', *Krasnaya Zvezda*, 29 June 1955.

Zacharoff, L., *We Made a Mistake—Hitler*, Grosset & Dunlap, New York, 1941.

Zavialov, A. S., et. al., *Bitva za Kavkaz, 1942–1943*, (The Battle for the Caucusus, 1942–1943), Voenizdat, Moscow, 1957.

Zhdanov, N., *Artilleriya i Protivotankovoi Oborone* (Artillery and Anti-Tank Defence), Voenizdat, Moscow, 1941.

'Bewaffnung und Ausrüstung der Armeen des Warshauer Paktes' (Arms and Equipment of the Warsaw Pact Armies), *Soldat und Technick*, No. 3, March 1965.

Bitva Pod Kurskom (The Battle of Kursk), Voenizdat, Moscow, 1963.

Boevoi Ustav Konnitsy RKKA (BUK–38) (Combat Regulations of the Red Army BUK–38), Voenizdat, Moscow, 1941.

Bronetankovye Voiska Sovetskoi Armii (Armoured Tank Troops of the Soviet Army), Voenizdat, Moscow, 1956.

'De Ontwikkeling van de T–54 Tank' (The Development of the T–54 Tank), *Herkenning*, No. 1, January 1964.

'Die Industriellen Grundlagen der Sowjetrussischen Kriegsrüstungen' (The Industrial Capacity of the Soviet Russian War Industry), *Militär-Wochenblatt*, No. 46, 1933.

'Die Militärische Bedeutung des Russischen Fünfjahresplans' (The Military Aspects of the Russian Five-Year Plans), *Militär-Wochenblatt*, No. 32, 1933.

'Die Panzerkampfwagen der Sowjet-Union' (The Tanks of the Soviet Union), 2 parts, *Die Panzertruppe*, Nos. 6 and 7, 1939.

'Die Panzerspähwagen der Sowjetunion' (The Armoured Cars of the Soviet Union), *Die Panzertruppe*, No. 8, 1939.

'Die Russische Heeresentwicklung seit 1945' (The Russian Army Development since 1945), *Schweizer Artillerist*, No. 7, July 1950.

Handbook on the Soviet Army, Department of the Army Pamphlet No. 30-50-1, Headquarters Dept. of the Army, Washington, DC., 1958.

Identification Handbook Soviet Satellite Ordnance Equipment, 6th Revised Edition, Parts I and II, USAEUR Pamphlet 30-60-1, 30 June 1966 (unclassified).

Istoriia Velikoi Otechestvennoi Voiny Sovestskogo Soiuza, 1941–1945 (The History of The Great Patriotic War of the Soviet Union, 1941–1945), Voenizdat, Moscow, 1961.

KPSS i Stroitelistvo Vooruzhennykh sil CCCP, 1918–Iiuni 1941 (The CPSU and the Development of the Armed Forces of the USSR, 1918–June 1941), Voenizdat, Moscow, 1959.

'L'Arme des chars en Russe Soviétique' (The Tank Arm of Soviet Russia), *Revue d'Infanterie*, No. 9, September 1937.

'L'Emploi Tactique des Chars à La Lumière du Nouveau Réglement Soviétique sur le Service en Campagne' (The Tactical Employment of Tanks in the Light of the New Soviet Field Service Regulations), *Revue d'Infanterie*, No. 9, September 1937.

'Les principeaux types des chars de combat de l'armée Soviétique' (The Principal Types of Tanks of the Soviet Army), *Bulletin Belge des Sciences Militaires*, No. 11, November 1938.

'Military Motor Vehicles—USSR', *Military Review*, No. 8, August, 1965.

'Motorisierte Kräfte in der Roten Armee' (Motorization in the Red Army), *Militär-Wochenblatt*, No. 10, 1932.

Nastavlenie dlia Motorizovannykh i Avtotransportnykh Chastei Krasnoi Armii (Manual for Motorized and Auto-Transport Units of the Red Army), Voenizdat, Moscow, 1941.

New Notes on the Red Army, War Office, London, August 1944.

Notes on the Red Army 1940, War Office (MI2b), London, 1940.

Obshchaia Taktika (General Tactics), Voenizdat, Moscow, 1940.

Polevoi Ustav (Field Regulations), Gosizdat, Moscow-Leningrad, 1929.

Polevoi Ustav Krasnoi Armii (Field Service Regulations of the Red Army), Voenizdat, Moscow, 1944.

Polevoi Ustav Krasnoi Armii, 1949 Goda (Field Service Regulations of the Red Army, 1940), Gosvoenizdat, Moscow, 1940.

'Schützenpanzer in Der Sowjetarmee' (Armoured Personnel Carriers in the Soviet Army), *Armee-Motor*, No. 12, December 1966.

Second Partial and First Consolidated Report on Russian Medium Tank T–34, Aberdeen Proving Ground, Maryland, USA, 1943.

'Soviet Employment of Armor', *Military Review*, No. 10, January 1949.

'Sowjetische Bergepanzer' (Soviet Armoured Recovery Vehicles), *Soldat und Technik*, No. 6, June 1969.

'Sowjetische Panzeraufklärer' (Soviet Armoured Reconnaissance), *Soldat und Technik*, No. 7, July 1965.

'Sowjetische Panzerwagenindustrie Vernichtend Getrossen' (Soviet Tank Industry Destruction Assured), *Wehrtechnische Monatshefte*, No. 1, January 1942.

'Sowjetrussische Panzerkampfwagen' (Soviet Russian Tanks), *Wehrtechnische Monatshefte*, No. 9, September 1942.

'Taktische Ansichten in Russland' (Tactical Theories in Russia), *Militär-Wochenblatt*, No. 11, 1932.

Tank Forces in the Soviet Army, Bulletin (Munich), Vol. I, October 1954, No. 7.

Tankistu o Borbie s Tankami Sredstvami PTO (Tankman's Guide with Tanks and Reconnaissance Means), Voenizdat, Moscow, 1941.

'The Adaptation of Soviet Ground forces to Nuclear War', *Military Review*, No. 9, September 1966.

The Red Army and Navy, State Art Publishers, Moscow and Leningrad, 1939.

Ubersichtstafel der Wichtigsten Panzerfahrzeuge im Sowjetrussland Stand (Descriptive Table of the Principal Armoured Vehicles in Soviet-Russian Use), Berlin OKH, 1 January 1944.

Uchebnoy Posobie po Podgotobkiy Mladshevo Komandira Avtobronevitch Chastiy (Training Manual for the Preparation of Junior Commanders in Auto-Armoured Units), Gosizdat, Moscow, 1933.

'Umfang und Gliederung der Panzertruppen der Sowjetunion' (Composition and Organization of the Armoured Troops of the Soviet Union), *Die Panzertruppe*, No. 9, 1939.

'Vamm—Russian Academy of Mechanization', *US Field Artillery Journal*, No. 5, September-October 1936.

Vooruzhennie Sily Soiuza SSR (The Armed Forces of the USSR), Voenizdat, Moscow, 1949.

Vooruzhennye Sily SSR v Velikoi Otechestvennoi Voine (The Armed Forces of the USSR in the Great Fatherland War), Voenizdat, Moscow, 1949.

Vremennyi Polevoi Ustav RKKA (The Provisional Field Regulations of the RKKA), Gosizdat, Moscow-Leningrad, 1925.

Vremennyi Polevoi Ustav RKKA, 1936 PU-36 (The Provisional Field Regulations of the RKKA, 1936 PU-36), Voenizdat, 1937.

Index

This index is arranged in two parts: firstly, a Vehicle Index and secondly a General Index. For each entry in the Vehicle Index the designation of the particular vehicle is followed by an abbreviated type description (in parentheses) as follows: (A)=Amphibian; (AASP)=Self-Propelled Anti-Aircraft weapon mounting; (AC)=Armoured Car; (APC)=Armoured Personnel Carrier; (ARV)=Armoured Recovery Vehicle; (BL)=Bridge-layer; (FT)=Flame-Thrower; (HT)=Heavy Tank; (H/T)=Half-Track; (LT)=Light Tank; (Ly)=Lorry/Truck; (MT)=Medium Tank; (RL)= Rocket/Missile Launcher; (SP)=Self-Propelled Gun; (Tr)=Tractor. This classification code is followed by the page numbers of text references. Pages on which illustrations appear are indicated in italic.